Brig. Gen. J. A. O'Connor
1945

Maj. Gen. W. M. Hoge
1945-1946

Brig. Gen. R. G. Moses
1946-1948

Col. L. H. Hewitt
1952-1954

Col. R. W. Pearson
1954-1955

Brig. Gen. R. K. Fleming, Jr.
1955-1957

Brig. Gen. R. R. Ploger
1965

Col. R. O. Renier
1966-1968

Col. F. P. Bane
1968-1972

DIVISION ENGINEERS

Col. J. P
1976-

ARMY ENGINEERS IN NEW ENGLAND
1775-1975

ARMY ENGINEERS IN NEW ENGLAND

THE MILITARY AND CIVIL WORK OF
THE CORPS OF ENGINEERS IN NEW ENGLAND
1775-1975

by

Aubrey Parkman

U.S. Army Corps of Engineers
New England Division
Waltham, Massachusetts
1978

This book is available through the New England Division of the U.S. Army Corps of Engineers, 424 Trapelo Road, Waltham, Mass. 02154

The Author

Aubrey Parkman is a professor of history at Tufts University, Medford, Massachusetts. A native of New England, he received the A.B. degree from Tufts University and the Ph.D. degree from the University of Rochester. His special fields of interest are American diplomatic and political history.

FOREWORD

New England is the birthplace of the U.S. Army Corps of Engineers. Here the Corps' military mission began at the outbreak of the American Revolution in 1775. Here, too, civil works projects were among the first to be undertaken by Army Engineers when Congress and the President entrusted the Corps with its civil mission in 1824. This is the story of the Corps' service and accomplishments in New England from the Battle of Bunker Hill to the present. Relating the activities of the Corps to broader regional and national developments, the book should appeal to a general audience as well as to specialists.

I commend Dr. Aubrey Parkman and the many members of the New England Division who assisted him for compiling a history in which the division can take pride.

JOHN P. CHANDLER
Colonel, CE
Division Engineer

PREFACE

The boundaries of the regional divisions and districts of the U.S. Army Corps of Engineers coincide generally with watersheds. The New England Division includes fifteen river basins and nine coastal areas that lie wholly or largely within the six New England states. It covers all of New England except western Vermont and small portions of western Massachusetts and Connecticut, which lie in drainage basins of the St. Lawrence and Hudson rivers. It also embraces small areas of southeastern New York that drain through the state of Connecticut, and Fishers Island, New York, located close off the Connecticut shore. This is the region, expanded on a few occasions to include military work performed in Long Island Sound and western Vermont, treated in this volume. The story of the Corps' work in New England, however, cannot be told as the history of an engineer division. It begins with the birth of the nation, and the New England Division was not created until 1942. Nor can it be recounted as the history of engineer districts. Districts were established in New England after the Civil War, but Army Engineers were active in the region long before then. And in 1946 New England districts were phased out and their functions assumed by the New England Division. This, then, is a history of "Army Engineers in New England."

In writing it, my objective has been to relate the work of the Corps in New England to larger regional and national events: to tell not only what happened but why it happened. Therefore I have examined not only the construction of military installations, the improvement of waterways, and the assumption of flood control and other more recent civil responsibilities, but also the factors that lay behind these undertakings, such as the early shortage of civil engineers in America, domestic and international political considerations, developments in military and naval weaponry, national economic growth, and changing public demands relating to the use and management of the nation's water resources. In narrating the early activities of Army Engineers in New England considerable emphasis could also be placed on specific individuals who supervised the construction of fortifications, carried out canal and railroad surveys, and improved river and harbor navigation. They were relatively few and the projects of the Corps comparatively limited. Since the Civil War, however, the Corps' work in New England has been directed by more than one hundred district engineers and over forty Northeast, North Atlantic, and New England division engineers. Corps personnel, mostly civilians, who turned concepts into plans and plans into countless projects, have numbered several thousand. Only a few are mentioned by name. This is nevertheless the history of them all—engineers and administrators, clerks and secretaries, specialists in real estate, law, and many other fields of expertise. They all played a part in the Corps' contributions to New England.

I am deeply indebted to all the present and past members of the New England Division who assisted in preparing this history. It would more than fill this page merely to list the people who gave generously of their time and knowledge in searching out materials scattered through the files of numerous offices, provided information from long association with the Corps, and offered helpful suggestions. Special thanks are due to Walter F. Mackie, Chief, Public Affairs Office, who provided guidance and help all along the way, to Susan Douglas, Public Affairs Specialist, who greatly assisted with typing and in securing photographs and other materials, and to Walter Avallone, Graphic Arts, who skilfully prepared the illustrations. I thank Jesse Remington, Lenore Fine, and Albert E. Cowdrey of the Historical Division, Office of the Chief of Engineers, for their aid and advice. I also thank Gerald Butler; Wilbar M. Hoxie; William Smith, Jr.; the National Archives; the U.S. Army Engineer Museum, Fort Belvoir, Virginia; and the U.S. Military Academy Archives, West Point, New York, for permission to use photographs from their collections.

Reading, Massachusetts

Aubrey Parkman

CONTENTS

I

Seven days after the first shots of the American Revolution were fired at Lexington on April 19, 1775, the Provincial Congress of Massachusetts, meeting in the village of Watertown, appointed Colonel Richard Gridley "chief engineer of the forces now raising in this colony, for the defense of the rights and liberties of the American continent."[1] Defiant delegates from the Massachusetts towns had taken the first step toward creating what was to become the United States Army Corps of Engineers.

A pensioned officer of the British army and one of few Americans with military engineering experience, Richard Gridley had learned his skills in England's colonial contests with France. Working in Boston in his early years as a surveyor and civil engineer, he became the friend of John Henry Bastide, a young British officer who was to become Director of His Majesty's Engineers and Chief Engineer of Nova Scotia. Bastide was engaged in drawing plans for fortifications at Boston, Marblehead, Cape Ann, and Casco Bay, and under his tutelage Gridley learned the elements of military engineering and gunnery.

Gridley's first military action came during King George's War, the American offshoot of the European War of Austrian Succession, when in 1745 he joined the audacious crowd of New England farmers, mechanics, and fishermen, led by Colonel William Pepperill, who dared to attack the great fortress of Louisburg on Cape Breton Island guarding the entrance to France's North American empire. Commissioned a lieutenant colonel and captain of the artillery train, and later made the chief bombadier of the expedition, he planted around the stronghold's mammoth ramparts the batteries that compelled its surrender. Some years later Governor William Shirley of Massachusetts, who had dispatched the expedition, commented that Gridley, and Bastide who had joined him during the seige, were the only engineers at Louisburg of any real service.[2]

Returning to Boston, Gridley was awarded a captaincy in Governor Shirley's regiment and ordered to ready defenses against a large French fleet, commanded by the Duc d'Anville, sent to burn the upstart Massachusetts town and retake Louisburg. Castle William, the island fortress lying in Boston's inner harbor, was strengthened, and cannon were planted on other islands in the harbor; hulls were sunk in the channel, and a boom was laid across it under the guns of the Castle. These preparations, taking several months, were never tested. Scourged by pestilence and struck by storm, the French armada was scattered off the American coast, with the admiral one of the victims.[3]

King George's War came to an inconclusive end in 1748. Louisburg, to the disgust of New Englanders, was returned to France in an exchange of all conquests. With nothing settled, French and British rivalries in America continued to simmer until the outbreak of the French and Indian War in 1754. Returning to active service, Gridley joined another expedition organized by Governor Shirley, this time up the Kennebec River of Maine to forestall a French thrust from Quebec along the River Chaudiere. At portages on the Kennebec near present-day Augusta and Winslow, he built Fort Western and Fort Halifax, each a typical frontier defense of pickets enclosing wooden blockhouses and barracks.

Fort Halifax, 1775.
Reprinted from Henry E. Dunnack, *Maine Forts* (Augusta, Maine, 1924).

The next year, because he "understood the artillery," Gridley was commissioned the colonel of a Massachusetts regiment raised to take part in Sir William Johnson's expedition to seize Fort Crown Point, the key French citadel on the classic Lake Champlain invasion route linking the French and British domains. Part of a larger unsuccessful campaign against Canada, the expedition failed to take the French fort. It did succeed, however, in throwing English barriers across the invasion route below it. Johnson built Fort William Henry at the foot of Lake George, while Gridley completed and took command of Fort Edward, a strong timber and earth structure on the Hudson River portage. "If all the Officers of his Rank in this Army were equal to him," Johnson wrote of Gridley at this time, "I should have thought myself verry happy in my Station and have flattered myself with Prospects equivalent to the hopes and expectations of the Goverments."[4]

Few things, however, went right for the English in the first years of the war; and in 1757 Fort William Henry fell to the army of the Marquis de Montcalm, though Fort Edward withstood his assault. Gridley, meantime, had formed a train of artillery for an expedition against Louisburg that never got beyond Halifax. The next year, following a shake-up of the British high command and revision of war strategy by William Pitt, the tide turned. Another expedition, this time of British regulars commanded by Generals Amherst and Wolfe, set out against Louisburg, and the fortress again fell to the English. Gridley again took part in the seige, supervising the expedition's carpenters and army stores. The campaign over, Amherst prevailed upon him, on orders from Pitt, to stay with the King's troops rather than rejoin a Massachusetts regiment. Remaining at Louisburg until the next year, he was given command of the provincial artillery that sailed with Wolfe against Quebec. He took part in Wolfe's daring nighttime scaling of the three-hundred-foot rock walls behind the towering fortress-city, and it was his corps that dragged up the only two British fieldpieces to reach the Plains of Abraham. Loaded with grapeshot, they did deadly work on the troops of Montcalm. For his services in the war, England conferred upon Gridley the Magdalen Isles in the Gulf of St. Lawrence, with an extensive seal and cod fishery, and half-pay as a British officer for life. In 1773 the governor of New Hampshire granted him three thousand acres of land that now lies in the town of Jackson.[5]

Gridley was a seasoned artilleryman, and since experienced gunners were about as scarce as engineers when the Revolution began, the Massachusetts Provincial Congress also commissioned him colonel of an artillery regiment with the rank of major general. His second-in-command was Lieutenant Colonel William Burbeck. In command of Castle William when the fighting started, Burbeck had deserted the British army to throw in his lot with his countrymen and had been appointed an engineer by the Massachusetts legislature on the same day as Gridley. Among the junior officers of the regiment was Burbeck's son, Lieutenant Henry Burbeck, who twenty-three years later became the Army's fifth Chief Engineer. The artillery train, however, was slow in forming. Cannon were hardly more plentiful than cannoneers, and for some time the regiment's total armament was only a half-dozen small iron and two brass fieldpieces.[6]

Gridley spent most of his time planning field fortifications for the New England militiamen who streamed in from the surrounding provinces, trapping the British army in Boston. The British were not strong enough to move out and crush the provincials, but their own position could be made virtually impregnable by occupying Dorchester and Charlestown peninsulas. Pointing like fingers at either side of Boston peninsula, both possessed heights from which an enemy could dominate the town and harbor. Learning through loose talk in Boston of the British plans to garrison these positions, the Massachusetts Committee of Safety recommended countermeasures, including the immediate occupation of Bunker Hill in Charlestown. Accordingly, on the evening of June 16, 1775 a detachment of about a thousand men, accompanied by Gridley, traversed the narrow isthmus of the peninsula and moved up the slopes of Bunker Hill. What followed is clouded by ambiguities in contemporary accounts. Apparently Gridley wanted to follow original plans and fortify Bunker Hill, which commanded all approaches to the peninsula by water or land, but General Israel Putnam, a legendary old warrior from Connecticut whose urge to fight was always stronger than his propensity to plan, insisted on putting breastworks on Breed's Hill, a lower elevation nearer and more threatening to Boston. As the field officers argued, the

4

cover of darkness slipped by, until finally Gridley remonstrated that he had to work somewhere and wanted a decision. Breed's Hill was chosen, Gridley marked out the lines of a redoubt, and about midnight the digging began.

By eleven o'clock the next morning earthen ramparts six to seven feet high formed a redoubt about 130 feet square. On one side a breastwork and then a reinforced stone and rail fence ran about 300 yards north to the Mystic River. On the other side, toward Charlestown, another fence and the houses of the town served as protection. To occupy Breed's Hill without first fortifying Bunker Hill, however, was a blunder. Its wide and gentle flanks were difficult to cover, and it could be cut off from the rear. But blundering was no American monopoly. The British, covered by guns of their ships, could have seized Charlestown Neck and isolated the American force. Instead, attacking that afternoon, they assaulted the American positions frontally. They took the hill on a third charge, when the patriots ran out of powder, but at a cost in casualties greater than any other engagement of the war. Gridley manned one of the brass fieldpieces of his artillery regiment, and near the close of the battle was struck in the leg by a musket-ball. Helped into a sulky to be carried off, he met with some obstruction and had just gotten out of the carriage when it was riddled by enemy shot and his horse was killed.[7]

Meantime, at Philadelphia, another event of importance to Gridley had taken place on June 16. The Second Continental Congress, functioning as an American government of sorts, had authorized a "chief engineer" for the "grand army" it had two days before resolved to raise.[8] Two and a half weeks later, when General Washington took command of the Continental Army at Cambridge, his choice was obvious. Gridley was already serving in that position by courtesy of the other New England provinces.

Not much bothered by what had been only a flesh wound, Gridley was by then back at work on fortifications. Strong redoubts and lines, Washington recorded shortly after arriving in Cambridge, formed "a complete line of circumvallation from Charles River to Mystic River." Helping Gridley were several younger officers, the most notable of whom was Henry Knox, destined to become the new nation's first Secretary of War. "On the Roxbury side," Washington also recorded, referring to south of the Charles River, "the enemy have dug across the Neck, and let the water through; and our people in turn have intrenched across the outer end of the Neck, and are strongly fortified there, and on the hill by the meeting-house." Here the redoubts were the work of Lieutenant Colonel Rufus Putnam, later famous in the history of western settlement as the leader of the Marietta pioneers. A veteran of three campaigns on the Champlain frontier during the French and Indian War, Putnam had enlisted at the outbreak of the Revolution in a Massachusetts regiment that took up station at Roxbury. Defensive works were needed, and since Gridley was occupied in Cambridge, Putnam was pressed into service when acquaintances mentioned that in the late war he had worked on fortifications under British engineers. Never having read a word on the subject, and claiming no knowledge of laying out works, Putnam nevertheless raised defenses at Roxbury, Dorchester, and Brookline as stout as those to the north.[9]

"The lines of both are impregnable," recorded an enthusiastic visitor to

Colonel Rufus Putnam.
Courtesy of the U. S. Army Engineer Museum,
Fort Belvoir, Virginia.

the camps at Roxbury and Cambridge in October, "with forts (many of which are bomb-proof) and redoubts, supposing them to be all in a direction, are about twenty miles; the breastworks of a proper height, and in many places seventeen feet in thickness; the trenches wide and deep in proportion, before which lay forked impediments; and many of the forts, in every respect, are perfectly ready for battle. The whole, in a word, the admiration of every spectator; for verily their fortifications appear to be the works of seven years instead of about as many months."[10]

Since August, Washington had been edging these fortifications nearer to the British in Boston and Charlestown. First he placed a redoubt on Plowed Hill, a low drumlin within point-blank shot of British-occupied Bunker Hill. Next he put a work, laid out by Putnam, on Cobble Hill, an elevation overlooking the Back Bay separating Cambridge from Boston. Then he located a strong redoubt, finished near the end of February, on Lechmere Point, directly across the Back Bay from the north end of Boston. Now the Commander in Chief was ready for his final move. Powder and shot had been gathered in increasing quantities, and fifty-nine large-caliber cannon and mortars, captured by Ethan Allen from the British at Fort Ticonderoga and hauled across New England on sleds by Henry Knox, were at hand. Washington's plan was to occupy Dorchester Heights, which the British had inexplicably still failed to garrison, command Boston and the harbor with his cannon, and force the British to take action or leave.[11]

The problem was how to make a lodgement in the frozen ground. It had taken three months to complete the earthworks at Lechmere Point, yet Dorchester Heights had to be fortified in a single night, for once the British discovered the attempt they would never allow the works to be finished. Inviting Rufus Putnam, who had recently returned from laying out works at Newport, Rhode Island, to dine one evening at Headquarters, Washington directed him to turn his mind to the matter. On his way home, Putnam called on General William Heath to pay his respects. On Heath's table he noticed a copy of *Mullers Field Engineer*, and after some difficulty he persuaded the general to lend it to him. Thumbing through it—the first engineering manual he had ever read—he came upon a description of chandeliers, which inspired the plan of fortification he submitted to Washington and Gridley the next day. His scheme was to use chandeliers—heavy pre-assembled timber frames—between which could be stuffed bales of hay, bundles of sticks, and baskets of earth. Raised overnight, these parapets could later be strengthened with earth. In front of them would be a line of felled trees with sharpened branches facing the enemy, the equivalent of a modern barbed wire entanglement. Stacked outside this barrier would be barrels filled with earth. Lending the works an appearance of greater strength, they could be rolled down on attackers to break their ranks and hopefully their bones.

On the night of March 4, 1776, while the attention of the British was distracted by cannonading from Cobble Hill, Lechmere Point, and Roxbury, a force of two thousand men with 360 oxcarts loaded with entrenching materials moved onto Dorchester Heights. Their passage was screened from eyes in Boston by bundles of hay placed along the north side of Dorchester Neck, across which the carts went back and forth until dawn. More than three thousand fresh troops were brought up during the night, and by daylight two formidable redoubts looked down on the British. "The rebels have done more in one night than my whole army could have done in a month," an astonished General Howe is said to have exclaimed. "It must have been the employment of at least twelve thousand men," he wrote to Lord Dartmouth, Secretary of State for the Colonies. Had Howe tried to take the Heights, Washington was ready with boats and troops to make a general assault on Boston. Exposed to the American batteries and not strong enough to force the American lines, the British army and fleet departed on March 17 for Halifax, Nova Scotia.[12]

The plan for fortifying the Heights was Putnam's, but Gridley, as Chief Engineer, had directed the work. It was his last exciting achievement. Sixty-five years made a man old in that day, and Gridley was slowing down. The previous September the congress at Philadelphia had placed him in command of Continental artillery, but two months later had felt compelled to replace him with Henry Knox. In April, when Washington moved the bulk of his army southward in anticipation of a British attack on New York City, Gridley stayed behind. He constructed coastal fortifications in and around Boston in case the British should return, and he manufactured mortars and howitzers, the first to be cast in this country, at a furnace in Sharon where he and a partner had begun smelting iron ore a few years before. He continued as Engineer General in New England until he retired from service on January 1, 1781. Gridley had contributed much to the patriot cause, yet two years later he was to suffer a rude blow. When the return of peace was celebrated in the Old South Church of Boston, he was not invited to participate. Inquiring from a friend as to the reason, he received the reluctant reply: "Because, General, you are not considered by those having that matter in charge a Christian." Gridley had become a Universalist.[13]

The military career of William Burbeck also ended on a plaintive note. Ordered to New York when Washington moved his army south, the old soldier refused to go. He was unwilling to leave the service of Massachusetts, he explained. It had voted him a salary for life, which at his advanced age he did not wish to give up. He asked to be excused from complying with the order. When General Washington apprised Congress of the matter, Burbeck was dismissed from Continental service.[14]

Washington's choice for chief engineer with his field army at New York was Rufus Putnam; and it was this Massachusetts soldier who laid out the fortifications arcund the city in Washington's unsuccessful attempt to hold it against British forces returning under General Howe. Putnam, however, had never been commissioned an engineer, and he was at this time in line for promotion to colonel of a regiment. Washington, dismayed by the prospect of losing his services, appealed to Congress to retain him. "The Public would sustain a capital injury," the general warned, "for although he is not a man of Scientific Knowledge, he is indefatigable in business and possesses more practical knowledge in the Art of engineering than any other we have in this Camp or Army." Several weeks later, on August 5, 1776, Congress promoted Putnam to full colonel and appointed him Chief Engineer of the Continental Army. But Putnam held this office for only a few months. Engineers were being commissioned and attached to army units by Congress in haphazard fashion whenever men with alleged credentials presented themselves. French adventurers for the most part, few had any real engineering ability that Washington could see. Putnam wanted Congress to create a specially trained engineer corps of officers and men, and when it failed to act on a plan he submitted through General Washington, he resigned in December to take command of a regiment of Massachusetts infantry.

Putnam's engineering talents, however, were to valuable to be wasted, and in March 1778, after campaigning against Burgoyne on the line of the Hudson, he was ordered with his regiment to West Point. While still with Washington at New York, he and several other officers had been ordered to inspect fortifications being built in the Highlands of the Hudson Valley, and his board had recommended defenses at West Point. A high wedge of bank forcing the river to bend sharply, the point was the key to the command of the valley. There redoubts were built by New York forces under the direction of a Dutch engineer, but the job was poorly done. In October 1777, when General Clinton's army advanced up the Hudson to join with Burgoyne coming down from Canada in a move to isolate New England, the British had no difficulty in capturing the fortifications and destroying them in two days. Burgoyne's surrender at Saratoga a few days later compelled Clinton's forces to withdraw to New York City. But since the British might push up the Hudson again, Washington ordered the construction of new fortifications, and a French engineer was sent to direct the work. But Lieutenant Colonel de La Radiere's plans were faulty, and quarrels over them with his superiors soon led to his departure. The task was now given to Putnam and to Colonel Thaddeus Kosciusko, the skillful Polish engineer with the army of General Gates. Together they laid out a stout chain of defenses. One fort, built by Putnam's regiment on a high rock commanding the point, was named for him. It still stands, now restored at the United States Military Academy.[15]

If Congress moved to create an efficient body of engineers with less haste than Putnam felt was urgent, it nevertheless by several acts lumbered piecemeal toward his proposal until finally, in March 1779, it authorized a separate and distinct ":corps of engineers." Commanded by Louis LeBègue Du Portail, an officer recruited by the American diplomatic mission in France, and largely staffed by other volunteers from the French Royal Corps of Engineers, the corps was a vital unit of the Continental Army until it was disbanded in November 1783 with the coming of peace.[16]

Engineers in the minuscule army maintained after the Revolution would perhaps have been a luxury, but only for the brief span of a decade. War broke out again between England and France in 1793, and the situation immediately became ominous as each belligerent tactlessly tried to whip the young republic into serving its ends. Fearing that a showdown might come, President Washington urged putting the coast in a condition of defense, and in March 1794 Congress authorized him to fortify specified ports and harbors along the coast. To begin construction of this "First System" of fortifications, Washington turned temporarily to the only engineers available— French emigrés residing in the United States, some of whom had served in the Continental Army. The coast was divided into sections, with New England assigned to Stephen Rochefontaine. A former captain in the Corps of Engineers, Rochefontaine had been brevetted a major by Congress for distinguished service at the siege of Yorktown. Returning to France at the end of the American Revolution, he had escaped back to America upon the execution of his king in 1793. Two months after providing for the new fortifications, Congress authorized a new army unit, the Corps of Artillerists and Engineers, to build and man them. Upon organizing the corps in February 1795, Washington placed Rochefontaine in command. In this capacity the French lieutenant colonel continued to supervise the construction of fortifications in New England until his retirement from the army in 1798.[17]

Rochefontaine's authority was narrowly circumscribed. Because appropriations were small, he was expected to adhere to estimates of the War Department relating to the cost of each fort and to its weapons and construction. He was instructed to submit his plans to the state governors and to take their orders. And he had limited control of his subordinates. The state governors appointed the superintendents in immediate charge of construction, and the Treasury Department appointed the agents who supplied materials and labor.[18]

By January 1796 local contractors had nearly finished erecting defenses at Portland, Portsmouth, Salem, Marblehead, Gloucester, and on either side of New London Harbor. Although Rochefontaine occupied good positions, mostly sites of earlier works, his forts were more in keeping with the views of Congress and the state of the treasury than with his own ideas of proper fortifications. Expenditures to date for all forts in New England totaled only about $30,000, and for all forts in the country only $132,000. His forts were small redoubts of stone and sod, mounting only ten to fourteen guns—skimpy armament for a time when cannon were pointed rather than aimed. These weapons were cast iron, smoothbore muzzle-loaders, the service guns used to the Civil War. They ranged in caliber, which was expressed in terms of the weight of the spherical shot they fired, mostly from 6 to 24 pounders, though a few were 32 and 42 pounders. Single stone or brick blockhouses, sheltering magazines and serving as barracks, covered the landward sides of the forts. Most were equipped with reverberatory furnaces for heating red hot the iron balls hurled at flammable wooden and canvas ships.

The town of Newport, Rhode Island, commanding the entrance to Narragansett Bay, demanded stronger fortifications. The bay—the only one on the coast that vessels could enter with a northwest wind—was the best naval refuge in the United States, and Newport's strategic importance had been demonstrated by its successive occupation during the Revolution by the Americans, the English, and the French. An enemy seizing it could menace the whole northern region with his ships and troops. On Goat Island, which lies in the center of Newport Harbor, Rochefontaine built Fort Wolcott, a masonry and earth redoubt of cross-moline form accommodating twelve guns. To protect the town from assault by land he built a blockhouse on nearby Tomony Hill, and to keep open communication with the mainland he placed a battery at Howlands Ferry.[19]

These defenses, which were totally inadequate to Newport's strategic needs, were strengthened between 1798 and 1800 under the spur of an undeclared two-year naval war with France brought on by French marauding on the sea. The engineer in charge was Lieutenant Colonel Louis Tousard. Another French veteran of the Continental Army, Tousard had come to America early in 1777, serving as an aide to Lafayette. Because of gallantry in action the next year on Rhode Island, where he lost an arm, Congress brevetted him a lieutenant colonel and awarded him a pension for life. Returning to the military service of France, he was later swept up in its revolutionary turmoil and imprisoned in 1792. After several months he was released through the intercession of the American minister at Paris. Joining his family which had fled to the United States, he was commissioned a major in the Corps of Artillerists and Engineers when it was organized in 1795.[20]

On Brenton's Point, which protects Newport Harbor on the west and commands the main passage into Narragansett Bay, Tousard built Fort Adams, a redoubt of irregular star design housing twelve guns. On Eastons Point, which lies above the town and was the site of a battery laid out by Rufus Putnam during the Revolution, he built Fort Greene, an elliptical stone-scarped battery sheltering another twelve guns. He added flank batteries to Fort Wolcott, increasing its firepower to thirty guns. He also began the construction of an elliptical stone tower to mount eight heavy guns on Dumpling Rocks on Conanicut Island, across the main channel from Fort Adams, and a large rectangular fort designed for sixty guns on Rose Island, located about a mile to the north. Neither was ever finished. During the next

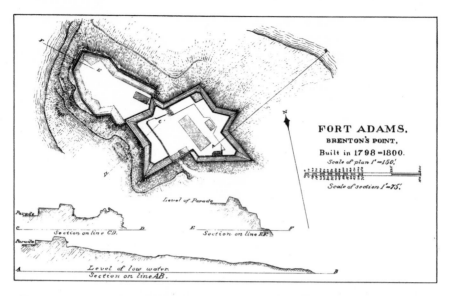

Fort Adams, Newport, Rhode Island, constructed by Lt. Col. Louis Tousard.
Reprinted from George W. Cullum, *Historical Sketch of the Fortification Defenses
of Narragansett Bay* (Washington, 1884).

century the Dumpling tower crumbled into a picturesque ruin, at one time
serving as an artillery target for a flamboyant commander of Fort Adams,
one Captain John Magruder. The fort on Rose Island was for a spell the
quarantine station for the Port of Newport. New construction in New England during the naval war was restricted to Newport. At other harbors
Tousard repaired a number of forts which, though built only a few years
before, had been left ungarrisoned and neglected.[21]

Boston, a bustling commercial community exceeded in size in the United
States only by New York and Philadelphia, had since the inauguration of the
First System relied for protection solely on Castle William. The Massachu-
setts legislature, which at first refused to cooperate at all with the War Department, would in any case have nothing to do with fortifications except on
Castle Island, where defensive works of some kind had existed since 1634.
Massachusetts finally ceded the island to the United States in October 1798,
and Castle William, renamed Fort Independence upon a visit by President
Adams the next year, was repaired by Tousard. But nothing more was done
to bolster Boston's defenses until the quasi war with France was over. The
first stone of a new Fort Independence was laid in May 1801; and in January
1803 a pentagonal, bastioned, fifty-gun brick and stone structure, not materially different in its dimensions from the fort that still stands on Castle Island, was completed. Its principal designer was Jean Foncin, a French
engineer who shortly before had been involved in the planning and
construction of Fort McHenry at Baltimore.[22]

On March 16, 1802, in anticipation of the signing of a treaty of peace by
the European belligerents at Amiens, France, Congress cut back and reorganized the army. Of otherwise no permanent significance, the act created a
separate Corps of Engineers, limited in size to sixteen officers. It provided

Plan of Fort Independence, Boston Harbor, by Jean Foncin.
The National Archives.

further that the Corps was to constitute the personnel of a military academy at West Point. In so doing the act recognized the almost complete absence of trained military and civil engineers in the United States. In effect it established a national college of engineering. Beginning with only four officers and three cadets, the new academy for some years did little more than hobble along with few instructors, few cadets, and few standards of qualification. Colonel Jonathan Williams, who commanded the Corps and the school, complained in 1808 that "the military academy, as it now stands, is like a foundling, barely existing among the mountains, and nutured at a distance out of sight, and almost unknown to its legitimate parents."[23] A decade later, however, the Academy was thoroughly reorganized, and thereafter grew in prestige and influence. Until 1835 it was the only school in the country to graduate engineers, and until nearly 1850 it remained almost the sole source of academically trained members of the profession. It continued under the supervision of the Corps of Engineers until 1866, when it was placed directly under the War Department.

Although headquartered at West Point until 1808, the Corps' first few officers were soon away much of the time inspecting coastal fortifications, a duty that began in April 1803 when the Secretary of War dispatched four officers to the maritime frontier. Major Decius Wadsworth went to New London and Newport, while Lieutenant Alexander Macomb checked over the fort at Portsmouth, New Hampshire.[24] While such tours appear to have been frequent, they were usually of short duration. Appropriations for the armed services in these years of "Jeffersonian economy" were meager, and there was little new fortification construction. In New England there was none at all.

This complacence, born of an untroubled foreign scene, lasted for only a brief time. The Peace of Amiens proved to be tenuous and short, and in 1803 France and England again went to war. Gradually the old troubles and worries of the 1790s reappeared as the impressment of seamen from American ships and the abuse of American shipping, especially by England, kindled resentments. A crisis came in June 1807, when the British frigate *Leopard*, seeking British deserters, fired on the American frigate *Chesapeake* off the

Brig. Gen. Joseph Gardner Swift.
Courtesy of the U.S. Army Engineer Museum, Fort Belvoir, Virginia.

Virginia capes. Twenty-one seamen were killed or wounded, and four of the *Chesapeake's* crew were impressed. America vibrated with exasperation and anger, and had it not been for the restraining hand of President Jefferson the outraged nation would probably have flung itself into war five years earlier than it did. By the time Congress convened in December the excitement was dying down, but the event nevertheless jarred the legislators into voting over $1 million for fortifying Atlantic harbors.

The Corps of Engineers was filled to its complement of sixteen officers, the Atlantic coast was divided into administrative sections, and the "Second System" of fortifications was begun. New England, which comprised the "Eastern Department," was assigned to Major Joseph Gardner Swift. The son of a physician from Nantucket, Massachusetts, Swift had been appointed a cadet of the Corps of Artillerists and Engineers in 1800 by President Adams. Assigned for a time to the fortifications at Newport under the command of Lieutenant Colonel Tousard, he was sent in October 1801 to a languishing military school at West Point organized by that corps earlier in the year. He was one of the three original cadets of the new academy opened by the newly formed Corps of Engineers in July 1802 and, at the age of eighteen, became its first graduate in October. Before taking charge in New England he had acquired several years of practical experience supervising the construction of Fort Johnston on Cape Fear, North Carolina, and for the past year had been in command at West Point.

Swift discovered that the "narrow redoubts" built by Rochefontaine, now badly damaged by the depredations of time, had never adequately protected New England's harbors. He also found that the War Department preferred the counsel of ancient worthies in Washington to the advice of its own young engineers. Advising that new works on Dumpling Rocks and at Coasters Harbor would be better expenditures for the defense of Newport than repairing Forts Wolcott and Adams, he was told that repairs on the old works must first be finished. He advised that any defensive system for Boston should include works on Georges and Long islands, commanding the main channels into the outer harbor, but the War Department chose to fortify Governors Island, located across from Castle Island in the inner harbor. Swift also thought that new fortifications should be designed on the spot where they were required, but he records that he received from the War Department "several plans of a species of Star Fort, contrived at Washington, too small for any flank defense and too complicated for a mere battery, unsuited to the positions for which they were devised." The only resort left to him "was to turn these plans on their centre until they might suit the sites as best they might, in Boston, Portland, and other harbors."[25]

Work was quickly carried out under the direction of locally appointed agents, and by October 1809 Swift could report that his engineering functions in the Eastern Department were ended. Because of the clamor of local apprehensions, many places were fortified, but the modest share of funds allotted to New England meant that the small works of Rochefontaine were repaired rather than replaced, and that most of the new works were not any larger. Connecticut's defenses were readied by the reparation of Fort Trumbull, Rochefontaine's work on the west side of New London Harbor, and by the construction of a small battery at New Haven and a brick gun house at Stonington. In Narragansett Bay, Fort Adams and Fort Wolcott were repaired, a small battery was placed south of Newport, and guns were mounted at Bristol, halfway up the bay. In Massachusetts, Rochefontaine's works at Salem, Marblehead, and Gloucester were repaired; an earthen battery was erected on Plum Island at the mouth of the Merrimack River; and small masonry "Washington Stars," mounting only five or six guns, were built at Plymouth and New Bedford. Boston acquired a larger star fort, supported at the urging of Swift by two outlying batteries, on Governors Island, and a sod battery and a brick gun house near the Charlestown Navy Yard. At Portsmouth, Fort Constitution, Rochefontaine's work on the New Hampshire shore of the harbor, was repaired; a masonry and earth battery, Fort McClary, was built in Kittery on the Maine shore; and a brick gun house was erected in town. At Portland, Fort Preble, another "Washington Star," was placed on Spring Point on one side of the main channel into the harbor, and Fort Scammell, a semi-circular brick battery with a wooden blockhouse, was put on House Island on the other side; a detached battery of Rochefontaine's old fort at the north end of town was repaired, and another of the ubiquitous brick gun houses was constructed.[26]

Responsibility for fortifications east of Portland, Swift learned after arriving in New England, had been assigned by the War Department to Colonel Moses Porter, a veteran artillery officer whose service in the Army extended from the Revolution to his death in 1822. Porter's works, strung along Maine's serrated coast at Georgetown, Edgecomb, Boothbay, St. George, Castine, Machias, and Eastport, were all small batteries of sod or stone. Several were covered by wooden blockhouses and furnished with barracks, but none mounted more than six guns.[27]

Because of the abundance and importance of its harbors, New England was fortified at twenty localities. Only fourteen additional harbors were fortified on the rest of the Atlantic coast.

Matching in 1809 its appropriations of the year before for coastal fortifications, Congress then drastically cut further spending on them. And dominated by anti-navy Jeffersonian Democrats, it trimmed back from already low levels its expenditures on the Navy. When war finally came in 1812 the United States, despite anticipating it for years, was as wretchedly prepared to constrain the power of the British fleet as it was to carry out its long-touted strategy of striking at England by seizing Canada. Bungling and ineptitude characterized much of the conduct of the war on land, while at sea British ships operating out of Halifax and Bermuda seized eastern Maine, plundered the coast almost at will, and blockaded every important Atlantic harbor and bay.

Reaping more humiliations than victories, the nation discovered that righteousness and rhetoric were poor substitutes for military preparations. And it took to heart, if only for a brief time, a few of the lessons the war had taught. On the assumption that England might have to be fought again at some future date, Congress in 1816 voted $838,000 to initiate a program of coastal fortification construction. It also authorized the President to employ a "skillful assistant" to aid the Corps of Engineers, an appointment that was given to General Simon Bernard, a military engineer who had served with Napoleon. To select sites and design works for a new defense system, the

War Department created a Board of Engineers for Fortifications, initially consisting of General Bernard, Colonel William McRee, and Major Joseph G. Totten of the Corps of Engineers, and a captain of the Navy. For a few years, however, things were stormy within the War Department. Bernard was given so much authority and deference by the department that Joseph Swift, who since 1812 had been Chief Engineer, protested. That plans already drawn up by the Corps and approved by the Secretary of War had to await the arrival of Bernard before being put into execution was in his view disgracefully humiliating to the Corps. He and other officers believed that the earlier imported engineers had been mostly bunglers, and that it was impolitic in any case to entrust defenses to any foreigner, whose first interests would likely be those of his own country. After two years of frustration, Swift felt compelled to resign. McRee did the same. Totten stayed in the Corps, but he believed that Bernard's appointment had been a mistake. Bernard remained in the service of the United States until 1831, when he returned to France to become the aide-de-camp of King Louis Philippe and, five years later, his minister of war.[28]

By 1821 the Board of Engineers had elaborated a comprehensive "Third System" of defense. Integrating naval and military planning, it recommended Charlestown, Massachusetts, and Burwell's Bay, Virginia, as sites for great naval arsenals; it designated Boston Roads and Hampton Roads as main harbors of rendezvous, with Narragansett Bay classed as an indispensable accessory to Boston Roads; and it fixed upon New London, Marblehead, Portsmouth, Portland, the estuaries of the Kennebec and Penobscot rivers, and Mount Desert Bay for the New England links of a coast-long chain of naval stations and ports of refuge. This naval design was complemented with projections for fortifications to guard the more important naval stations and anchorages, to protect principal cities and the mouths of navigable rivers, and to hold strong positions that an enemy might seize for his own use. Each proposed fortification was classed in a schedule of construction according to its relative importance. Those in the First Class were to be started as soon as possible; those in the Second Class at a later period; and those in the Third Class at a still more remote time. Although in the course of continued planning priorities were changed and the number of works proposed was greatly increased—in 1825 twenty works were listed for New England; in 1851 the number, including old works to be repaired and new works to be constructed only in the event of impending war, exceeded sixty-five—the essential features of this system of defense remained unchanged for the next half century.[29]

The construction of fortifications began in a climate of reinvigorated nationalism. Wartime divisions quickly gave way to unexampled national unity born of a sense of common participation in a great cause; and the sentiment prevailed that true independence having been preserved, it must not again be imperiled. But as the War of 1812 receded in time, revived sectional antagonisms eroded national enthusiasm; military, naval, and civilian officials assailed permanent fortifications as unnecessary; Congress grew neglectful; and tariff and other policies ate away treasury surpluses. Appropriations for fortifications became more or less perfunctory, and sometimes were not voted at all. Although construction costs increased greatly over the decades with a general rise in prices, the average annual appropriation to the outbreak of the Civil War was considerably less than the initial one of 1816. Many forts urged by the War Department were never begun, and those that were rose with agonizing slowness. The slow pace of construction forced by limited funds was made even more halting by the frequent failure of Congress to vote appropriations early in the year, which often caused the loss of half the working season and created difficulties in arranging contracts, through which practically all work was done, and in securing artisans, mechanics, and laborers when they were needed. Another curb on construction was that the Corps of Engineers was too small for the burden of work assigned to it. Congress had increased the size of the Corps in 1812 to twenty-two officers, but it was not until 1838 that it authorized another increase, permitting a maximum of forty-three officers. Even when forts were readied, because appropriations for ordnance lagged behind those for the forts themselves, completed placements often stood empty of guns.[30]

The Third System of fortifications was no doubt overly ambitious, and many works were never really needed. Certainly some forts were unnecessarily elaborate, the threat of an enemy was seldom clear, and the forts never faced a hostile foreign force. A congressional policy of constant evaluation of the recommendations of the War Department was required. A policy of drift was followed.

Nevertheless, a number of fortresses were built on American coasts under the Third System. And again New England received the heaviest concentration of defenses, with eight localities fortified out of a total of nineteen on the Atlantic coast. Mostly enclosed works, the forts were massive structures of stone or brick depending upon materials available. In New England they were made of granite. Because masonry walls were vulnerable to concentrated cannon fire, the exterior walls, or scarps, on the landward sides of the forts were shielded by structures that had been employed on land fortifications since the invention of gunpowder. The essential components were a ditch in front of the scarp wall, a counterscarp wall on the other side of about the same height, and a glacis, or earthen slope, descending away from the top of the counterscarp. Protecting scarp walls from direct fire, they still preserved traditional impediments to storming assaults. On sea fronts these structures were usually omitted, permitting the installation behind the exposed scarps of one or two tiers of guns in casemates, or bombproof-roofed chambers. With their rows of casemated guns, and with guns mounted close together behind earthen parapets on the tops of the walls—that is, mounted en barbette—the forts could bring a tremendous volume of fire on any ship coming within range. Built as close to the shore as possible to make the fullest use of comparatively short-range guns, the forts were preferably located where the conditions of navigable channels made it necessary for passing vessels to come in fairly close. Since sailing ships could not lay down breaching fire without anchoring, and their wooden hulls were no match for walls of stone or brick, the American pre-Civil War forts were extremely effective installations.[31]

Construction in New England began in 1824 when plans were completed for a new Fort Adams at Newport. Of massive proportions and spreading over twenty acres, the fort was to be an irregular pentagon, prominently bastioned on its sea fronts and casemated on all sides for gun-rooms and quarters. With two tiers of casemate guns on its main sea front, one tier on each of its other two sea fronts, and upper batteries en barbette all around, it would mount nearly five hundred pieces of ordnance.[32]

Supervision of its construction was given to its designer on the Board of Engineers, Major Joseph G. Totten. A native of New Haven, Totten had

Maj. Gen. Joseph Gilbert Totten.
Courtesy of the U.S. Army Engineer Museum,
Fort Belvoir, Virginia.

been graduated from West Point in 1805 at the age of sixteen. In 1808-09 he had assisted Major Swift on harbor defenses in New England and directed the construction of forts at New York City. During the war with England he was chief engineer for the Armies of Niagara and Champlain. Appointed a member of the Board of Engineers in 1816 and serving on it for more than two decades, he developed principles of coast defense construction that were followed for a century. Of special note were his experiments with casemate embrasures. Employing new designs, he reduced their openings to less than a quarter of that on many European forts and still provided scope for guns to swing laterally through sixty degrees as compared to the forty degrees that was standard abroad. He introduced on the world scene the use of armor plate in seacoast fortifications when he designed iron throats for embrasures and two-inch-thick iron shutters that were opened when a gun was fired and then automatically slammed shut.[33] Appointed Chief Engineer in 1838, Totten commanded the Corps until 1864, a length of time never close to being equalled.

If Totten had few peers among nineteenth century engineers, he could not speed the construction of Fort Adams beyond limits set by small and irregular appropriations. The fortress rose inchmeal. It was not ready to receive any ordnance until 1841, and it was not until 1858 that all its batteries were completed and its quarters equipped to receive a full garrison. Some measure of benefit, however, did result from this long period of construction. Little was known in the United States about building such great defense structures, and various principles and details of the art of fortification were used at Fort Adams in new combinations, compelling Totten to make numerous experiments to test materials and ideas. He made the first experiments on the expansion and contraction of building stone by natural changes in temperature and on the relative stiffness and strength of certain kinds of timber. He experimented with the composition of mortars, the thickness of sustaining walls, and the thrust of arches. In this work he was assisted over the years by a large proportion of the young officers of the Corps sent to serve apprenticeships with him. Fort Adams thus became for the Corps a kind of graduate school of applied science.[34]

Fort Adams, Newport, Rhode Island, c.1930. The outer defenses employed on the landward side of Third System forts appear at the right.

Boston Harbor was of key importance in the new defense system, but for more than a decade other demands on the Corps of Engineers were too numerous and pressing for it to do more than build a seawall on Georges Island, on the harbor's outer rim, to protect it from erosion and preserve it as a site for fortifications. This project, carried out between 1825 and 1829, was also directed by Totten. The construction of a fort on Georges Island was begun in 1833. A sprawling, bastioned pentagonal of Quincy granite, with a single tier of casemates all around, Fort Warren was designed to take three hundred guns. Major Sylvanus Thayer was placed in charge.[35]

Major Sylvanus Thayer.
Courtesy of the U.S. Army Engineer Museum,
Fort Belvoir, Virginia.

Born in Braintree, Massachusetts, Thayer had attended Dartmouth College, had transferred to West Point in 1807, and a year later had joined the Corps of Engineers. Like Totten, he had assisted Major Swift in constructing batteries in New England and during the War of 1812 had served on the Canadian frontier. In 1815 he and Colonel William McRee were sent abroad to study fortifications, army workshops, and military schools in France. Returning in 1817, he was appointed superintendent of the Military Academy. Taking over a chaotic institution without entrance qualifications, definite course of study, or set period of residence, he transformed it within a few years into an American version of the famous École Polytechnique at Paris, making a West Point education stand for a solid program of study and high standards of efficiency and honor. His fame as "Father of the Military Academy," however, has eclipsed his later, lengthier service in New England. From 1833, when, tired of having his authority undermined by President Jackson, he was relieved of command of the Academy at his own request, until 1857, when he took leave of absence because of broken health, he was in charge of most of the work of the Corps of Engineers from Boston northward. During this period he was also on the Board of Engineers for Fortifications, serving after 1838 as its president.[36]

Taking up residence in Boston, Thayer directed work on Fort Warren for the next twenty-four years, experiencing the same difficulties and delays as did Totten at Fort Adams. Nine years passed before the fort's exterior walls were finished and provisions could be made for the temporary mounting of a few guns in a crisis. Fifteen more years went by before it was fully ready for its armament bearing on the main channel and partially ready for guns on its other fronts. When the Civil War broke out, three more years later, Fort Warren was ready for its casemate guns and about three-quarters of its barbette armament, but was still not finished.[37]

Fort Warren, Boston Harbor. View of the parade. Courtesy of Gerald Butler.

Fort Independence, Boston Harbor. Rebuilt by Colonel Thayer as a casemated work. Courtesy of Gerald Butler.

A year before Thayer came to Boston, Congress had voted a small sum for repairs on Fort Independence. Because no engineer was available, however, nothing was immediately done. Taking up the project in 1833, Thayer found that the funds could be stretched only to building a protective seawall and repairing the island's wharf. The appropriation had been based on 1831 prices, and construction costs in the area had meantime risen twenty-five percent. Partial repairs of Fort Independence would in any event have been a waste. According to the Board of Engineers, which at this time consisted solely of Totten and Thayer, the outmoded and dilapidated fort needed to be wholly rebuilt to provide a secondary line of defense to Fort Warren and other projected works in the outer harbor. Thoroughly redesigning it to guard the inner harbor with seventy-nine guns and to house stores, recruits, and hospitals in time of war, the two engineers planned to replace its decaying brick scarps with walls of granite more than double in height, replace its tumbling-down quarters, magazines, and storerooms with bombproof casemates, and replace or reshape most of its accessory structures. With an optimism as to congressional largess difficult to comprehend, the House Committee on Military Affairs approved their plan on the ground that since Fort Warren would not be finished for five or six more years, a reconstructed Fort Independence would take less time. The reconstruction of Fort Independence, however, consumed more than a dozen years. Begun in 1836, the fort was ready to receive some armament in 1845, and by the end of 1848 was nearing completion. Then a want of funds and the presence of a garrison brought work practically to a standstill.[38]

In 1838 Congress voted $25,000 for fortifications at New London Harbor, where Rochefontaine had built two small redoubts, Fort Trumbull and Fort

Griswold, in the 1790s. On the recommendation of Colonel Totten the money was applied to Fort Trumbull, on the west side of the harbor, and plans were prepared for a new pentagonal of granite housing fifty-two guns in its main structure and additional armament in two exterior batteries. Captain George Washington Cullum was placed in charge of construction. Graduated from the Military Academy five years before and sent to Fort Adams as an assistant engineer, Cullum was another officer of the Corps who was to spend many years in New England. The author of numerous technical and historical papers, he is best known for his monumental *Biographical Register of the Officers and Graduates of the United States Military Academy*, a work that has been brought down to recent date by later compilers. Fort Trumbull, smaller and less costly than the other new forts in New England, took less time to build. Planning his work with an eye to quick defense, Cullum had one of the exterior batteries ready to receive some guns by 1841. By 1845 the main structure was capable of resisting assault and of defending the harbor with more than half its proposed armament. Five years later the fort was completed.[39]

Captain George W. Cullum.
U.S. Signal Corps photo (Brady Collection) in the
National Archives.

The contruction of the next fort in New England came about more by accident than design. In 1837 peaceful relations with England were suddenly threatened by incidents connected with rebellions in Upper and Lower Canada, causing the Senate to request from Secretary of War Joel Poinsett "a plan for the protection of the north and east boundaries of the United States." Poinsett replied in January 1838 by reminding the Senate that a thorough plan of defense was already in existence. Had it been prosecuted with the same vigor with which it was begun, he commented caustically, inland posts might now be properly garrisoned and coastal fortifications ready to afford some protection to points of attack. But as it was, "after a period of more than twenty years and expenditure of many millions of dollars, there is not a fortress on our long line of sea defenses capable of resisting an armed brig." What was needed, he advised, was to complete without delay the defense system long proposed by the Board of Engineers, especially all forts of the First Class. But Congress, apparently not greatly disturbed after a brief flurry of excitement, did not materially increase appropriations for defense.[40]

Then in February 1839 a crisis came. Wrangling frontiersmen and self-important local officials set aflame a dispute over the boundary between Maine and Canada, the legacy of imprecise language of the Peace Treaty of 1783, that diplomats had hitherto kept within the safe bounds of negotiation and arbitration. When a party of Canadian lumberjacks began operations on the Aroostook River, the state of Maine sent an armed posse of American lumberjacks to arrest them. But New Brunswick sent a larger force, and fifty of the Maine men were captured and put in jail. Maine called out its militia, New Brunswick did the same, and troops glared nervously at each other across a stream only thirty yards wide. Canadian provinces voted war credits; and Congress, on March 3, voted $10 million to resist invasion. Fortunately, General Winfield Scott, troubleshooting for President Van Buren, had already arranged a truce several days before. The "Restook War" was destined to go down in history as bloodless.

On the same day that it excitedly voted millions to defend a disputed patch of woods, Congress voted only $327,000 for fortifications, less than a quarter of which applied to New England. The next year it voted considerably more, but the condition of the treasury forbade the use of the funds until the following spring. When Poinsett made his annual report in December 1840, he had to state that fortifications on the Canadian frontier had not been much advanced. He advised that since the Maine boundary was still unsettled, works in that region should be confined to the erection of barracks at the juncture of the Mattawamkeag and Penobscot rivers, which was well below the area in dispute. Congress voted $25,000 for this purpose, Army Engineers made a reconnaissance, but before anything further was done the Webster-Ashburton Treaty of August 1842, setting the boundary far to the north, removed the need for this backwoods installation.[41]

Totten now requested permission to apply the funds to a fort on the Penobscot River at the narrows in Bucksport near its mouth. A fort at this locality, originally in the Third Class of works proposed by the Board of Engineers, had by 1835 been advanced to the First Class. Perhaps because Maine had long been petitioning for such a defense, Congress consented, and in 1843 the construction of Fort Knox began. Built of granite quarried from nearby Mount Waldo and planned for 145 guns, the fort was designed as an irregular pentagon skirted on its river fronts by two earthen barbette batteries. Construction for the first several years was entrusted to First Lieutenant Isaac Stevens. Initially an assistant to Colonel Thayer, Stevens took full charge of the work in December 1843 when Thayer left for Europe on an extended leave of absence because of ill health. Like Cullum at Fort

Trumbull, Stevens centered his attention first on the fort's exterior batteries and by the fall of 1845 had one of them ready for armament. The main structure of the fort, however, went up at the more familiar pace. In 1858 Captain John D. Kurtz, then in charge, reported that it was only half finished. When the Civil War began Fort Knox was ready for most of its guns on the water fronts, but much work still remained to be done.[42]

After 1838 a definite pattern of construction was discernible at the forts going up in New England. Fort Adams, which remained under the general supervision of Colonel Totten after he became Chief Engineer, was finally readied by 1841 to mount some ordnance. Thayer pushed ahead vital parts of the forts at Boston. Cullum and Stevens started Fort Trumbull and Fort Knox by concentrating on their external barbette batteries. This was in line with policy laid down by Totten upon becoming Chief Engineer in December 1838. Working with limited funds, Totten aimed at achieving the greatest measure of defense possible by bringing portions of forts successively into serviceable condition rather than raising them in more uniform fashion. Totten also launched a program for repairing old forts at important positions where new works had not been authorized. Several of the long-neglected older forts in New England were thus put in working order, primarily by replacing decaying wooden gun platforms with granite ones now permitted by a new model seacoast gun carriage, but sometimes also by other repairs and alterations.

Among the works repaired were the exterior batteries of the old star fort on Governors Island in Boston Harbor. But the Board of Engineers believed that stronger defenses here were especially necessary, and by 1845 it had completed plans for a casemated tower surrounded by several outlying batteries. Congress approved the project the next year. Captain Cullum was assigned to supervise it, and the construction of Fort Winthrop was begun. Cullum immediately prepared three exterior batteries for service, readying them for guns within a year, before even starting to clear away the old star on the site of the new tower. It was not until 1855, however, that the tower's foundations were completed and any superstructure began to show. By 1861 the tower could in a pinch be equipped with barbette guns, but neither it nor all the exterior batteries were close to being finished.[43]

Also repaired was the diminutive Washington Star that Swift had built at New Bedford. Because it was entirely too small for the important position it occupied, Totten stated in his report of 1842, it deserved no further expenditures. For the next fifteen years a new work here was among those the Chief Engineer repeatedly urged upon Congress, but to no avail. Sometimes Totten could not hold in his exasperation. In his annual report of 1855 he noted that for seventeen years he had pressed strenuously for the means with which to complete the nation's military defenses, and had Congress granted the sums asked, the most important points on the Atlantic would now be secured. "If, therefore," he admonished, "circumstances of peril should awaken the nation to a sense of the backwardness of defensive preparations at any important place, it must be understood that the Engineer Department is in no way responsible for the delay."[44]

Two years later Congress provided for several works that Totten had long been urging—and for several more that he had not. Finally authorized to build a modern fort at New Bedford, plans for which had been prepared a decade before by Major Richard Delafield and Captain Robert E. Lee, the War Department purchased a site on Clarks Point, commanding the harbor's entrance. The purchase, however, did not include existing roadways, and there were citizens of the town who preferred the pleasures of a popular drive along the shore to the protection of a fortress that might never be needed. It was two years before a special board of engineers reached a compromise whereby the shore road was rerouted for a short stretch, enough to permit the building of the fort but still leaving New Bedfordians with their scenic drive only slightly interrupted. Work on the fort—it was unnamed for four decades—was now rapidly pushed forward under the direction of Captain Cullum. Pentagonal in shape, with two tiers of gun casemates on four water fronts and barbette armament above, it was designed for seventy guns. By 1861 the preparatory work was done, the foundations were in, and the fort's scarps were just beginning to show.[45]

Interior view of the gun casemates of the fort at Clarks Point, New Bedford (named Fort Rodman in 1893). Courtesy of Wilbar M. Hoxie.

Two new forts were also authorized for Maine. Fort Popham was to be located on Hunnewells Point at the mouth of the Kennebec River in Georgetown, where Colonel Moses Porter had built a small battery in 1809. Plans called for a forty-two-gun fort shaped like a half-moon, with two tiers of casemates on its convex, or water, side. But here too hitches developed. The tip of the point was government owned, but difficulties in getting clear title to necessary adjoining property delayed the breaking of ground until after the Civil War had begun. Fort Gorges was to be built in Portland Harbor. No site had been selected nor plans prepared for it by the Engineer Department. The fort's proponent appears to have been Secretary of War Jefferson Davis, who decided upon it after a visit to Portland in 1857, "to the great rejoicing of the Democrats." Hog Island, an acre and a half of bare ledge in the harbor, was chosen as the site, apparently by the local engineer, Captain John D. Kurtz. Kurtz also seems to have been the principal designer of the fort. Whenever defenses were planned, the local officer was always an ad hoc member of the Board of Engineers. Hexagonal in design, with two tiers of gun casemates on its five channel fronts and a barbette tier all around, the fort would mount ninety-five guns. Situated so that it could rake vessels coming down the main channel while they were engaged with the guns of Forts Preble and Scammell, it also would cover two other deep water entrances into the harbor. With planning quickly accomplished, Kurtz began work on the fort in 1858.[46]

Fort Gorges, Portland Harbor.

The "circumstances of peril" that an exasperated Chief Engineer Totten had hypothesized in 1855 materialized a short six years later. But they arose in a way never contemplated under the defense system. When the Civil War broke out the Confederacy had no navy and was apparently without the means of constructing one. Yet Northern ports were not immune from attack. For more than a year intervention by European powers on the side of the South was a worrisome possibility. The South acquired several crack cruisers from abroad, and it came dangerously close to getting from British shipbuilders two ironclads reputedly powerful enough to destroy the Union fleet and lay Northern coastal cities under tribute.[47] In March 1862 the brief but murderous career in Hampton Roads of the South's improvised ironclad, the *Virginia*, better known as the *Merrimac*, threw both Washington and Northern coastal cities into near panic.

The speed with which fortifications now went forward in New England, after nearly four decades of sluggish activity, was striking. Forts Warren, Winthrop, and Independence at Boston were all essentially finished by the end of the war. Fort Knox on the Penobscot River and the new work at New Bedford were nearly so. Fort Gorges at Portland was brought to the point where its gun casemates were ready for armament, and Fort Popham on the Kennebec River, although not begun until 1862, was nearly completed on its water fronts. The old forts on opposite sides of Portland and Portsmouth harbors were redesigned in 1862 and 1863 (all except Fort McClary in Kittery as casemated works), and by the close of the war work on them was well under way. To defend the west passage into Narragansett Bay two permanent earthen batteries were erected on Dutch Island, in the center of the passage. And to protect smaller commercial towns against attack by Confederate cruisers like the famed *Alabama*, old forts dating back to 1795 were hastily repaired or rebuilt, and temporary earthen works, sometimes nothing more than trenches on a hill, were installed up and down the coast.[48] The war came to an end, however, without any of these defenses being challenged.

By this time there had been several turnovers of Army Engineers in New England. The names of Totten, Thayer, and Cullum are most closely associated with the imposing Third System forts that were strung from New London to the Penobscot. They designed most of them and for years directed their construction. During the 1850s, partly because of a rule instituted in 1854 that officers at stations must be rotated at least every four years, no less than fourteen officers had charge of fortifications in New England. Usually the number at any one time was four, and upon the outbreak of the war it was three. These officers—Lieutenant John C. Palfrey, Lieutenant C. Seafort Stewart, and Captain George W. Cullum, who was back on New England's south shore after several years' service elsewhere—were hastily given more crucial assignments. For some months New England's forts were left in charge of civil agents. But upon the acceleration of defense construction, engineer officers again took over. When the war drew to a close five officers—Lieutenant Colonel John D. Macomb, Majors Thomas L. Casey and Charles E. Blunt, and Captains Henry M. Robert and Samuel M. Mansfield—were constructing and keeping in order defenses from the Canadian border to the New York state line.[49]

But the era of the Third System of fortifications had come to an end. Special boards of engineers, studying New England's major harbors, were already planning modifications on the forts. Years in the building, they had suddenly become obsolete. During the war revolutionary developments had taken place in naval weaponry, both in the United States and abroad. Corresponding changes now had to be made in the art of fortification.

II CIVIL WORKS BEGIN

From the southeastern corner of Massachusetts the sandy arm of Cape Cod thrusts more than thirty miles into the Atlantic. Flanked on the east and south by shoals, frequently shrouded in fog, and taking the full brunt of northeast storms, the cape was dreaded by all mariners. Yet because coastal shipping was the only practicable way of transporting goods along the seaboard in the early nineteenth century, an estimated five thousand coasters compassed the cape in the single year 1823. Since the first settlers had come to Massachusetts, men had talked about eliminating this dangerous passage and shortening the sailing distance to New York by the construction of a canal, and it was to determine the feasibility of this idea that three men came to New England in October 1824. General Simon Bernard, Major Joseph Totten, and John L. Sullivan, a civil engineer, appointed a Board of Engineers for Internal Improvements by President Monroe the previous May, were on a signal mission. A new and non-military function had been assigned to the Corps of Engineers. This was the consequential task of planning transportation facilities to link together the sprawling parts of the still raw and undeveloped nation.

Sixteen years earlier, considerations of commerce and defense—the easy movement of produce and of military units and supplies—had led Secretary of the Treasury Albert Gallatin to prepare at the request of the Senate a plan for tying the new nation together with government-sponsored roads and canals. Foreign difficulties had pushed his scheme aside, but in 1819 Secretary of War John C. Calhoun elaborated a similar program at the request of the House of Representatives. Calhoun advocated the extensive use of Army Engineers in making surveys and plans, for, inevitably, the Corps of Engineers was already becoming involved in the work of improving internal communications. On essentially military assignments Army Engineers were projecting transportation routes while making western explorations. They were making navigational surveys of the nation's great inland lakes and rivers. They were laying out military roads and occasionally other highways. Local governments and private corporations, faced with a critical shortage of civil engineers, were calling on the War Department for the Corps' assistance in making canal surveys. Congress also turned to the Corps when engineering talent was needed to formulate plans for a breakwater in Delaware Bay and to determine how to improve a harbor on Lake Erie. In 1823 President Monroe recommended that Army Engineers survey a proposed canal to be built by private enterprise between the Potomac and Ohio rivers.[1]

With federal encouragement of "internal improvements" conspicuously on the increase, Congress on April 30, 1824 passed a General Survey Act authorizing the President to employ army and civil engineers to make surveys, plans, and estimates of roads and canals of national importance. It was to administer this act that the Board of Engineers for Internal Improvements was created the next month. The board performed this function until 1831, when its duties were taken over by the War Department's Topographical Bureau.

The Topographical Bureau, like the Corps of Engineers, had roots in the American Revolution, when three "geographers" had been appointed by Congress to carry out topographical duties for the army. There was no organized corps, however, until 1813, when Congress provided for sixteen topographical engineers to serve with armies in the field. At the conclusion of the War of 1812 the corps was disbanded, but in April 1816 it was reestablished with the appointment of ten topographical engineers to the general staff. Later that year, upon the creation of the Board of Engineers for Fortifications, the corps was placed under the orders of the board to carry out coastal and harbor surveys. Two years later Secretary of War Calhoun assigned the topographers directly to the Engineer Department, a recently established special command consisting of the Corps of Engineers, the Military Academy, and now the Topographical Bureau. In 1831 Secretary of War John Eaton made the bureau an independent office within the War Department; and in 1838 Congress reorganized it into the Corps of Topographical Engineers. Existing separately within the War Department until March 1863, the Topographical Corps was at that time merged into the Corps of Engineers. Signifying this fusion, the title of Chief Engineer was changed to Chief of Engineers.[2]

The Board of Engineers for Internal Improvements, assisted by surveying brigades of topographical engineers, officers borrowed from the line, and civil engineers, examined all the major land and water routes proposed by Gallatin and Calhoun, and many other routes as well. And in accordance with the purpose of the General Survey Act it began formulating plans for great national arteries of transportation. But enthusiasm for internal improvements at federal expense was a fragile sentiment. Part of a magnificent scheme inspired by the nationalist feelings prevailing after the War of 1812, internal improvements would bind the nation together physically while protective tariffs and a national bank united its sections economically, each region complementing the others to the benefit of all. Grand in concept but unworkable in practice, the "American System," as it was later named by Henry Clay, was soon wrecked on obstacles of constitutional objections, partisan politics, and state and sectional rivalries. Ultimately, the development of transportation in America was left largely to state and private enterprise.[3] Nevertheless the General Survey Act of 1824 remains a landmark measure, for it inaugurated the extensive and continuing use of Army Engineers in works of a civil character.

Both Gallatin and Calhoun had recommended a canal bypassing Cape Cod as part of a chain of artificial waterways creating a sheltered passage stretching from Boston to Savannah. Gallatin had been specific, believing that the only feasible route was from Boston Harbor to Narrangasett Bay along a course between Weymouth and Taunton surveyed by the state of Massachusetts in 1806. The Board of Engineers for Internal Improvements reconnoitered this route during its investigations of October 1824 and, agreeing that a canal here would be of great value, recommended an instrument survey. The board also examined a long-advocated route between the towns of Barnstable and Hyannis, about halfway out to the elbow of the cape, but found the terrain too high. It was a third route, cutting across the base of the cape between Barnstable Bay and Buzzards Bay, that most interested the board. There seemed to be no doubt of its practicability, no serious obstacles to construction, and no great costs involved. Less than eight miles long, the route was traversed most of the way by rivers flowing north and south, with the ridge between them rising only about thirty feet above sea level and at one point only three-quarters of a mile wide. The colonists of Plymouth had begun using this natural artery as early as 1623 to trade with Indians south of the cape and later with the Dutch at New Amsterdam. By 1676 they were talking of cutting "a passage from the South Sea to the North." In 1697 and again in 1776 the General Court of Massachusetts appointed committees to investigate the feasibility of this idea, but these efforts came to nothing. In 1791 the Massachusetts legislature again appointed a committee, two surveys were made, and from that time on the question was intermittently before the General Court. Private interest in a canal had also been strong, and in 1818 another survey was made by a Boston corporation chartered that year.

Examining the route with the data of these earlier investigations in hand, the board assigned Major Paul H. Perrault to begin a survey immediately. An old-timer in government service, Perrault had been one of the civilian engineers employed by Washington in 1794 and was one of the first officers appointed to the Corps of Topographical Engineers when it was formed in 1813. Although Perrault's survey was finished in February 1825, complete plans and estimates for the canal were not forthcoming from the busy board until nearly five years later. The plans called for a ditch sixty feet wide at the

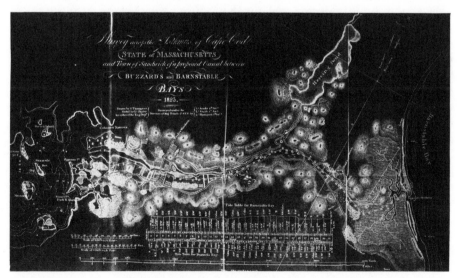

Route of the proposed Cape Cod Canal surveyed by Mayor Paul H. Perrault in 1824-25.

top, thirty-six feet wide at the bottom, and eight feet deep. Because of considerable differences in the heights and times of tide at Barnstable Bay and Buzzards Bay, the canal was to be equipped with locks at each end. Helping to draw up the plans was one Major William Tell Poussin, a protégé and assistant of General Bernard enlisted into the Topographical Engineers from France. Leaving the service of the United States soon after Bernard departed, Poussin published in Paris in 1843 a report on internal improvements in the United States in which he described the Cape Cod canal as one of the greatest pieces of construction contemplated on the American continent. But since neither Congress, nor Massachusetts, nor private enterprise took any further action, the project languished until 1860, when it was again taken up by the Massachusetts legislature.[4]

The Cape Cod canal was not the only artificial waterway contemplated for New England. A near-mania of canal-building soon seized the nation; and as New England communities eyed the success of New York's Erie Canal, opened in 1825, and the prosperity of the counties through which it passed, they pressed their claims for waterways in their own regions. Since the extensive building of canals, and later of railroads, caused a greater demand for civil engineers than the profession could supply, both states and chartered companies looked to the federal government for assistance; and for some years the services of Army Engineers were lent to them. One result of this technical aid was that by 1830 a round dozen other canal routes in New England had been surveyed by United States Topographical Engineers.

One route was the Weymouth-Taunton course linking Boston Harbor with Narragansett Bay. Another was between Rutland, Vermont, and Whitehall, New York, to connect with the newly opened Champlain Canal running to the Hudson River. The other routes, while each had its own state or private sponsors, would together have formed three great lines of communication reaching across northern New England from Lake Champlain to the Atlantic. Intersecting the principal rivers of the region—the Connecticut, the Merrimack, the Androscoggin, and the Kennebec, which were also surveyed with a view to improving navigation—the canals would have formed with the rivers a huge transportation grid serving five states. The northernmost line of projected canals ran east and south like a jagged, descending set of stairs from north of Burlington on Lake Champlain to Casco Bay in Maine, where Portland would serve as its Atlantic terminus. The second series of proposed waterways ran in an almost straight southeasterly line from Burlington to Portsmouth, New Hampshire. Roughly paralleling this line forty to fifty miles to the south, the third great projected artery ran from Montpelier, Vermont, where it connected with the second line, to the Merrimack River, joining it just north of Concord, New Hampshire. Following river valleys for most of their lengths, the routes were meticulously planned for utility, adequate supplies of water, and economy of construction.

The Weymouth-Taunton route was lined by a brigade under the command of Major John Anderson. Appointed a Topographical Engineer when the Corps was formed in 1813, Anderson was kept on topographical duty after the war in order to complete surveys that he and Major Isaac Roberdeau were making on the northern frontier. Believing that the Corps should be reinstituted, he and Roberdeau submitted a memorandum to the Secretary of War that was instrumental in bringing this about. While surveying the Weymouth-Taunton route, Anderson was also making the first river and harbor surveys in New England, where he continued to be stationed until his death in 1834. A Vermont segment of the northern string of canal routes and the upper Connecticut River were surveyed by Assistant Civil Engineer DeWitt Clinton, Jr., while a lower stretch of the Connecticut River was lined by another civil engineer, Holmes Hutchinson. The rest of the surveys were directed by Major John J. Abert, assisted by eight artillery lieutenants.[5] A West Point graduate of 1811, Abert was another of the War of 1812 topographical engineers. Reappointed to the Corps in 1816, he was engaged in topographical surveys until he became chief of the Topographical Bureau in 1829, a position he held for the next thirty-two years.

Colonel John James Abert.
Courtesy of the U.S. Army Engineer
Museum, Fort Belvoir, Virginia.

The New England canal surveys were completed by 1830, but because of the small size of his corps, Colonel Abert reported in 1835, his engineers were still working on the drawings and reports. This was the last mention of the canals in Abert's annual reports. By this time railroads were gripping the nation's attention. Less obliged to conform to the lay of the land and not freezing up for part of the year, rails had pushed ditches from the scene of new enterprise in the East. The plotting of the great New England canal system became only a brief, unrealized, and rather romantic adventure.

In 1825 Robert Stephenson opened the Stockton and Darlington Railroad line in England. Interest in railroads immediately spread to the United States, and numerous companies were formed to construct roads along the eastern seaboard. The first was the Baltimore and Ohio Railroad Company, chartered in 1827. With only a few exceptions, the engineers who conducted the surveys and made the plans and estimates for these early railroads were Army Engineers. Being roads of a kind, they were accepted as within the terms of the General Survey Act. As early as 1828 a New England company, the Hudson and Berkshire Railroad, applied for engineering assistance, and upon orders of the Secretary of War, Major Perrault surveyed a route from Hudson, New York, to Pittsfield, Massachusetts, part of a projected road extending to Boston. The Secretary instructed that the expenses of the survey, except for the personal compensation of Perrault and his assistants, were to be borne by the company, these being the terms on which government assistance had been given to the Baltimore and Ohio Railroad. This set the pattern, and these were the terms on which all future technical assistance was given to railroads. Horsepower would probably be used on the line, Perrault said in a report to the War Department in January 1829. But should locomotive engines be adopted and perform as they were represented to do, he added, then "every and all difficulties in the way of transportation would disappear at once."[6]

The first trial of a steam locomotive in the United States took place in August 1830, and crude as these screaming, wood-burning monsters belching fire and steam were, they worked. Railroads were not to be another passing enthusiasm. In the next several years a number of surveys were made for them in New England by Army Engineers whose names are the most famous in the history of early American railroading.

Captain William G. McNeill and Lieutenant George W. Whistler had closely connected army railroading careers. They had been close friends at West Point, and when McNeill was assigned to make a survey for the pioneer Baltimore and Ohio Railroad, he requested that Whistler be also assigned. In 1828 the company sent them to examine railroad building in England, and upon their return to the United States they worked together on a number of roads. Until 1837, when he resigned from the Army to continue a notable engineering career, McNeill was permitted by the War Department to engage almost exclusively in railroad activities. Whistler, although commissioned in the artillery, spent his army career assigned to topographical duty. Graduating from West Point in 1819, he spent the greater part of the next two years making surveys for military defenses in New England. His first assignment was at Salem, Massachusetts, where it was desired to show on a map the differences in elevation between the shore line of the harbor and the terrain commanding it. Whistler accomplished this by a system of contour lines that showed at a glance the height of every part of the surveyed area above an assumed datum plane. Contour lines had previously been used only on nautical charts to indicate depths. After Whistler's application they became universally employed in topography. Resigning from the Army in December 1833, Whistler was a civil engineer in the United States until 1842, when he was invited to Russia to construct his greatest work, the St. Petersburg-Moscow Railroad. Seven years later he died in Russia.

Major Stephen H. Long, a native of Hopkinton, New Hampshire, and a graduate of Dartmouth College, joined the Topographical Corps when it was reinstituted in 1816. He was already famous as a Western explorer when he was assigned in 1827 to the Baltimore and Ohio Railroad as a consulting engineer. He later became the president of its board of engineers. The author of the first railroad manual published in the United States, he developed tables relating to grades and curves that eliminated the necessity of field computations. He also invented a truss-type wooden bridge that was widely used. Devoting his life to the Topographical Corps, he later spent many

Captain William G. McNeill. Courtesy of the U.S. Military Academy Archives.

Lieutenant George W. Whistler. Courtesy of the U.S. Military Academy Archives.

Major Stephen H. Long. U.S. Signal Corps Photo (Brady Collection) in the National Archives.

years supervising the improvement of the great rivers of the West. In 1861 he became the last chief of the Corps.

A fourth army engineer involved in New England railroading was Captain William H. Swift. The brother of Chief Engineer Joseph Swift, William entered West Point in 1813 at the age of twelve. Enjoying the permissiveness that then prevailed, and given more to frolic than to study, he had little chance of receiving a commission when Major Thayer began reorganizing the academy in 1817. To salvage William's army career, the Chief Engineer had him attached to Major Long's expedition to the Rocky Mountains that left Pittsburgh in 1819. Two years on the western rivers and plains had the desired effect of making the boy a man. On one occasion Swift was captured by a band of Pawnee Indians. The chief wanted to adopt him, but after some months he allowed William to rejoin the expedition. Upon his return from the West, Swift was commissioned in the artillery and assigned to topographical duty. Transferred to the Topographical Bureau in 1832 upon the resignation of Poussin, he spent much of his subsequent army career in New England. Resigning from the army in 1849, he became a prominent railroad executive.[7]

In 1832-33 McNeill was placed in charge of railroad surveys made in New England between Boston and Providence, Providence and Stonington, and New London and Worcester. As usual, Whistler was detailed to assist him. McNeill was also assisted by William Swift, who after making several railroad surveys in New York was assigned to make the Providence-Stonington survey. Later McNeill carried out surveys between Taunton and New Bedford, Boston and Lowell, and Boston and Albany. Stephen Long, headquartered from 1834 to 1837 at his home in Hopkinton, New Hampshire, was in charge of surveys in northern New England. He reconnoitered a route from Boston to Whitehall, New York, which prominent citizens of New Hampshire had petitioned the Secretary of War to have surveyed; and he instrument surveyed the segment of it between the Connecticut River and Concord, New Hampshire. For the state of Maine he surveyed a route from Portland to Bangor, which would extend a road from Boston already under construction. Maine also wanted a railroad that would connect with a projected Canadian line running to Quebec. Long therefore reconnoitered routes from Portland, Wiscasset, and Belfast to the Canadian border near the headstream of the River Chaudiere, and finding the Belfast route the best, surveyed it. The route from the Canadian border to Quebec, following the River Chaudiere, was reconnoitered by Captain Patrick Yule of the Royal Engineers.[8]

The shortage in America of men capable of directing large engineering operations caused the War Department to permit Army Engineers not only to make surveys and plans for railroads but also to supervise their construction. William McNeill was a company engineer for all of the railroads he surveyed in New England. The Western Railroad of Massachusetts, as the Boston and Albany line was then called, also later employed William Swift as its superintending engineer. Railroading by Army Engineers for private enterprise, however, lasted for only a few years. The failure of the federal government to initiate a national system of internal improvements had resulted in the General Survey Act becoming merely a vehicle for providing engineering assistance to state and private agencies. Complaints against this practice and the pressure of other duties on Army Engineers finally resulted in new legislation. In 1838 the provision of the General Survey Act authorizing the employment of civil engineers was repealed; the practice of borrowing officers from the line for the development of internal improvements was prohibited; and the employment of officers by incorporated companies was forbidden.[9]

By this time, however, the law did little more than register the current situation. It affected only four officers—in New England only Captain Swift—and it had no bearing on what by now was a more important civil function of Army Engineers. For since 1824 Army Engineers had also been at work developing the nation's harbors and improving navigation on its rivers. The small amount of such work that had been done earlier had been carried out almost wholly by the states. What little the federal government had done had been under the direction of the Treasury Department, which from an early date had assisted navigation by erecting lighthouses, beacons, buoys, and public piers. Although the Corps of Engineers had recently been called upon a few times to develop plans, its role in improving rivers and harbors really began in May 1824, when Congress voted appropriations for improving navigation on the Ohio and Mississippi rivers, for deepening the channel of the harbor of Presque Isle on Lake Erie, and for repairing Long Beach at Plymouth, Massachusetts.[10] Although no agency was designated to carry out these projects, they appear to have been entrusted by the President to the Corps of Engineers as a matter of course. Less than a month before, by the General Survey Act, Congress had assigned the Corps a comparable civil function.

In 1826 Congress voted appropriations for more than twenty works and surveys. Thereafter until 1838 it annually enacted similar river and harbor bills. Under their provisions Army Engineers surveyed more than forty riv-

Long Beach, forming Plymouth Harbor. A congressional appropriation of $20,000 on May 26, 1824, "to repair Plymouth Beach, in the state of Massachusetts, and thereby prevent the harbour at that place from being destroyed," initiated river and harbor work by the Corps of Engineers in New England.

ers and harbors in New England, and at most of these localities carried out works of improvement.[11] The surveys of the rivers and harbors and the plans for improving them were usually made by Topographical Engineers. The plans and estimates of cost were then reported to Congress for its decision whether to vote appropriations for the projects. If funds were provided, regular engineers of the Corps supervised the work.

The beach at Plymouth, the Corps' first project in New England, was a long narrow sandspit forming the town's harbor. Constantly endangered by water and wind erosion, it had been a subject of concern to citizens of the town as early as 1702, when they had made it a crime to fell trees on it or fire its grass. The work of the Corps was begun by Lieutenant William H. Chase, who planned to build a cribwork breakwater along the beach's outer shore and to arrest the drifting of sand by erecting brush fences and planting beach grass. The next year the project was taken over by Major Totten, now stationed at Newport to construct Fort Adams. Totten maintained general oversight of the project, while daily supervision was exercised by a hired local agent. This was the manner in which most of the early river and harbor work by the Corps was carried out. Engineer officers supervised a number of works in an area, local agents were immediately in charge, and work was performed by contract. Totten was in general charge of all civil works in New England until 1836, when Major Thayer took charge from Boston northward.

Just to the north of Plymouth lies the harbor of Duxbury, also formed by a long, narrow, and vulnerable spit of sand. Totten's method of combatting erosion here was to drive a double row of stakes, spaced a few feet apart, with four to six feet exposed, along most of the spit's six-mile length. Seaweed was then laced along the stakes, creating hurdles that in a year or two were covered by sand. Soon beach grass took root, holding the sand in place. Made of timbers from two wrecked vessels and of refuse boards, Totten's barrier was simple and cheap, yet effective: the protective wall of the harbor was raised and firmed. Directly eastward from Duxbury, on the tip of Cape Cod, the harbor of Provincetown was similarly dependent on low sandy beaches enclosing it. Deep, capacious, and with convenient approaches, it was one of the most important harbors of refuge on the Atlantic coast. Its beaches, within the hook of the cape and protected from easterly storms, were preserved for years merely by planting beach grass every spring where it would most assist natural seeding. Sand piled up around the grass, whose roots, reaching down ten to twenty feet, held the beaches firm.

These simple expedients, proof of ingenuity if not of professional engineering talent, were not sufficient to preserve other harbors of New England. Boston Harbor, fronting directly on the Atlantic, was sheltered by numerous islands. But the easterly storms to which these covers were exposed threatened to destroy them and fill the harbor's channels and anchorages with debris. Because the islands were important sites for fortifications, Congress in 1825 voted funds for preserving those "necessary to the security of that place."[12] Thus began the building of the massive granite seawalls that still protect the harbor's islands and headlands. The first was built on Georges Island by Major Totten with stone quarried on Cape Ann. Similar walls were later built on Deer, Rainsford, and Castle islands by Major Thayer. Seawalls to preserve harbor covers were also constructed by Totten on Cedar Point, Westport, Connecticut, and on Fayerweather Island, Connecticut.

At harbors designated for improvement that did not have suffcient natural cover, Totten and Thayer constructed rubblework breakwaters. Thus by 1839 shipping could find protected anchorages at Belfast and Portland in Maine; Rockport, Bass River, and Hyannis in Massachusetts; Church's Cove in Rhode Island; and Stonington in Connecticut. At Southport Harbor, Connecticut, a breakwater and dike were constructed to confine the entrance channel and prevent sand from washing into it.

Less massive in construction and designed for different purposes were the piers—now generally called jetties—built by New England's Army Engineers. They built a pier in Warren River, Rhode Island, to carry a navigational beacon, and another at Edgartown, Martha's Vineyard, to catch sand carried by currents into the harbor. But their most significant use of piers was to deepen navigable channels by the scour of concentrated water currents. The Corps had narrowed the entrance to the harbor of Presque Isle on Lake Erie by piers and had succeeded in deepening the channel, but it was not known if this could be done in tidewater. The first test, begun in 1829, was at Newburyport Harbor, at the mouth of the Merrimack River. The first pier was hardly constructed before a section of it was undermined and swept away by the tide. Rebuilding it, and extending another pier out from the opposite shore, Totten scheduled several delays so that the sturdiness and the scouring effect of each section could be observed. In 1835 Chief Engineer Charles Gratiot reported that the influence of the piers in widening

Seawall and jetty under construction at Fayerweather Island, Black Rock Harbor, Connecticut, 1914. A seawall was first constructed here in 1836-37 under the supervision of Col. Totten.

Breakwaters at Rockport Harbor, Massachusetts. The long breakwater on the left was originally constructed under the supervision of Col. Thayer in 1836-38. It was rebuilt and the short breakwater on the right was constructed in 1902-5.

The inner breakwater at Stonington, Connecticut, 1914. This work was originally constructed under the supervision of Col. Totten in 1828-31.

and straightening the channel had been very great, and although it was impossible to state what their ultimate effect would be on the entrance bar, it was satisfactory to know that vessels drawing seventeen feet could now pass over it without difficulty. Reports on work at the harbor later in the century indicate that he must have meant at high water.

Piers were built for the same purpose in several other New England rivers. A pair of protective piers at the mouth of the Kennebunk River in Maine, constructed earlier by the Treasury Department and soon wrecked by storms, were rebuilt and extended considerably so as to confine the channel more narrowly and obtain more water over the bar. In the Saco River of Maine ten timber and stone fender piers were built to prevent vessels from being swept on ledges and two piers were constructed at the river's entrance to create a channel through the bar, where the depth was only two feet at mean low water. A much larger project was initiated in the Thames River of Connecticut, which for a distance of three miles below the city of Norwich was obstructed by a number of shoals. The project, begun in 1835 with plans prepared by topographical engineer Hartman Bache, consisted of the construction of fourteen piers, or wing-dams, jutting out from the shores of the river, the scouring effect of which would be supplemented by dredging. When work on the project was closed down four years later by the cutoff of funds, seven wing-dams were nearly completed and two dredging machines were at work on the bars.

Dredging operations were also employed at several other places in New England. The first dredging machine used by the Corps in the region was on an experimental project at Nantucket Harbor. Here Lieutenant Jonathan Prescott, an artillery officer on engineering duty, undertook in 1829 to im-

Jetties at the mouth of the Kennebunk River, Maine. The original jetties, constructed by the Treasury Department in 1820-21, were timber cribs filled with stone. They were soon destroyed by storms and worms. Between 1829 and 1838 new stone and granite jetties were constructed by the Corps of Engineers to confine the river channel and obtain more water over the bar.

prove the entrance channel. Narrow, tortuous, and only six feet deep at mean low water, the channel wound through a bar a mile and a quarter wide. Encountering no difficulties for several work seasons, Prescott reported in 1831 that prospects for the permanent improvement of the channel continued to be promising. But shortly thereafter his work of three years was obliterated by a single storm, and the project was abandoned. More successful dredging projects were carried out at Southport and Bridgeport harbors in Connecticut, where channels through the bars were considerably deepened. At Saybrook Harbor, where the Connecticut River flows into Long Island Sound, two dredging machines, one driven by horsepower and a new model driven by steam, were cutting through the entrance bar when river and harbor work was brought practically to a standstill after 1838 by the stoppage of appropriations.

Most New England waterways were strewn not only with shoals but with ledges and boulders that had to be blasted or raised. Thus improvements by rock removal as well as the excavation of shoals were made on the Berwick, Saco, and Kennebec rivers in Maine, the Cocheco River in New Hampshire, and the Saugatuck River in Connecticut. New England's Army Engineers also on several occasions arranged by contract for the removal from harbors of wrecked ships that were hazardous to navigation.

For most of the projects carried out in New England, topographical engineers John Anderson, John Abert, Hartman Bache, and William Swift made the surveys and drew up the plans and estimates, while Joseph Totten and Sylvanus Thayer superintended operations. This was in accordance with the division of responsibility for river and harbor improvement between the Topographical Bureau and the Corps of Engineers that had been established at the outset of this work by the Army. Neither corps, however, was happy with this system. Colonel Abert argued that the corps that designed improvements was best qualified to carry them out; while Totten and other officers of the Corps of Engineers felt hardpressed to fulfill their military duties. In 1836 the Secretary of War transferred a number of works in the interior to the Topographical Bureau; and two years later, upon the organization of the Topographical Corps, the War Department assigned to it all civil work not connected with fortifications.

Letter from Col. Alexander Macomb, Chief Engineer, to Lt. Col. Joseph Totten, in charge of all Corps projects in New England, June 1, 1827. The letter refers to surveys for civil works at Hyannis Harbor, Massachusetts, Saugatuck River and Harbor, Connecticut, and Kennebec River, Maine, made by Topographical Engineers Lt. Col. John Anderson and Lt. Col. John Abert.

Captain William H. Swift was now placed in charge of civil works in New England. But his active superintendency was brief. The depression opening in 1837, presidential opposition to federal improvements of a local nature, and unabated state and sectional rivalries combined to spell an end to the annual river and harbor acts of the past dozen years.[13] Except for a limited measure in 1844 providing for works in the interior, there was not another general river and harbor act until 1852. A few appropriations continued to be made by special acts, but those for New England were solely for seawalls in Boston Harbor, work that related to fortifications and therefore remained with the Corps of Engineers. Topographical Engineers were still assigned duties in New England, but of different kind. They continued to make occasional harbor surveys related to the planning of fortifications. A surveying party staked out and mapped the nation's northeast boundary. And Captain Swift assisted the United States Coast Survey and constructed towers for the lighthouse service.

The Webster-Ashburton Treaty of August 1842 awarded the United States some 7,000 of the 12,000 square miles on its northeast frontier that had been in dispute with Great Britain. The treaty described the boundary agreed upon in terms of rivers, highlands, and lines between them. To locate and map the line, a brigade of Topographical Engineers, covering the ground in conjunction with a party of British engineers, spent several seasons pinpointing by astronomical determinations the exact geographical positions of the reference points named in the treaty. The American party was led by Major James D. Graham, another veteran of Long's western explorations and later of canal and military surveys in New England. Stationed in Washington when not in the field, Graham and his assistants prepared a set of boundary

Major James D. Graham.
U.S. Signal Corps Photo (Brady Collection)
in the National Archives.

maps of meticulous detail. They had scarcely completed them when they were ordered to join the armies of Taylor and Kearny in the war that had opened with Mexico. The maps were left in an office of the Topographical Bureau, and there they were completely destroyed in a fire. The loss was serious, but fortunately under a rule of the bureau the field books had been placed in a different repository. Graham, upon returning to Washington in 1848, was therefore able to start work on a new set of maps. Merely to replot the boundary would have been no great task, but the original maps had depicted the topography on either side of the line, exhibiting features valuable from a military point of view, and it was desirable that the new maps should do the same. Consequently Graham and several assistants spent three more years on the job, finally turning out a new portfolio of forty-five large and precise maps.[14]

The United States Coast Survey was first established in 1816 with the appointment within the Treasury Department of surveyor Ferdinand R. Hassler, a Swiss engineer who had once taught mathematics at West Point and had introduced in this country the subject of analytical trigonometry. In 1818 Congress transferred the responsibility of charting the coast to the Army and Navy but neither service initiated systematic surveys. In 1831 Colonel Abert reported that, because of their small number, Topographical Engineers had done nothing under the law of 1818 except surveys relating to military defense. Two years later the Coast Survey was reestablished in the Treasury Department, again under Hassler. At Hassler's request Captain Swift was assigned to assist him, a job Swift filled on a part-time basis for the next decade, making surveys in Fishers Island and Long Island sounds. In 1840 Swift went to Europe for about a year to procure instruments for the Coast Survey. While there he took the opportunity to examine hydraulic works in Holland and inspect lighthouse structures of a new design in Great Britain. The latter investigations were to lead to Swift's most interesting assignments, and to his greatest engineering failure.[15]

The administration of lighthouses in the United States was also under the Treasury Department. Usually contracting for the construction of towers itself, the Treasury had, however, in 1831 and in 1834 called upon the Army to construct several lights, including one on Goat Island in Newport Harbor, built by Lieutenant Cullum. In 1843 it called upon the Army again. Between 1829 and 1842 it had three times had a stone beacon built by contract at Black Rock Harbor, near Bridgeport, Connecticut. Each tower had been destroyed by storm within a year. When Congress in 1843 appropriated another $10,000 for a beacon, the Secretary of the Treasury was John C. Spencer, who formerly had been Secretary of War. While in the War Department, Spencer had discussed with Colonel Abert the lighthouses inspected by Swift on the coasts of England and Ireland, where British engineers, using newly invented mooring-screws for forcing iron piles into muddy or sandy shoals, had erected skeleton towers of simple and inexpensive design that offered almost no resistance to waves. Discussing the subject with Abert again, and asking the colonel's opinion of the practicability of erecting a pile structure at Black Rock Harbor, Spencer was assured that while ledge footing at the harbor prevented the use of mooring-screws, a pile tower could still be designed. Spencer asked Abert to accept the project, which Abert assigned to Swift, who was now serving as his principal assistant in Washington. Designing a structure consisting of six iron piles wedged into holes bored in a heavy granite platform laid on the ledge, with the piles tied together by wrought iron bars and topped by a cage that was visible from a great distance, Swift in three months constructed a beacon thirty-six feet high that cost less than half the sum allotted by Congress. Three days after it was finished the beacon was hit by a storm as severe as those that had wrecked the earlier stone towers. A number of steamboats in the sound were disabled and a lightship was driven from its moorings, but the beacon stood the test without injury.[16]

Could pile structures be used successfully on American coasts for the larger towers of lighthouses? A few years later Swift made the first attempt by an American engineer to find out. In 1847 Congress for the firt time assigned the construction of several lights directly to the Army, in this case to the Topographical Engineers. All the towers were to be built at difficult and hazardous places, but the worst was Outer Minots Ledge off the southern chop of Massachusetts Bay. Part of a reef that had caused more wrecks than any other on the coast, the ledge was exposed to the full brunt of the Atlantic wave. Rarely, even at low water and in calm weather, was an area more than twenty-five feet in diameter left bare by the sea—never was it more than thirty feet—and never was any part of the rock more than three feet above water. Working with less than $40,000, Swift designed a tower of nine piles sunk five feet into the ledge and rising sixty feet high. Bedded on a twenty-five-foot diameter and closing to fourteen feet, the piles supported a combination lamp and keeper's house ten feet high. To bore the nine pile holes took most of two whole working seasons. During the first year men could get on the rock only twenty-five days; and twice a specially designed drilling machine, pintled and chained to the rock, was swept away. Men were frequently washed from the rock, but no lives were lost. Once the drilling was completed, work progressed more rapidly, and by the autumn of 1849 the tower was finished and turned over to the Treasury Department.

Swift was sure that all doubts about the practicability and modest cost of using pile lights on this side of the Atlantic had been removed. Critics of the tower were not lacking, but he rejected their dire predictions of its destruction. But the technique of building skeleton iron lighthouses was still in its infancy, and Swift's structure could not stand the strains to which it was exposed. On April 16, 1851 it was carried away by a gale of hurricane force lasting for several days. Apparently waves reaching mountainous heights struck against the keeper's house, which became a fatal point of resistance at the end of a sixty-foot lever. The ten-inch piles of the tower were bent and snapped off a few feet above the surface of the rock.[17]

Another lighthouse was to be built on Minots Ledge, but before this was done Army Engineers in New England were again assigned, for a short time at least, projects of river and harbor improvement. In the election campaign of 1852 the Whig and Free Soil parties, both more attuned to the interests of eastern businessmen and western farmers than the Southern-controlled Democratic party, proclaimed themselves in favor of internal improvements. Swaying with the political winds, Congress in August passed a bill for more than a hundred river and harbor works, fifteen of which were in New Eng-

land. With the Whig Millard Fillmore in the White House, the bill was en-
sured against a presidential veto. Because the Topographical Bureau already
had numerous duties, while the fortification work of the Corps of Engineers
had been practically suspended for the past two years for want of funds, the
War Department assigned the public works on the Atlantic and Gulf coasts
to the Corps of Engineers.[18]

The New England projects were carried out by Colonel Sylvanus Thayer,
Captains William D. Fraser and George Dutton, and Lieutenants John Newton, Zealous B. Tower, and Charles E. Blunt. These officers built new
breakwaters at Owls Head Harbor and Richmond Island Harbor in Maine;
repaired the old breakwaters at Portland and Hyannis and the piers at the
mouth of the Kennebunk River; and patched up seawalls at Marblehead and
a dike at Woods Hole, built years before by other agencies. At Plymouth
Beach they closed several large breaches, opened by the storm that brought
down Minots Light, by the old method of giving nature a hand with brush
fences; they strung a timber bulkhead along a beach at Provincetown and
planted more beach grass; they dredged again at Bridgeport Harbor until
funds ran out; and they blasted out rock obstructions in New Haven Harbor
and in Cobscook Bay, Maine. They also made five river and harbor surveys
called for by the act of 1852.

Another project, seemingly a simple one, was the improvement of the
Kennebec River for a few miles below Augusta. When Lieutenant John
Newton finished his reconnaisance and set about to arrange contracts, however, he discovered that the sudden demand for dredging machines
everywhere in the country resulting from the act of 1852 had skyrocketed
bids for work in his area beyond all reason. For nearly two years the project
was stalled. In 1854 Newton was succeeded by Captain William Fraser. Giving up attempts to arrange for dredging by contract, Fraser devised a raking
apparatus suspended between two scows towed by a steamer and began the
job with workers on day wages. His machine scraped away sand and gravel
from the river bars with great success, but Fraser soon had another problem.
He uncovered dozens of large boulders, some weighing up to seventy tons.
Drilling holes in them, into which he drove iron rods to serve as hafts, he
raised and floated them away with flat-bottomed boats when the tide rose.
Ingenious though his methods were, Fraser was able to clear only a short
stretch of the river with the $6,000 at his disposal.[19]

The River and Harbor Act of 1852 also provided for the preservation of
Great Brewster Island, lying on the outer fringe of Boston Harbor. In 1840
Colonel Thayer had made a detailed report on the islands of the harbor,
recommending repairs on some of the seawalls already built and the construction of walls on other islands. In the next three years Congress voted
appropriations for the repairs and for the construction of a seawall on
Lovells Island, to which Thayer had given first priority. But three later appropriations for seawalls on Great Brewster Island, included in broader river
and harbor bills, were killed by presidential vetoes. In 1848 an appropriation
for Great Brewster was finally approved, and the construction of seawalls on
two heads of the island began. Apparently because Thayer was burdened
with other duties, Captain Henry W. Benham was placed in charge. Spending most of his subsequent career in the Corps at Boston directing the con-

Colonel Henry W. Benham.
U.S. Signal Corps Photo (Brady Collection)
in the National Archives.

struction of seawalls and fortifications, Benham shares honors only with
Thayer for length of service in New England. The funds voted in 1848 for the
seawalls on Great Brewster ran out in 1850. When the new appropriation
was made in 1852, Thayer took over the project, carrying it on until late
1854, when it was again suspended for want of money.[20]

The product of election-year pressures, the River and Harbor Act of 1852
failed to restore an ongoing program of civil public works. The Democrats
won the election; and with preponderant influence in government for the rest
of the decade resting in the party that from 1840 to 1860 consistently declared against internal improvements, Congress did not pass another general
river and harbor bill until after the Civil War. Occasionally it voted funds for
a project or two, but none of these was in New England. When the 1852
appropriations ran out, river and harbor work in the area by the federal
government again came to a halt.

Two more construction projects of different kind, however, were carried
out in the decade of the 1850s. One was the Marine Hospital at Chelsea,
Massachusetts, built between 1855 and 1859. The supervising engineer was
Captain Barton S. Alexander, transferred from Washington where he had
been directing work on public buildings. The hospital, however, was not
Alexander's principal assignment. He had been sent to New England to direct the construction of a new lighthouse on Minots Ledge.

In August 1852 Congress created a Lighthouse Board, composed of army
engineers, naval officers, and civilians, that was to have entire charge, under
the Secretary of the Treasury, of the construction, maintenance, superinten-
dence, and operation of lighthouses. One of the board's first decisions was

Bvt. Brig. Gen. Barton S. Alexander.
Courtesy of the U.S. Army Engineer
Museum, Fort Belvoir, Virginia.

to build a stone tower on Minots Ledge. Chief Engineer Totten, who was a member of the board, designed the structure. It was a masonry shaft, purely conical in shape because of its limited base, 112 feet high. Solid, except for a small central well, for half its height, it had a cylindrical hollow space above, divided into several stories by iron floors. Using the holes for the piles of the former skeleton light, Totten pinned the tower to the rock with gun-metal dowels rising to the twelfth course of masonry. Each course of masonry throughout the tower was also doweled to the one above and the one below. Personally selecting Alexander to construct the work, Totten assigned him to the duty in April 1855.

Minots Ledge had to be cut across its whole surface to receive the foundation stones of the tower, and cut to the extent that the stones were all bedded below low water. Because part of the ledge was at all times under water, and the rest was bare for only an hour or two at low spring tides when the sea was dead calm, there were weeks together when workmen could not land on the rock. To have men ready to work on the ledge whenever it was possible—men disciplined and physically qualified for the hard labor and exposure—Alexander employed the same working party ashore to cut and dress the stones for the tower, thereby giving them constant work and full wages.

The first blow on the ledge was struck on July 1, 1855, and the first stone was laid on July 9, 1857. In 1855 only 130 hours could be spent on the rock. In 1856 men were on it for 157 hours, and in 1857 for 130 hours. During the second season's work Alexander erected an iron scaffold to make the cutting operations safer, using the holes of the former skeleton lighthouse. The following January a gale threw the bark *New Empire*, loaded with cotton, against the scaffold, breaking off the iron posts and shattering the rock in places, making it necessary to do some of the work of the preceding year over again. Once the foundation was in place, more time could be spent on the rock, and the stones of the tower, all previously fitted together on shore, went up with less trouble. In 1858, 208 hours were put in on the rock; in 1859, 377 hours; and finally on June 29, 1860 the last stone was laid.

Minots Ledge Light.
Photo by Kevin Cole. Courtesy of the *Boston Herald American.*

"The lighthouse on Minot's ledge is the most important *engineering* work that belongs to our lighthouse system;" said Colonel J. G. Barnard, reputedly one of the best civil and military engineers of his day, speaking nearly two decades later on the subject of lighthouse engineering. "Indeed," he added, "it ranks by the engineering difficulties surmounted in its erection, and by the skill and science shown in the details of its construction, among the chief of the great sea-rock lighthouses of the world."[21] Still standing and in service, Minots Light was the last civil work in New England by the Corps of Engineers before the war broke out between the states.

THE DISTRICTS AND THE DIVISION

The Civil War settled the long-debated issue of river and harbor improvement. It opened a period of tremendous growth in transportation, trade, industry, and agriculture. Old political patterns dissolved before new dynamic forces, and new ruling groups emerged anxious to provide expanding economic enterprise with a federal helping hand. And this assistance included the development of the nation's navigable waterways. The Republican party had begun its national career with a declaration in its platform of 1856 that appropriations by Congress for the improvement of rivers and harbors were constitutional and justified by the obligation of the government to protect the lives and property of its citizens. The postwar Democratic party, forsaking its earlier opposition to internal improvements, was no less eager to give river and harbor improvement steady and generous support.[1] The civil works function of the Corps of Engineers, sporadic and uncertain since its inception in 1824, began to burgeon.

Even before the war ended, river and harbor work was resumed in a small way. In June 1864 Congress authorized the Secretary of War to expend $350,000 to repair harbors on the seaboard and the Great Lakes. Two of the five projects opened on the Atlantic coast were in New England, where Army Engineers again took up the work of preserving the delicate beaches that formed the harbors of Plymouth and Provincetown. In July 1864 Congress reopened projects in Boston Harbor with appropriations for continuing the seawalls on Great Brewster Island and repairing those on Deer and Lovells islands. Colonel James D. Graham, the cartographer of the nation's northeastern boundary twenty years before, was placed in charge of these works and of all harbors on the Atlantic coast. Graham had drawn up plans and got construction under way when, late in December 1865, he died at Boston. Lieutenant Colonel Henry Benham, recently assigned to fortification work in Boston Harbor, took over the seawalls and the Provincetown beaches, while Major George H. Mendell took charge at Plymouth.[2]

River and harbor improvement began on a broad scale in June 1866 with a congressional appropriation of nearly $3.7 million for over fifty works and nearly forty examinations and surveys throughout the country. Thereafter river and harbor appropriations, voted annually with but few exceptions, grew by large amounts. For the decade of the 1870s they totaled nearly $54 million; for the decade ending in 1972 they came to $5,757 million, exclusive of large sums provided for maintenance.[3]

A project began with a directive in a river and harbor act, usually inserted at the representation of local interests, for the preliminary examination and survey of a waterway to determine if it were worthy of improvement. The engineer making the investigation would inspect the waterway, hold public hearings to learn the views of local citizens, and establish whatever liaison might be necessary with other governmental agencies. If the examination report, after being reviewed by a division engineer, a Board of Engineers for Rivers and Harbors, and the Chief of Engineers, recommended the proposed improvement, the Secretary of War was authorized to order a detailed survey so that plans and estimates might be submitted to Congress. The survey report would go through the same gantlet of review, and additional public hearings and consultations with other governmental agencies might be held.[4] Reports had to include information relating to the commercial importance of the waterway. After 1909 they had to include any obtainable data relating to terminal and transfer facilities, to the development of waterpower, and to any other subject that might properly be connected with the project. After 1920 they had to include recommendations as to what local cooperation should be required if the improvement would bring special benefits to the localities involved.

Many reports were unfavorable. But navigational demands upon a waterway sometimes changed, local interests were often persistent, and congressmen were almost always anxious to have as much federal money as possible spent in their districts. Therefore Congress, in 1913, legislated that requests for reviews of reports, to determine if any modifications should be made, might be submitted to the Chief of Engineers merely by resolutions of appropriate committees. These "review report" requests became so common that more investigations were ordered by them than by regular legislation. Another significant modification of the report procedure was the abandonment by law, in 1958, of preliminary examination reports. Originally designed to avoid the expense of surveys and plans for waterways manifestly not worth improving, the two-stage report process had become both inefficient and uneconomical as the Corps' water resources responsibilities broadened and investigation and planning grew more complex. Whenever preliminary studies indicated the desirability of further investigation, the Corps could now proceed directly with more detailed surveys.[5]

In reporting a waterway worthy of improvement, Army Engineers meant only that the project was feasible and that the resulting increase in commerce would warrant the expense. As the Chief of Engineers stated in his annual report of 1884, they were not recommending the execution of the work. He noted that of the 147 localities enumerated in the River and Harbor Act of 1882 for examination and survey, 76 were reported as not worthy. The act of 1890 provided for 203 examinations and surveys, more than half of which resulted in unfavorable reports. "The chief of engineers is required by law to make the estimates," wrote an investigator of the 1890s, "but were he to name the works that Congress ought to undertake, he would recommend far fewer than Congress now authorizes." Between 1902 and 1940 the Board of Engineers for Rivers and Harbors reported on approximately 4,800 investigations, including 400 for flood control. The recommendations were unfavorable to 60 percent of the navigation improvements and to 85 percent of those for flood control.[6] Engineers in New England, required at one time or another to examine almost every waterway that could float a boat, contributed proportionately to these unfavorable reports; the records of some waterways, in fact, reveal a series of unfavorable reports. Occasionally Congress would appropriate funds for works prior to investigations, and sometimes it would vote appropriations despite unfavorable reports, but usually the procedure described for instituting projects was followed. Although the nineteenth century river and harbor pork barrel won considerable notoriety, the Corps succeeded at least in keeping a lid on it.

Until 1920 river and harbor acts specified the amount appropriated for each project, usually a sum sufficient for only one or two working seasons. This "driblet system of appropriations," as a report of the House Committee on Rivers and Harbors in 1892 styled it, not only encouraged Congress to initiate more works than it might otherwise have done but made projects more costly by precluding large and continuing contracts. The problem had been only slightly alleviated by the practice beginning in 1890 of occasionally permitting long-term contracts on some projects, to be paid for as appropriations were from time to time provided. After 1920 Congress voted lump sums each year to be apportioned to projects by the Chief of Engineers. Work could now be prosecuted more efficiently since rapidly moving projects were less subject to interruption and funds were not tied up on inactive projects pending the fulfillment of requirements of local cooperation. Congressional control, however, was not relinquished. Congress continued to specify where examinations and surveys were to be made and to authorize new works; and in appearances before the Bureau of the Budget and before appropriation committees, the Chief of Engineers had to justify the portions of the Budget Bureau's recommended appropriation that were to be allotted to various projects during the fiscal year under consideration.[7]

With works and surveys rapidly multiplying after 1866, local river and harbor engineer offices were established to plan and carry them out. And by practice, rather than by specific directive, an administrative system of district engineers in charge of all projects within certain geographical areas came into being. The informal development of the district unit is indicated by a letter from the Chief of Engineers to the Secretary of War, dated May 20, 1884, which speaks of "districts, as that term is now understood."[8] Although the first district engineers sometimes supervised fortification work, most military construction in the immediate postwar years was directed by other officers. In New England, district engineers were not given jurisdiction over fortifications everywhere in the region until 1883, and since defense construction had by then come to a standstill, the added responsibilities were for some time more nominal than real.

New England's first river and harbor office was established at Portland, Maine, in the autumn of 1866. The River and Harbor Act of the previous June had provided for a half-dozen works and surveys in the state, which were initially assigned to Major Barton S. Alexander, then reconstructing fortifications at Portland. By a series of directives from the Engineer Department in October and November, however, these civil works were turned over to Lieutenant Colonel George Thom, a former Topographical Engineer who was also working on Maine fortifications, as his primary responsibility.[9] In charge of the Portland Engineer Office for over sixteen years, Thom supervised a district that eventually embraced all of Maine and New Hampshire. From 1871 to 1883 it also included eastern Massachusetts south to Provincetown.

A second district office was operating at Newport, Rhode Island, by the next year. The River and Harbor Act of 1866 had provided for only one work and one survey on New England's south coast, both in Connecticut, which were assigned to Major David C. Houston, in charge of defense work at Fort Adams. The next year seven more works and surveys on waterways in Connecticut and Rhode Island were also entrusted to Houston. Although Houston remained in charge of modifying batteries at Fort Adams, his chief responsibility was now river and harbor improvement, and an engineer district covering the two states had been created.[10] In May 1870 Houston was succeeded by Major Gouverneur K. Warren, who remained in charge of the Newport District until his death twelve years later.

In Massachusetts river and harbor work was for several years under various officers. Colonel Graham and then Colonel Benham and Major Mendell were in charge of the first few works. Several new projects were then assigned to Lieutenant Colonel John C. Foster and Captain Jared Smith. By 1869, however, most work in Massachusetts had either been directly assigned or transferred to Foster, and a district had thus come into being. Apparently because work on the seawalls of Great Brewster, Lovells, and Deer islands had initially been authorized by a fortification act, they remained under Benham; but Foster had charge of new seawalls begun in Boston Harbor on Long and Gallops islands and on Point Allerton, the harbor's southern chop. Two other works in Massachusetts, the beach at Plymouth and newly authorized repairs on the breakwater at Hyannis, were assigned in 1869 to the Newport District.

Because the Corps had few officers and many duties, and since the volume of work in sections of New England changed from time to time, so did the size and number of New England engineer districts. On May 25, 1871 the Boston Office was closed, Foster went to Washington to be Assistant Chief of Engineers, and all river and harbor projects in Massachusetts south to Provincetown, except Benham's seawalls, were transferred to Colonel Thom at the Portland Office. On April 1, 1873 the seawalls were also transferred. On June 11, 1874 the projects in Massachusetts were returned to Foster at Boston, and the district was reestablished. But two months later, on August 24, Foster died. Colonel Thom was again instructed to take over, and works in Massachusetts thereafter remained under the Portland Office until January 18, 1883. On that date the Boston District Office was reopened under Major Charles W. Raymond.

In southern New England districts were reorganized a half-dozen times in less than thirty years. In 1870 the Newport Office relinquished the works at Plymouth and Hyannis to the Boston Office and acquired jurisdiction over all projects on the south, or New York, shore of Long Island Sound. Two years later, in July 1872, it was given charge of the southern coast of Massachusetts and the islands of Nantucket and Martha's Vineyard. By July 1874, however, its work load had apparently become unwieldy, for a new engineer office, under Major John W. Barlow, was opened at New London with jurisdiction over all harbor work on both shores of Long Island Sound. Although the new district included the entire Connecticut coastline, projects on the Connecticut River remained under the Newport Office. This arrangement lasted until May 1883, when the New London Office was closed and all works on Long Island Sound and on the Connecticut River were transferred to an engineer office at New York City. Thirteen years later, on August 5, 1896, in a reorganization that was to last for still a longer time, the engineer office at New London was reopened, with Major Smith S. Leach in charge.

52

Major Gouverneur K.
Warren. Courtesy
of the U.S. Military
Academy Archives.

Major Charles W.
Raymond. Courtesy
of the U.S. Military
Academy Archives.

Major John W. Barlow.
U.S. Signal Corps
Photo in the National
Archives.

Major Smith S. Leach.
Courtesy of the U.S.
Military Academy
Archives.

Major Walter L. Fisk.
Courtesy of the U.S.
Military Academy
Archives.

The New London District took over all works on the Connecticut shore and
the Connecticut River, while projects on the south shore of Long Island
Sound remained under the New York Office.

A series of jurisdictional changes now took place in northern New Eng-
land. On September 30, 1899 an engineer office, headed by Major Walter L.
Fisk, was opened at Portsmouth, New Hampshire, which was assigned all
projects between Portland, Maine, and Lynn, Massachusetts. On April 30,
1901, its jurisdiction was extended to works in Vermont and New York on
Lake Champlain, which previously had been under the First New York,
New York, District. But the Portsmouth District had a short life, for on
August 31, 1903 the office was closed and its works were transferred to the
engineer office at Boston. A year and a half later, on March 31, 1905, all

projects in Maine and New Hampshire were again put under the Portland Office. The works on Lake Champlain continued to be supervised by the Boston District until 1911, when they were returned to the office at New York City.

Until 1920 New England continued to be divided into four districts. River and harbor projects in the area, however, had by then greatly fallen off, and another reorganization was in order. On January 1 the Newport and New London districts were combined into a single district with its office at Providence, Rhode Island. Initially including the states of Rhode Island and Connecticut, the southern coast of Massachusetts, and the Connecticut River valley in Massachusetts, the Providence District later assumed jurisdiction, when flood control work began in the 1930s, over the entire drainage basin of the Connecticut River in Massachusetts, New Hampshire, and Vermont. On June 9, 1920 the Boston and Portland districts were merged, with the office at Portland becoming a suboffice of the Boston District. Extending from Eastport, on the eastern tip of Maine, to Chatham, on the elbow of Cape Cod, the Boston District embraced most of eastern New England.

New England was to have still another district, but it was one of ephemeral life and microscopic size. On May 17, 1935 an engineer office was opened at Eastport, Maine, for the prosecution of the Passamaquoddy Tidal Power Project, Lieutenant Colonel Philip B. Fleming in charge. On November 1, 1936 the office was closed and its activities were turned over to the Boston District. Sharing between them the Corps' work in New England, the Boston and Providence districts remained in existence until October 1, 1946. On that date they were discontinued and their functions were absorbed into the office of the New England Division.

Engineer divisions had existed since December 3, 1888. With river and harbor work growing enormously, direct supervision of all districts from Washington had become difficult. Chief of Engineers Brigadier General Thomas L. Casey therefore divided the country into five administrative divisions, assigning to each division engineer supervisory responsibilities over all districts within his division whose engineers were below the grade of lieutenant colonel.[11] The Northeast Division, whose office at New York City was opened by Colonel Henry L. Abbot, included six districts with territory stretching from the Atlantic coast to Michigan. The Newport District came under its jurisdiction, but the Boston and Portland districts, whose engineers were lieutenant colonels, continued to report directly to Washington. The Portland District was not absorbed into the division until April 1897, when Major Richard L. Hoxie became the district engineer. The incorporation of the Boston District occurred in two stages. Military construction came under divisional jurisdiction in June 1901, when District Engineer Lieutenant Colonel William S. Stanton transferred fortification work in the district to Captain Harry Taylor, then engineer of the Portsmouth District. Two years later, following the fusion of the Boston and Portsmouth districts, civil work was also placed under divisional control, even though Stanton, a lieutenant colonel, was still the district engineer.

Like the engineer districts, the engineer divisions were frequently reorganized. In 1901 the Northeast Division was redefined to include only the

New England districts. The division engineer was usually also engineer of the First New York, New York, District, but the district itself did not become part of the division until 1909. Over the next two decades there were several shifts in and out of the division by first three and then two New York, New York, districts, and the division was expanded to include the Philadelphia, Wilmington (Delaware), Baltimore, and Washington districts. In 1929 the Northeast Division was superseded by a less extensive North Atlantic Division consisting of the Boston, Providence, First and Second New York, Philadelphia, and Wilmington districts. Within a dozen years, however, through the addition of the Baltimore and Washington districts, the North Atlantic Division had grown to the size of its predecessor.[12] Finally, on May 1, 1942, because of increased military construction on the eastern seaboard, the New England Division was carved out of the North Atlantic Division. Its office at Boston was opened by Colonel Leonard B. Gallagher. Four years later, when the Boston and Providence district offices were closed, the New England Division became an operating division with both district and division functions, the only such administrative unit within the continental United States.

Although planning and supervising large volumes of work, the New England district offices until the mid-1930s were surprisingly small establishments, employing only three or four army and civilian engineers. District engineers were for some time assisted by a junior officer or two assigned to gain practical experience, but the perennial shortage of engineer officers forced the curtailment of this practice in 1908. Assistant Engineer Lieutenant Ulysses S. Grant, III, remained with the Boston Office until July 1909, but thereafter the districts had no Corps officer assistants for many years. A handful of civilian assistant engineers and other technical people, and a few clerks, made up the permanent personnel of an engineer office. In 1908 the Newport District employed an assistant engineer, a junior engineer, a draftsman, and three clerks in the office, and three inspectors, a foreman, a master and steam engineer of the district's launch, a diver, and a clerk in the field—a total of fourteen people. In 1918 the district's personnel numbered twenty-six, with more than half engaged in coastal defense construction.[13] Districts sometimes expanded their staffs, as when extensive surveys were being made on the Connecticut River in 1872-73 and ten assistant engineers were on the payroll of the Newport Office, but usually a district did not employ more than two or three civilian engineers. In addition to permanent personnel, who were under Civil Service examinations and regulations, the districts hired artisans and laborers on a daily or monthly basis as they were needed.

District engineers inevitably had to be acquainted with almost every detail of the projects and problems of their lightly-staffed offices. Until about 1912 some district engineers were inspectors of lighthouse districts and in this capacity were responsible for the maintenance and construction of lights under the Lighthouse Service. District engineers were also officers of the United States Army and as such were subject to the same rules and regulations as all other officers. Occasionally this could lead to inconveniences, as Major G. W. Pillsbury, engineer of the New London District, discovered in November 1912 when the Commanding General of the Department of the

East ordered him to take a test ride in the vicinity of New London and arrange with the commanding officer of Fort Wright for a physical examination before and after the ride. Since no mounts were available at Fort Wright, which was a seacoast battery on nearby Fishers Island, Pillsbury had to use his private mount. "As I have anticipated that this animal would not be used for military purposes, it has not been foraged at government expense and has not been kept in condition," Pillsbury explained to the Commanding General. "I am now taking steps to have her placed in condition for the ride." The required army test, it appeared, would probably be less one of army officer than of non-army horse. But arrangements were still not settled, for the test ride required that one night be spent under canvas. "On account of the lack of transportation," Pillsbury informed the Commanding General, "I know of no way in which this can be done unless a tent is pitched in the yard of my house. Information is requested as to whether such a course is desired, particularly in view of the fact that it might be considered undignified in a civilian community."[14] Records do not reveal whether the major was forced to shock the citizens of New London with the odd ways of the Army.

Flood-control work in the 1930s and military construction in the 1940s enlarged the New England engineer offices beyond recognition. The pressure of World War II, especially, swelled their personnel. Competing during the war with the military services and private industry in a tight labor market, the districts sent out recruiting teams to scour key New England cities for the engineers, technicians, clerks, and other people they needed. By the end of the war the Boston District employed about 170 engineers among a total personnel numbering about 565, not counting ungraded employees. The Providence District was about the same size, and the New England Division Office had a staff of 21 military personnel and 205 civilians. Simple office

Members of the Structural Section of the Design Branch, Engineering Division, of the Providence District, 1939. Left to right: (seated) John Pack; William Smith, Jr.; section chief John Dingwall; Roy Martin; Eugene Vaughn; Eli Viner; (standing) Scott Baird; Robert McAleer; Robert McCormack. Courtesy of William Smith Jr.

structure, where organizational problems had not extended beyond the best location of the desks, had necessarily given way to bureaucratic arrangements. Organization position charts of the Boston District Office for 1946 carried more than ninety neatly connected blocks representing the offices, suboffices, divisions, branches, sections, subsections, and other units into which its personnel was divided, sorted, and arranged.

With a return to normal peacetime work the personnel of the New England Division, which in October 1946 absorbed employees from the discontinued districts, rapidly shrank. By January 1947 only 614 people from the large wartime organization remained. In June 1950, when hostilities broke out in Korea, the employment figure was 556. The communist attack galvanized Congress into providing for a defense posture the National Security Council had recommended, a huge new military construction program was authorized for New England, and to carry it out the division hurriedly searched for qualified people. Recruiting teams were again sent out, newspaper publicity was employed, and spot announcements on the need for engineers, inspectors, and other employees were made over radio stations. One Boston station donated to the Corps a five-minute broadcast five days a week for ten weeks in place of a paid commercial. By September 1951 the personnel of the division had been increased to a force of 1,065. The division

Some senior members of the New England Division enjoying an outing at Hingham, Massachusetts, 1958. Left to right: (front) Joseph Keefe, Finance and Accounting Branch; William Schmidt, Construction Division; George Smith, Finance and Accounting Branch; Dominic D'Agostino, Finance and Accounting Branch; William Steinmetz, Comptroller; John Ferullo, Finance and Accounting Branch; William Conners, Chief, Budget Branch; (standing) William Smith Jr., Construction Division; George Messier, Budget Branch; Robert Taylor, Chief, Management Branch; Thomas Moran, Budget Branch; John Murphy, Procurement Branch; Henry Pickersgill, Construction Division; Harold Gamble, Engineer in Charge, Cape Cod Canal; John Eklund, Chief, Construction Division; Robert Lafrenz, Executive Assistant; John Dooley, Finance Officer; John Wm. Leslie, Chief, Engineering Division; Thomas Kehoe, Budget Branch; Francis Czernicki, Chief, Finance and Accounting Branch; Charles Sieman, Audit Branch; John Gale, Chief, Audit Branch. Courtesy of William Smith, Jr.

remained at about this strength until 1955, when the resumption of civil work on a large scale again pressed up the employment figure until by 1958 it reached a peak of 1,750. Then as both military and civil projects in New England tapered off, the personnel of the division dwindled almost every year until by May 1975 it numbered 659.[15]

In the days of few personnel and simple organization, the quarters of the New England engineer offices had consisted of only a few rented rooms in the business sections of their cities. Scattered and incomplete records reveal a number of changes in location. The Boston District Office appears to be typical. In 1869 it was housed in Boston City Hall. Three years later it was at No. 2 Bulfinch Street. In 1895 rooms were maintained in the Winthrop Building at 7 Water Street. Upon incorporating the Portsmouth District in 1903, the Boston District took larger quarters in Rooms 1015-17, Barristers Hall, at 25 Pemberton Square. There it stayed until December 1919, when it moved to the thirteenth floor of the Boston Customs House. These accommodations sufficed until 1936, when the start of flood control work made more office space necessary. Additional rooms were rented at 148 State Street until September 1937, when the whole office was moved to the Park Square Building at 31 St. James Avenue.

Headquarters of the New England Division since 1958. The former Murphy Army Hospital, Waltham, Massachusetts.

When the New England Division was established its office was in the Second National Bank Building at 75 Federal Street. Upon absorbing the Boston District in 1946 it took over the district's quarters in the Park Square Building. The next year it moved to Building 21 of the Boston Naval Annex in South Boston. Following the outbreak of the Korean War, arrangements were made through the recently established General Services Administration for still larger accommodations, and on May 21, 1951, the office was relocated at 857 Commonwealth Avenue. In the fall of 1955 the division moved again, this time to the North Station Office Building at 150 Causeway Street. Finally, in October 1958, the division settled down at the former Murphy Army Hospital in the rolling environs of Waltham, about ten miles west of Boston. A sprawling maze of small brick buildings linked by corridors, the cantonment-type hospital had been built by the Boston District during World War II for the care of soldiers stationed around Greater Boston.[16]

IV
NAVIGABLE RIVERS AND SAFE HARBORS

The coasts of New England are stabbed with several large and many small waterways. Between 1864 and 1975 the Army Engineers improved 172 of them.[1] Naturally shallow and cluttered with shoals, ledges, and boulders, all but a dozen rivers and harbors required dredging or rock removal for the construction of channels, anchorages, and turning basins. At about seventy localities improvements included the building of breakwaters, jetties, or other structures. Projects ranged from building sand-catchers at Westport Harbor for $1,000 to developing Boston Harbor at a cost of over $25 million.

During the nineteenth century small rivers and harbors absorbed much of the attention of the New England districts. Some of these minor waterways served small commercial ports where coastal sailers brought in coal, grains, and other bulky goods and carried away lumber, quarry stone, ice, seafood, and local manufactures. Others sheltered fishing and lobstering fleets, and still others were mainly collecting points for their catches. Projects at New England's larger harbors, though fewer, were generally more ambitious and prolonged. Often work seemed to be in a race with increasing commerce and bigger ships. Providence River, for example, which stretches eight miles from the city of Providence to Narragansett Bay, was initially obstructed by several shoals, and at one point the low-water depth of the channel was only four and a half feet. Continuing work first begun in 1852, Newport District engineers deepened the channel first to nine feet at mean low water, then to twelve, then to fourteen, and then again to twenty-three feet. In 1882 they begun cutting a twenty-five-foot-deep, 300-foot-wide channel and a capacious anchorage basin, a project that would permit the largest ocean steamers then plying the seas to reach the city.

At the turn of the twentieth century, when there were five New England districts, improvements were concurrently underway at no less than sixty-six localities, excluding those on Lake Champlain, which lie outside the present limits of the New England Division. River and harbor projects then tapered off in number. Almost every waterway considered worthy of improvement by current standards had been or was being improved. By 1917, the year the United States entered World War I and retired officers and civilians temporarily took charge of the New England districts, projects had been completed on ninety-five rivers and harbors. On sixty-eight of these waterways, no further improvements have been made; on twenty-seven, nothing more was done until after World War II. Improvements on thirty-eight waterways were continued or renewed between the wars, but projects were begun at only seven new localities.

As projects became fewer in the twentieth century, they generally became larger and more restricted to localities of major commercial importance. Shipping at small ports declined as trains and trucks took over the business of the coastal sailers. The scene of greatest river and harbor activity shifted southward to the more heavily industrial states, and projects in Maine, whose sawtoothed coastline had earlier seen the largest number of works,

Clamshell dredge *State of Maryland*, 1947.

Dredges at work in New England waterways

Sea-going hopper dredge *Comber*, 1956.

Dipper dredge *Governor Herrick*, 1914.

Hydraulic dredge *General*, 1947.

dwindled to a handful. Although some small waterways used primarily by fishing fleets were improved, most work centered on harbors important mainly for their commercial traffic.

World War II, swamping the Boston and Providence districts with military construction, restricted river and harbor work to a trickle. The war over, congressional authorization between 1945 and 1950 of forty-seven new projects promised a strong revival of navigation work. Operations had begun at only a dozen places, however, when hostilities erupted in Korea. Military construction again took priority, and river and harbor work, except for maintenance, diminished to two dredging projects. In 1955 work was resumed on a broad scale, and by 1975 improvements had been made at thirty-two new and fifty old localities. Some sixteen additional projects were authorized but remained inactive pending compliance with requirements of local cooperation. Projects actively underway in any one year ranged from twenty-one in 1957 to three in 1972.

The resurgence of navigation work after the Korean War meant a preponderance again of projects on small harbors, with Maine again becoming the scene of more works than any other state. The new burst of activity also evidenced a new public demand upon the civil function of the Corps of Engineers—the development of recreational facilities. While some of the small projects were at minor commercial ports and fishing and seafood processing centers, more were at harbors used as much or more by recreational fleets, and some were at localities used almost exclusively by recreational craft. Work on nineteen of these small harbors was carried out under Section 107 of the River and Harbor Act of 1960, which permits the Corps, without specific congressional authorization, to accomplish certain small projects with general funds appropriated annually.

At major harbors, channels, anchorages, and turning basins continued to be developed to allow deep-draft oil tankers and other large vessels to come in at any tide stage. The main channels of Boston and Providence harbors were deepened to forty feet at mean low water, and a forty-foot channel was authorized for Fall River, the second largest port in Massachusetts. At Portland Harbor, where about 75 percent of the tonnage is crude oil brought in large tankers and transshipped by pipelines to refineries in Canada, the entrance channel was cut to forty-five feet. Thirty-five foot channels were constructed at Bridgeport, New Haven, Portsmouth, and Weymouth Fore River, the last being the location of one of the largest shipbuilding plants on the Atlantic coast. Channels thirty to thirty-three feet deep were dredged at New Bedford, Salem, and New London.

Boston Harbor, the largest and busiest in New England, was the object of the most extensive planning and development. Before the Civil War the great need of the harbor had not been improvement for navigation, but preservation. About forty-seven square miles in extent, sufficiently deep for vessels of the time, and fronting directly on the Atlantic yet protected by a screen of islands and headlands, the harbor was generously endowed by nature. It was nevertheless a fragile harbor. Tides and storms were rapidly wearing away its natural breakwaters, not only to the detriment of these covers themselves and of channels being filled with debris, but also to that of navigation in the loss of guide marks for sailing directions. Consequently,

Portland Harbor.

the years between 1825 and 1854 saw Colonels Totten, Thayer, and Benham building the huge granite seawalls protecting the bluffs of Georges, Deer, Rainsford, Castle, Lovells, and Great Brewster islands.

The politics of sectionalism and the coming of the war between the states interrupted this work, leaving the comprehensive recommendations made by Colonel Thayer in 1840 for protecting the Port of Boston only partially carried out. Therefore for a decade after the war, the building of more seawalls was a principal item in broader plans for improving the harbor. In 1864 Colonel Graham resumed work on the walls of Great Brewster Island and began repairing those on Deer and Lovells islands. By the early 1870s Colonel Benham had completed this work and built a new wall on Lovells Island. Meantime Colonels Foster and Thom had constructed walls on Long and Gallops islands and on Point Allerton. The walls, which rose to fourteen feet or more above mean high water, were most vulnerable at their foundations, and to protect them the engineers designed stone aprons and numerous projecting jetties for the faces and angles most exposed to storms and currents. Subsequent Boston District engineers extended some of the walls until they reached a total length of about three and three-quarter miles.

By the 1850s the art of shipbuilding was making giant technological leaps, and soon Boston Harbor no longer satisfied all standards of a safe and adequate port. For a few years there was a frenetic construction of clipper ships, a daring new type of vessel characterized by long, sharp lines, clouds of canvas, and deep draft. No sailing vessel ever approached the clippers in power, majesty, or speed. But winds had to be favorable, and even before

Seawall on Gallops Island, Boston Harbor.
Photograph by 101st Photo Sect., 26th Div. Aviation, Mass. N.G.

the "clipper fever" began it was evident that iron steamships would soon replace wooden sailing vessels in the carrying of ocean freight. After the British-built *Great Western* crossed the Atlantic in fourteen and a half days in 1838, a number of steamship companies were organized in the United States and abroad. The British companies, especially, rapidly improved the design and construction of their steamers, and by 1860 they were driving the clippers from the seas. Becoming bigger and deeper than men had once thought ships could be, the iron steamer was soon necessitating the deepening of Boston and other hitherto satisfactory harbors.

The first project for channel improvement in Boston Harbor was drawn up by Colonel Foster and adopted by Congress in 1867. It provided for a main ship channel 23 feet deep and 600 feet wide at mean low water. The chief obstacle to the entrance of large vessels into the inner harbor was the "Upper Middle Bar," a 2,200-foot-wide formation of hardpan that restricted the channel to 18 feet deep and 100 feet wide. Before tackling this compacted barrier the contractor had a powerful new dredging machine built expressly for the purpose, but still found the work immensely slow and difficult. Further slowdowns were occasioned by the discovery of a number of huge sunken ledges that had to be chipped away by drilling and blasting. But finally in 1879 the project was completed. As shipping increased and vessels became larger, other projects followed. By 1966, when the last project was completed, the main ship channel had been deepened to 40 feet and widened to a maximum of 1,100 feet; two more entrance channels, 30 and 35 feet deep, had been cut to the sea; an anchorage 40 feet deep, 2,700 feet wide, and 6,000 feet long had been constructed; and over a dozen tributary channels in the harbor and its arms had been dredged and blasted to depths of from 12 to 40 feet.

Boston Harbor was well provided with good natural covers, but not all

Boston Inner Harbor.

New England harbors were so favored. Breakwaters, which Corps engineers designed and built at about two dozen localities, were necessary for their improvement. Varying in cross section and design according to particular requirements, the breakwaters range in length from a few hundred feet at tiny harbors like that at Criehaven, Maine, to more than two and a third miles, the aggregate length of three structures forming a wholly artificial harbor nearly a mile square at Point Judith, Rhode Island. A primary purpose of many of the earlier breakwater projects was to provide harbors of refuge for the sailing vessels that continued to dominate the coastal trade until after the turn of the century.

Breakwaters for constructing a wholly man-made harbor were first employed at Block Island, twelve miles off the Rhode Island coast. The island had no natural harbors, no ships could find anchor in a storm, and no decked vessels were owned there. The open boats of the island's inhabitants were hauled upon a beach by oxen. In 1867 Congress ordered an examination and survey at the island for creating a harbor of refuge. Newport District Engineer Major Houston made the survey, and in 1870 his successor, Major Warren, began the construction of an anchorage on the east side of the island. By 1873 Warren had built a temporary harbor about 300 feet square, dredged to 7 feet at mean low water. Another enclosure about 800 feet square was then constructed outside this small basin; and a third, still larger, sheltered anchorage was formed by extending the main breakwater beyond the enclosed areas to a distance of 1,950 feet from shore. Although work on retaining walls, a jetty, dredging, and portions of the breakwaters continued

The small breakwater at Criehaven Harbor.

The long breakwaters at the Point Judith Harbor of Refuge.

until 1916, the original project was essentially completed in 1879. Two years later Lieutenant Colonel Warren reported that the harbor was crowded to capacity in active seasons and that local business had so increased that a new dredging project was underway to accommodate a small steamer now belonging to the island. Ultimately the harbor was dredged to 15 feet at mean low water.

Block Island Harbor of Refuge.

The breakwaters at Block Island cost about $825,000 to construct. Those at Point Judith, built between 1890 and 1916, the longest in New England and until the inflationary 1970s the most expensive, cost nearly $2.5 million. Almost as expensive as the Point Judith complex was a breakwater at Sandy Bay, Massachusetts, that the Corps was never anxious to build and was finally left only about one-quarter completed. A large bight on the northeastern shore of Cape Ann, Sandy Bay lies almost exactly halfway between Boston and Portland, and apparently for this reason Congress in 1882 ordered a survey for the construction of a harbor of refuge. Submitting a report in 1883, Boston District Engineer Major Charles Raymond presented a plan for a breakwater 9,000 feet long, estimated to cost $4 million. He made no recommendation, however, as to the worthiness of the project. "The proposed harbor will have great accessibility in the daytime in weather when the adjacent coast can be seen," Raymond said. "In the night and in thick weather, when the lights are obscured, it is a serious question whether an attempt to enter it could be made with safety." Explaining that a slight error at the northern entrance would bring a ship upon a rocky shore and that the eastern entrance was always dangerous because of outlying reefs and ledges, he left it to qualified mariners to answer whether it would be safer to try to enter the harbor in a storm or stay outside.

Evidently not finding this conclusive enough, Congress in 1884 appropriated $100,000 for the construction of "a national harbor of refuge of the first class," provided that a board of engineers decided that Sandy Bay was the best location between Boston and Portland. The special board that was convened displayed no greater enthusiasm for the project than had Raymond. It reported that it did not consider the construction of the harbor necessary or expedient at that time, but should Congress decide otherwise, both the location and Raymond's plans were the best that could be adopted. It increased the estimated cost to $5 million and figured that another $2.5 million would be necessary for lighthouses, buoys, and defense.

The matter would probably have ended there had not "interested parties" approached Secretary of War William C. Endicott in April 1885. Arguing that the expenditure of the $100,000 available would be to the substantial benefit of commerce by clearly marking a ledge from which the breakwater was to be extended, they asked him to direct that operations be commenced.

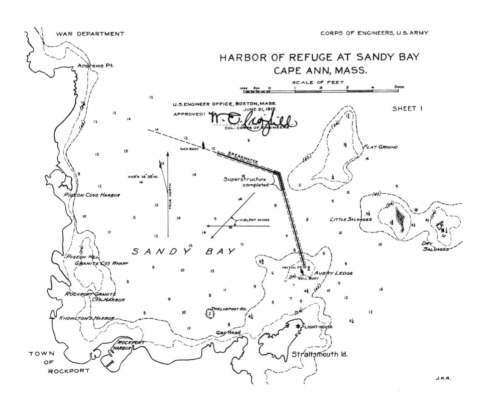

The Secretary referred the question back to Raymond, who agreed that the construction of a visible pier on the ledge would no doubt benefit navigation whether or not the breakwater was built. Endicott thereupon authorized the construction of the pier. The next year, in reply to Senate questioning, Endicott overrode the advice of the board of engineers and stated that in his opinion work on the breakwater should be continued and completed.[2]

The politics of inertia then took over. Voting appropriations for the next thirty years, Congress did not again question the expediency of the project. In 1899 it asked if any modifications should be made, and a special board of engineers proposed strengthening the breakwater, thereby raising its estimated cost to nearly $7 million. In 1909 further modifications were proposed after severe winter storms proved the earlier changes to be insufficient. The worthiness of the project, however, was not brought under review until 1915, when the Chief of Engineers was directed to report on any projects that should be modified or were no longer desirable. The engineer of the Boston District at that time was Colonel William E. Craighill, who thought that thirty years of dumping stone in Sandy Bay was enough. Pointing out that coastal sailing ships had by now been largely superseded by steamers less dependent on harbors of refuge, and expressing doubt that any mariner would attempt to enter the harbor in thick weather, Craighill recommended that the project be abandoned. When his recommendation was followed the next year, about two-thirds of the substructure and one-tenth of the superstructure of the breakwater, or 26 percent of the project, had been completed. Ironically, the portion that was to mark the ledge to the benefit of commerce was never brought above high water level. The cost of this great white elephant was nearly $2 million, and the only beneficiaries were the granite companies of Cape Ann who had supplied two million tons of rubblestone.[3]

In an account of breakwater construction by the Corps in New England, however, the breakwater at Sandy Bay is merely an interesting and perhaps instructive episode. The breakwaters sheltering New England harbors have significantly reduced hazards to navigation and improved anchorages for local craft. The artificial harbor of refuge at Point Judith provided a haven for numerous commercial coastal sailers and now sees heavy use by recreational boats; and the other harbors have similarly been used extensively by both commercial and recreational craft. At a major commercial harbor the most notable construction of breakwaters was at New Haven, where a broad estuary opens more than four miles wide on Long Island Sound. To shelter the harbor from storms sweeping in from the sound and to provide anchorage grounds for vessels seeking refuge, the Engineers constructed, between 1879 and 1915, three riprap breakwaters that extend for an aggregate distance of 12,100 feet in a rough arc across the wide harbor entrance.

The most recent breakwaters built by the Corps in New England are at Plymouth and Provincetown. Originally improved in the interests of commerce, both harbors are now popular centers of recreational boating and the homes of large commercial fishing fleets. Trips in and out of Plymouth Harbor were estimated in 1962 at about 42,400 annually, consisting of 17,000 by fishing vessels and 25,400 by recreational craft. Anchorage facilities were inadequate for this heavy use, for although a natural harbor is formed by

Long Beach, it is exposed to storms from north through east. The break-water completed by the New England Division in 1971, which runs easterly and then southeasterly out from shore for about 3,500 feet, creates a protected anchorage sixty acres in extent. Provincetown Harbor, lying within a sandy hook on the tip of Cape Cod, was splendidly protected by nature from Atlantic storms from the east, north, and west, but was exposed to bad weather sweeping up from the south across Cape Cod Bay. The new Provincetown breakwater, a 2,500-foot-long offshore barrier completed in 1972, now provides a safe anchorage for Provincetown's fishing fleet and the large number of transient vessels that put into the harbor.[4]

Plymouth Harbor Breakwater.

Several breakwaters built in New England by the Corps were designed, not to shelter anchorages, but to arrest dangerous tidal cross currents or to protect river or harbor entrances. The largest breakwater of the latter type was built at the mouth of the Saco River in Maine. Navigable for about six miles to the cities of Saco and Biddeford, the Saco wound over numerous ledges and shoals before discharging into the sea through a wide sandy beach where the depth over the bar was only two feet at mean low water. In 1866 Congress authorized the repair of the piers built inside and at the mouth of the river thirty years before. But since the piers at the entrance had failed to deepen the water over the bar, Major Alexander, during his brief supervision of projects in Maine, recommended replacing them with a long breakwater extending from the north side of the river's mouth, which would better hold the channel out into the sea. Lieutenant Colonel Thom began the project the next year. Reporting in 1869 that 2,550 feet of the breakwater had been completed, Thom claimed with too much optimism that it had already accomplished everything expected of it: it had closed the old circuitous channel and formed a deeper, more uniform, and more direct one. Under succeeding projects to 1938, the breakwater was raised, strengthened, and extended 6,600 feet into the sea; a jetty was built out 4,800 feet from the south side of the river's mouth to contract the channel and obtain more water over the bar; small fender jetties within the river were repaired and two jetties were built to serve as contraction works; and dredging and ledge excavation was carried out to a depth of eight feet at mean low water. Although the works at the mouth of the river did not achieve the permanent seven-foot depth that had originally been expected, they did succeed in creating a straighter and deeper channel. While the depth over the bar varies from time to time, five feet at mean low water is generally available by action of the river's current. A project depth of eight feet to the head of navigation, adopted in 1925, is maintained by periodic dredging.

Saco River Breakwater and Jetty.

Jetties were built by New England's Engineers at more than thirty localities. Some were intended as fender piers, others were built to control river or tidal currents or to protect shores from erosion, and still others were designed as contraction works. One of the largest jetty projects was at Nantucket Harbor, where Lieutenant Prescott's pioneer efforts at dredging in New England earlier in the century had been erased by a single storm. Except for the small harbor of Hyannis on the north side of Nantucket Sound, Nantucket Harbor offered the only shelter between the harbors of Martha's Vineyard, thirty-two miles to the west, and Provincetown, eighty miles to the north, for vessels navigating the dangerous waters of the sound. Pursuant to a congressional directive in 1879, Lieutenant Colonel Warren prepared plans that he believed would increase the mean-low-water depth over the harbor's wide bar from six to twelve or fourteen feet. He proposed the construction of a jetty, or if necessary, two jetties, across the bar so as to arrest the motion of littoral sand and concentrate tidal currents in the channel. Unlike other places were contraction works had been built, Nantucket Harbor had no river currents to assist outgoing tides, but it had been observed that outgoing tides had a greater scouring effect by themselves than incoming ones, and thus more material would be carried out of the channel than carried in. If the project were successful, the harbor would be available as a harbor of refuge. And any increase in channel depth, Warren figured, would aid communications with the island, which was already becoming an important summer resort. Begun in 1880, the project dragged on for nearly sixty years, appropriations for it averaging only about $8,000 annually. One benefit of this long period of construction was that it provided time to experiment and observe results. Before two converging jetties were finally completed in 1937 to lengths of 6,987 and 5,000 feet, they had been built to varying heights and cross sections to find the best proportions for controlling the scour. Dredging, provided for by a modification of the project in 1886 if scouring did not result in the expected channel depth, was begun in 1905 and completed in 1930. Since then the controlling depth has never been less than twelve feet, and dredging has been necessary only a few times to maintain a depth of fifteen feet. More than doubling the depth of a former shallow and tortuous channel by natural scour, the Nantucket project is an outstanding example of the successful application of contraction works.

Jetties built at the mouth of the Connecticut River at Saybrook and at

Contraction-works jetties at Nantucket Harbor.

several other places were also successful in deepening water over the bars. The most troublesome jetty project was at Newburyport Harbor. By the close of the Civil War the long-neglected jetties designed by Major Totten in the Corps' first tidewater experiment with contraction works had been destroyed, and the channel over the bar was only from five to seven feet deep. Unlike the bars at most river entrances, the bar at the mouth of the Merrimack was not formed by the dropping of debris as the river's current slowed down upon entering the sea, but by the rolling in of sand by ocean waves. The river struggled to keep its entrance open at even a shallow depth, and the channel and the sandy points on either side of the entrance were constantly shifting their positions. The plan of improvement for the harbor, drawn up by Lieutenant Colonel Thom and modified by the Board of Engineers in 1880, aimed at securing a depth of seventeen feet across the bar by the construction of converging rubblestone jetties extending from Salisbury and Plum Island points. An actual depth of seventeen feet, it was assumed, would guarantee, even during storms, a navigable depth of thirteen and a half feet.

By 1885 the north jetty had been pushed out from its anchoring point about 2,000 feet, and the south jetty about 1,000 feet. Major Raymond, who had taken over the project two years before on the reestablishment of the Boston District, reported that the depth over the bar had increased three feet since the beginning of the project, and that half the gain had been made in the past year. "These works, being an attempt to improve the mouth of a river on a sandy coast, are of great scientific interest," he commented. "Such attempts have generally proved failures, but in this case there is reason to expect success."[5] But the constant action of storms driving in sand was to limit the success of the project severely. Construction on the jetties continued until they were completed in 1914. The south jetty measures 2,415 feet in length, and the north jetty, 4,118 feet. They converge until 1,000 feet apart and then extend seaward parallel to the axis of the channel for 1,000 feet. During the period of construction the channel changed in depth from year to year, measuring anywhere from eight to thirteen feet; and the completion of the jetties had little effect on this constant variation. The jetties provided somewhat more water over the bar—the usual minimum depth was nine feet—but shifting sands continued to change conditions rapidly and frequently.[6]

Damage to the Newburyport jetties by storms necessitated major rehabilitation of them in 1936 and again in 1970; and between 1937 and 1942 government dredges twice deepened the channel to fifteen feet. In 1945 a project was adopted, subject to local cooperation, providing for a channel fifteen feet deep through the bar and twelve feet deep to the city's wharves. Pending compliance with the requirements of local cooperation, the channel would be improved to depths of twelve and nine feet. Nothing more was done at the harbor, however, until 1958, when the channel was dredged to the lesser depths of the project, the plans for the greater depths having realistically been relegated to the inactive category. Since then maintenance dredging to maintain twelve feet of water over the bar has been carried out every few years.

Jetties, or wing-dams, as well as training walls and dikes, were also con-

The jetties at Newburyport Harbor, March 1969.

structed upstream in several New England rivers, including the Kennebec, Thames, and Housatonic. Most of these projects were small works built in the nineteenth century, and by deepening water somewhat over shoals they were of benefit to the shallow-draft commercial river vessels of that time.

The most extensive efforts to improve river navigation were naturally made on the Connecticut River, New England's longest navigable waterway. In the early development of central New England, freight had been moved on the river in small boats of light draft to points more than two hundred miles above its mouth. Rapids at several places had been surmounted by dams and navigation canals constructed by private enterprise. By the post-Civil War era, however, all that remained of these works was the Windsor Locks Canal, and a rock-filled, timber-crib dam to divert water into the canal, at Enfield Rapids, about sixty-three miles from the river's mouth. Since the canal, built by the Connecticut River Company in the early 1830s, could not accommodate vessels drawing more than three feet of water, navigation for all practical purposes ended at Hartford, fifty-two miles up the river from the sea. Thirty-four miles above Hartford, a power dam at Holyoke, Massachusetts, completely interrupted navigation.

Below Enfield Rapids the major obstructions to navigation were river bars scattered for about ten miles on either side of Hartford. The Connecticut at this point flows through an alluvial region. Its banks are easily eroded, causing constant changes of its bed and the formation of shoals at every flood stage. Major Houston, who made the first postwar survey of the river in 1867, observed that piers for confining the channel built some years before by private agencies were now either dangerous obstructions or covered by deposits. He therefore advised against the construction of permanent works in the area. The channel could be kept open, he believed, only by annual dredging.

The Windsor Locks Canal, 1914.

One of the three small navigation locks at the downstream end of the Windsor Locks Canal, 1940.

Gouverneur Warren, coming to the Newport District in 1870, thought differently. Between Hartford and Enfield Rapids, a distance of about eleven miles, shoaling sometimes left depths of only eighteen inches at low water, and Warren hoped to secure a permanent depth of three to four feet by the use of wing-dams. Since the Windsor Locks Canal could not pass vessels of more than three-foot draft, no greater depth in the river was necessary for the time being. During the next decade Warren constructed jetties at five bars. He never regarded them as more than temporary improvements of limited capacity, however, and by the time he had finished the last of them, he obviously thought they did not have even that value. In his annual report of 1881 he noted that while at locations where work had been done the results were still satisfactory, changes that had taken place elsewhere in the river had left it at extreme low water in about its original unnavigable condition.

Below Hartford the river was kept open after 1870 to steamers running between Hartford and New York City by annual dredging to a depth of nine feet. Hoping for more permanent improvement of the channel, Warren in 1880 began the construction of training walls and jetties at six of the worst bars. In 1887, however, when works had been completed at two places and the bars still had to be dredged every year about as much as before, the project was abandoned. Permanent works in the river were not tried again until 1911, when a project was adopted to provide a twelve-foot channel to Hartford by dredging and by the construction, for sixteen miles below the city, of spur dikes, training walls, and revetments. Under this project some construction was carried out every year, largely by hired labor, until 1929. Training walls and spur dikes of timber and stone, and revetments of riprap and brush, were built along the river at more than a dozen places bearing intriguing names such as Cys Hollow, Press Barn Reach, and Pistol Point Bar. In 1935 a new project provided for a fifteen-foot channel to Hartford and for additional dikes, training walls, and revetments. The channel was dredged to project depth by 1937, but only a few of the regulatory structures were completed. The channel to Hartford was kept open by maintenance dredging, and new work on the Connecticut focused on improvements at recreational boating centers near the river's mouth.

While navigation was being improved on the Connecticut River below Hartford, projects for improvement between Hartford and Holyoke remained on the drawing board, the victims of complexities that often exist in the planning of public works.

In 1878 Gouverneur Warren submitted plans for opening this upper stretch of the river to larger vessels by the construction of a seventeen-mile-long canal from below Hartford to the head of Enfield Rapids. The canal, and dredging above it, would provide an eight-foot channel to Holyoke. Justifying the proposal, Warren observed that it would reduce transportation costs of bulky articles into a large manufacturing region reached only by railroads. Although river and harbor improvement received much of its support in this period of largely unregulated private enterprise precisely because it offered a competitive means of reducing railroad rates, Warren's scheme was shelved. He estimated that the improvement would cost about $3 million, a figure that seemed to outweigh expected benefits of the plan.

No further studies were made until 1896, when Congress ordered a new

Construction of a training wall at Clay Banks, Connecticut River, 1914.

Construction of brush and riprap revetments at Cys Hollow, Connecticut River, 1915.

survey. The next year Major Smith S. Leach, in charge of the newly reopened New London Office, submitted a favorable report, estimating that the cost of improvement, including locks and dams for surmounting the rapids, would be about $2 million. The river towns of southern Massachusetts, suddenly seeing themselves again the thriving ports they had been a century before, energetically backed the proposal, and the Massachusetts legislature sent lobbyists to Washington. Hartford interests, on the other hand, were not at all eager to see commerce bypassing their city. For the next dozen years a controversy raged over the desirability of the improvement, and Congress ordered several more surveys and reviews of reports. Each time, however, the Corps submitted an unfavorable recommendation. The cost of surmounting the rapids would be at least $3 million, the Engineers reported, and unless waterpower could be developed by private interests in connection with the project, the cost to the United States would be out of proportion with expected benefits to navigation and commerce.[7] Development of power by the federal government itself was a recommendation the Corps had no authority to advance; it was outside the thinking of most people of the time, and beyond the reach of political possibilities.

In 1909 the Connecticut River Company, which was already using the canal at Enfield for small power plants and had not previously been disposed to enlarge its facilities, and a newly organized corporation, the Northern Connecticut Power Company, both petitioned Congress for the privilege of developing waterpower at Enfield Rapids; and in this context Congress ordered another examination and survey. The Board of Engineers, in keeping with policy set by President Theodore Roosevelt that the government be compensated for waterpower rights, recommended that private interests assume responsibility for all damage claims and for constructing a lock and dam at Enfield Rapids, which would become the property of the United States.

In 1913 this scheme for making the navigation project justifiable was modified when a bill authorizing the Connecticut River Company to construct a power dam was referred by the Senate to Secretary of War Henry L. Stimson for comment. On the advice of the Chief of Engineers, Stimson recommended that the company be required to pay a reasonable annual return to the federal government for the power rights, this compensation to be applied to the improvement of navigation. The United States would pay for construction work on the dam that was exclusively in the interests of navigation and would have title and control of such property. In this revised form the bill passed the Senate but was killed in the House by congressmen who claimed that federal legislation respecting waterpower on the Connecticut River violated states' rights. Meanwhile Congress had ordered still another examination and survey. Reporting in 1915, New London District Engineer G. P. Pillsbury came to the same conclusions as had the Board of Engineers earlier. He deemed the improvement of the river advisable, provided that waterpower or other interests assumed all responsibility for damage claims and constructed a suitable lock and dam at Enfield, to be deeded to the United States.[8]

There the matter rested until 1928, when the Northern Connecticut Power Company, which had meantime acquired the water rights at Enfield Rapids from the Connecticut River Company, was granted a license by the Federal Power Commission (established in 1920) to construct a lock and dam. This revived interest in the navigation question, and the House Committee on Rivers and Harbors requested the Board of Engineers to review the Corps' last report on the improvement of the river. Submitting its findings in April 1930, the board noted that ten highway and railroad bridges lay between Hartford and Holyoke, all of which would have to be provided with draw or lift spans to allow passage of the type of freight steamers now plying the lower river. Since local interests were opposed to modifying the bridges, the board recommended that no improvement be made. The Massachusetts towns thereupon immediately about-faced and agreed to modify the bridges, and a week later the board issued a second report favoring improvement. The project it recommended provided for the extension of the twelve-foot channel from Hartford to Holyoke by dredging and suitable regulatory works; for the construction by private interests of a lock and dam at Enfield Rapids; and for the lengthening by the federal government of the lock at Enfield and the construction of a low dam and lock near Hartford, which would create a pool covering the shallow stretch of the river to Enfield. Terms of local cooperation included the modification of the bridges and the provision of satisfactory terminal facilities by the upriver cities.[9]

Despite strong opposition from Connecticut forces, Congress included the project in the River and Harbor Act of 1930, and at last it appeared that a channel would be cleared from Holyoke to the sea. Then suddenly the power company decided not to build the dam; and in September 1931 the Federal Power Commission was forced to revoke its license. Why the company made this decision remains a subject of conjecture, but most likely it was simply that the economic collapse of 1929 made the power enterprise less attractive than it had seemed the year before.[10]

The Massachusetts towns now clamored for the federal government to construct the entire works, including the power dam at Enfield; and again the Corps of Engineers was ordered by the House Committee on Rivers and Harbors to review the project. Providence District Engineer Major Charles J. Taylor, reporting early in 1933, recommended the construction of a lock and dam so designed that the work could later be modified for the development of power. He was overruled, however, by all his superiors, who thought the costs involved too great and the public benefits too limited. The Chief of Engineers therefore recommended no alteration of the authorized project except a change of wording to permit the construction of the lock and dam at Enfield by any state, municipal, or private interest under license by the Federal Power Commission, a modification that was included in the River and Harbor Act of 1935.[11]

This was hardly the action the upriver towns wanted, and even before the final passage of the act of 1935 the House Committee on Rivers and Harbors had again requested the Board of Engineers to review the Corps' last reports. New studies, changing circumstances, and a somewhat altered approach to the problem resulted in a reversal of the Corps' previous findings. The new proposal, drawn up by Providence District Engineer Lieutenant Colonel John S. Bragdon, was sent to Congress in January 1939. Bragdon recommended that the authorized plan of improvement be modified to provide for the construction and immediate operation of a combined navigation-power development at Enfield Rapids, the combined benefits of which would, in view of prospective river traffic and present power values, be in excess of costs. Bragdon also proposed, as another necessary modification to make the project economically feasible, that the terms of local cooperation regarding bridge draws or lifts be changed to require vertical bridge clearances of twenty feet. The principal transportation line operating barges on the river promised to provide vessels to handle the twenty-foot clearances, which meant that only four bridges would have to be raised and one drawspan installed. Bragdon estimated the cost of the project to the government at about $12 million.[12]

At hearings conducted by the House Committee on Rivers and Harbors Bragdon's proposal was supported by the Massachusetts river cities and a number of industries and was opposed by the entire Connecticut congressional delegation and by power, railroad, railroad labor, coal (because considerable petroleum would be transported), and other interests. The committee, after first rejecting the project by a close vote, ultimately approved it. But the full House, which in 1939 had few supporters of public power schemes, decisively defeated the proposal. Attempts by proponents of the Enfield project to secure its adoption by Congress in 1941 and again in 1943 also failed to secure favorable action.[13]

Yet the Enfield power and navigation project was still not dead. In 1946 Congress called for another examination and survey of the Connecticut River, and the next year the House Committee on Rivers and Harbors requested a review of the 1939 report on the river between Hartford and Holyoke. Under these authorizations the New England Division conducted more studies, on which it reported in June 1949. The division recommended providing a sixteen-foot channel to Hartford and a twelve-foot channel from Hartford to Holyoke. Rather than building a low dam at Hartford to back water to Enfield, as previously contemplated, it proposed dredging a navigation channel. At Enfield it proposed to construct a somewhat higher dam, with considerably greater generating capacity, than had been envisioned under the previous plan. The cost to the government of the project would be close to $32 million.[14]

At public hearings on the project, old alignments rather startlingly went somewhat topsy-turvy. The power company that now controlled the water rights at Enfield no longer opposed the project, but applied to the Federal Power Commission for permission to construct the powerhouse and install the generating equipment. Connecticut state authorities followed in train and abandoned official opposition to the proposal. A number of Massachusetts interests, on the other hand, no longer favored it, claiming that the higher dam by backing water upstream would in one way or another cause them financial injury. But in general most Massachusetts spokesmen still tended to favor the project, and had it been considered by Congress it apparently would have received greater local support than in the past. The project, however, was not approved by the Board of Engineers, which felt that its navigation benefits had not been clearly established.[15]

The enthusiasm of upriver interests for improving the stream for commercial navigation, however mixed it may have been in 1949, was in later years to wane. When the House Committee on Public Works, in June 1964, issued another request for the Corps to review its reports of 1939, its concern was not cargo carriers but a new and expanding business—recreational boating.

Various state and local officials, as well as private interests of the communities between Hartford and Holyoke, wanted a navigable channel between the two cities that would permit small craft to run the whole river from Long Island Sound to Holyoke. Division engineers, looking for the best means of providing safe and dependable passage for recreational craft, at first considered the construction of a low-elevation dam at Hartford that would form a navigable pool extending upstream to Windsor Locks. Federal, state, and local fish and wildlife agencies, however, said that the plan would result in the loss of 60 percent of a shad spawning area. When the engineers considered placing the dam several miles up the river beyond a tributary stream, the fish and wildlife agencies protested that it would still flood 45 percent of the shad spawning area. The engineers then decided upon a dredged channel six feet deep to Windsor Locks, where a small navigation lock would lift boats thirty-three feet into the Windsor Lock Canal, whose channel would also be deepened to six feet. The plan further required the construction of a small dam in the canal downstream from the lock to maintain adequate pool elevation and the replacement of the existing lock at the head of the canal with a flood-control gate. The cost of the improvement was estimated at $9 million, to which local interests would be required to contribute half. They would also be responsible for operating and maintaining the project, acquiring Enfield dam and the upper four miles of the canal from their owner, and various lesser obligations. These requirements were more than local interests cared to meet. Although expressing interest in the plan, they claimed that they could not participate in it financially. Thereupon Division Engineer Colonel John H. Mason, winding up the matter in 1973, recommended that no improvement be made for the present.[16]

For over one hundred years Army Engineers thus devoted an enormous amount of time and expertise to studies and plans for improving a thirty-four-mile stretch of the Connecticut River. Technically, improvement was always feasible, but technical feasibility was only one of many considerations that had to be taken into account. Costs in relation to benefits, conflicting economic interests, reversals of attitudes, changing navigational needs, problems relating to non-federal contributions, and recently emphasized considerations of ecological impact all helped to shape the history of this proposed navigation improvement.

Dredging waterways and building breakwaters and jetties were the major river and harbor activities of Army Engineers in New England, but by no means the only ones. At Plymouth and Provincetown they continued the work of preserving the harbor-protecting beaches by the construction of bulkheads, jetties, dikes, and catch-sand fences; and at several other harbors they carried out smaller but similar projects. At Woods Hole, Massachusetts, they constructed an anchorage basin for the use of the United States Fish Commission and other governmental agencies. They constructed dikes for a variety of purposes, erected spindles and beacons to mark rocks in channels, and at a number of places removed wrecks and old bridges that were hazards to navigation.

Plan of pier to form an anchorage basin at Woods Hole, 1883.

Like most river and harbor work of the Corps until fairly recent years, these projects were directed wholly to the improvement of navigation. That was what public and congressional interest dictated. But at least one small project was of a different kind. At Newport, Rhode Island, a causeway between Coaster Harbor Island and Rhode Island closed off a small cove, water could not flow freely through the causeway's one small opening, and deposits built up, creating noxious odors. In 1891-92 the Newport District dredged the cove and pierced the causeway with several bridge trusses. An insignificant project, and perhaps from the viewpoint of a later generation one that only permitted sewage to flow out to sea, it nevertheless appears to have been the first in New England directed toward environmental improvement, which currently absorbs much of the Corps' attention.

The causeway to Coaster Harbor Island did not impede navigation, but

New England district engineers encountered the problem of man-made obstructions in other waterways. "Throughout the country," writes the historian of the Refuse Act of 1899, "industries were building wharves and piers, municipalities were filling in open water, sawmills and factories were dumping refuse, and cities were disposing of rubbish, dredged spoil and sewage without regard to the effects on navigable streams. Bridge building had become a splendid art carried on in a legal wilderness of special laws by Congress and the states."[17] All these activities encroached upon constitutional powers over navigable waterways claimed by the federal government since the time of John Marshall. Before the Civil War there had been little need to exercise this authority. The aggravation of abuses and the growing federal investment in waterways after the war, however, made its invocation more compelling.

Portland District Engineer George Thom called attention to the obstruction of streams in Maine as early as 1867. Directed to improve the St. Croix River, which marks the lower portion of the boundary between Maine and New Brunswick, Thom reported that the river was choked with slabs, edgings, and sawdust, which had been accumulating for more than thirty years from sawmills near Calais. If the river were cleaned out, he cautioned, it would soon be closed again unless this dumping of waste was stopped. The next year Thom made a survey of the Penobscot River below Bangor and reported even worse obstructions. Sawmill waste thrown into the stream for more than fifty years had accumulated to an average depth of ten feet, and in places to more than eighteen feet. To restore the channel to its original condition for a three-and-a-half mile stretch below the city would require the excavation of more than five million cubic yards of material. Thom, therefore, recommended for the present merely the cutting of a passable channel. And again he advised that permanent improvement was impossible unless the mills were prevented from throwing in waste. He added, however, that recent state laws had in great measure accomplished this prohibition.

The Maine laws proved to be wholly ineffective. Beginning work on the Penobscot in 1871, Thom was soon complaining that millwaste continued to be thrown into the stream. Finding the same situation on several other rivers in his district for which appropriations had been made, he repeatedly recommended that Congress withhold funds for their improvement until this obstruction of navigable rivers was prevented by federal legislation. But Congress continued to vote appropriations, and Thom was obliged to carry out the work. In each case it was not long before the river was again impassable or more work was necessary to keep it open.

Only on the St. Croix was work postponed, and this was because of its international nature. The appropriation of 1867 had been made with the proviso that New Brunswick contribute a like amount. Between 1873 and 1909 Congress three more times voted funds for the river and five times ordered new surveys. But the government of Canada steadfastly refused to cooperate in the project until satisfactory assurances were made that the dumping of waste would be permanently stopped.[18] Portland District engineers invariably agreed with this position and favored improvement of the river only if the practice were brought to an end. "To remove the refuse of the mills from the river without taking any measures to prevent the necessity for repeating the expense at some future day," said Jared Smith politely in 1886, "is a proposition which cannot be commended."[19] It was not until 1911 that sufficient assurances against dumping were obtained and an agreement with Canada was made. On the basis of the commercial benefit of the improvement to each side, Canada agreed to bear ten percent of the cost. Dredging of a twelve-foot channel began in 1912 and was completed in 1916. By this time, however, the project was of little value. During most of the fifty years of delay Calais had been a busy port. Even though vessels in the lumber trade had had to drop down river nearly four miles after being partially loaded and it had been necessary to lighter a large part of the freight of all kinds to deep water, the annual value of waterborne commerce had often been several million dollars. In 1920 it was less than $350,000. The river is now used chiefly by a small fishing fleet.

Colonel Thom's suggestions for legislation prohibiting the obstruction of waterways were the first voiced by the Corps of Engineers. They were soon being echoed by other army engineers and other interests. At the instigation of the New York City Chamber of Commerce, Representative Abram S. Hewitt introduced a bill in Congress in 1876 to prohibit the dumping of waste materials in navigable waters. It died in committee. The next year the Chief of Engineers, Andrew A. Humphreys, sent to Congress the draft of a new bill that covered not only dumping but also the obstruction of waterways by bridges or any other construction.[20] The broader nature of Humphreys's bill owed something to New England district engineers. Thom had added the building of bridge piers and draws to his complaints coming down from Portland, and Major Warren at Newport was complaining about present and prospective bridge obstructions in the Pawtucket River of Rhode Island and wanting to know if there were any legal means to control bridge construction.[21]

Humphreys's bill, like Hewitt's, was set aside in the House of Representatives, as were several later bills. Despite increasing federal appropriations for waterways, the obstruction of them did not arouse much interest in Congress. It was easy to view most obstructions as petty and local, and opposition to corrective action from railroads, bridge companies, and other interests was strong.[22]

But the problem of obstructions was of growing concern to the Corps, and at the urgings of the War Department some progress was made, usually by attaching proposals to river and harbor bills, which few congressmen cared to endanger or delay. Minor gains were made between 1880 and 1890 by giving the Secretary of War greater authority to clear wrecks from navigable waters. Under this authority the New England districts by 1917 had arranged for the removal of 315 wrecks, over half of them in the vicinity of Cape Cod and Nantucket Sound. More important was the authority given to the Secretary of War in August 1888 to order the alteration of bridges that obstructed navigation. The act was hardly printed before the Boston and Newport districts recommended the alteration of nine bridges across the Charles River and one spanning the Taunton River. When the Old Colony Railroad Company refused to alter the Taunton River bridge, the Secretary filed a complaint with the Justice Department as provided in the law. During the next three decades the New England districts required the owners of forty-six bridges to meet specifications they made for changes.[23]

The act of 1888 also empowered the Secretary of War to establish harbor lines beyond which no piers or wharves could be extended or deposits made except under regulations that might later be prescribed by law. Two days after the law was passed the Chief of Engineers appointed a board of engineers, which included the Boston District engineer, to determine harbor lines at Boston. The next three New England localities at which harbor lines were established were the unlikely small ports of Stamford, Connecticut, and Lubec and Bath, Maine. The appointment of a board of engineers to draw lines at Stamford resulted from a petition to their senator from citizens of the town objecting to a pier that was about to be built into a channel the Engineers had just dredged. At Lubec and Bath, narrow channels and rapid tidal currents prompted District Engineer Jared Smith to nip quickly proposals for the extensions of wharves that were arousing protests. Two decades after the passage of the act of 1888, lines had been established at thirty-five New England harbors either by district engineers or special boards of engineers. In each case consideration was given to all interests involved. The district engineer or board was required to make a full report to the Engineer Department as to the necessity of the action, to hold a public hearing, and to consult with municipal authorities.[24]

Complete success in the protection of waterways appeared to be won with the River and Harbor Act of September 1890. A bloated piece of legislation making appropriations for 413 projects and 203 examinations and surveys, the bill was amended by senators in conference committee to include all the regulatory provisions for which the Chief of Engineers and other advocates of protective legislation had long been asking. Upon being sent back to the House, the revised bill was accepted without debate by members anxious to vote for the great pork-barrel measure and get home for the November elections. The act made it unlawful to dump into waterways waste of any kind that obstructed navigation; to build any structure that might impair navigation or to change the course or condition of a navigable channel without permission of the Secretary of War; or to construct any bridge over a navigable waterway until the location and plan had been approved by the Secretary of War.[25]

The provision relating to the construction of bridges worked well. Its first application in New England was to a bridge connecting Little Island with the mainland at Osterville on Cape Cod, plans for which were recommended for the Secretary's approval by the Newport District engineer in May 1891. Plans for 130 other new or reconstructed bridges were investigated and recommended by the New England districts during the first two decades after the passage of the act.[26]

Other sections of the act soon proved to be less effective. An unfortunate phrase in the prohibition against dumping obliged the government to show that each act of dumping had individually obstructed a waterway—a crippling requirement since obstructions generally resulted from an accumulation of deposits. With respect to structures that impaired navigation, a resounding declaration prohibiting "the creation of any obstruction . . . to the navigable capacity of any waters" was followed in the next sentence by the exemption of "structures erected for business purposes"—an exception that practically vitiated the prohibition. No provisions were made for gathering evidence against violators, nor was authority given to appropriate government officers to make arrests.

Wanting new legislation, the Corps got its first real opportunity in 1896 when the House Committee on Rivers and Harbors asked for its assistance in drafting that year's omnibus bill. An astute attorney was sent to the Hill, who inserted a provision in the bill directing the Secretary of War to compile all existing laws relating to the protection and preservation of waterways and suggest necessary revisions. The Corps now had the chance to draft a bill containing the reforms it desired. Three years later Senator William P. Frye of Maine inserted the proposals in the river and harbor bill of 1899 and adroitly maneuvered them through Congress with bland assertions that the amendments prepared by the Chief of Engineers involved no real changes but only codification of existing laws.[27]

The changes were actually of enormous significance. Section 10 of the act of 1899 forbade any obstruction to navigation not "affirmatively authorized" by Congress and made it unlawful to build any structures or make any excavations or alterations in navigable waters except by plans recommended by the Chief of Engineers and approved by the Secretary of War. Section 13—the Refuse Act of 1899—was equally comprehensive because of its simplicity. It uncomplicatedly prohibited the discharge or deposit of "any refuse matter of any kind or description"—except municipal sewage—in navigable waters of the United States and their tributaries. Since the phrase, "which shall tend to impede or obstruct navigation," of the act of 1890 was discarded, it was no longer necessary to show that any particular act of dumping obstructed navigation. Customs officials and Corps personnel were empowered to arrest violators. As in the earlier act, the Corps was authorized to issue permits prescribing conditions under which deposits of material not obstructing navigation might be made.[28]

The sweeping assertions of federal authority over waterways contained in Sections 10 and 13 provided the legal bases for a program of permits set up by the Corps to protect navigation. The administration of the program, at first rather improvisional, was gradually developed and improved until by 1917 detailed regulations defining permit procedures had been worked out. Printed regulations explained the law and provided form letters and specimen drawings to assist applicants. Such instructions have been periodically reissued, and investigations have been carried out, permits granted, and abuses checked by small staffs in the engineer offices, all as a routine, not very visible, but important part of the Corps' daily activities.[29] From the beginning of the program through 1946, the Boston District and its earlier components issued about 5,000 permits for dredging, filling, or construction of some kind, while the Providence District and its predecessors issued some 6,000 permits. Between 1947 and 1973 the New England Division issued 8,085 permits, the number in any one year ranging from 234 in 1948 to 363 in 1968. Alleged violations of the law were routinely checked. Between 1966 and 1974 the Permits Branch of the division carried out 248 such investigations. When necessary, reports were sent to the Division Counsel with recommendations for litigation. Of nineteen investigations made in 1974 by the month of September, for example, reports on six were submitted to the Division Counsel with recommendations for legal action, and reports on two were sent to the Office of the Chief of Engineers for administrative action. One permit was issued and the rest of the cases were still under consideration.[30]

By the Department of Transportation Act of October 15, 1966, the supervisory functions of the Secretary of War over bridges and causeways were transferred to the Secretary of Transportation. The administration of permits relating to them thus passed from the Corps of Engineers to the Coast Guard, which the act separated from the Treasury Department and placed under the new secretaryship.[31] Four years later it appeared, at least for a brief time, that this loss of authority would be more than compensated for by the extension of the Corps' permits responsibilities in another area.

Section 13 of the act of 1899—the Refuse Act—was shaped by ideas and interests prevailing in 1899, and was intended solely for the protection of navigation. The possibility that it might be used to protect public health, and thus encroach upon the police powers of the states, was in fact closed off by the exemption of municipal sewage from its broad definition of refuse. The function of the Corps under the act was to protect the navigability of United States waters, not their quality. Yet navigation ends sometimes faded into environmental ones, as when, upon the passage of a law in 1924 forbidding oil discharges in tidal waters, the Corps began to apply the Refuse Act to spills on inland streams as well.

During the 1960s the federal courts, reversing seven decades of legal interpretations, began construing the Refuse Act as covering the discharge of pollutants; but definite authority to extend the Refuse Act to environmental purposes was not granted the Corps until 1970. The mercury scare of that year revealed the inadequacy of existing laws against water pollution, and several congressional leaders urged that a permits program already being planned by the Corps be set up to control the discharge of pollutants at their source. On December 23, 1970 President Nixon directed the Corps to do so under Section 13 of the act of 1899. Under the resulting program, the regulations for which were published in the *Federal Register* on April 7, 1971, permits were required for all discharges into navigable waters and their tributaries, and applicants had to specify in detail the nature and quantity of the discharge or deposit. Decisions whether to issue permits, made in coordination with the regional offices of the Environmental Protection Agency and other appropriate federal and state offices, were to be based on an evaluation of the impact of the discharges or deposits on anchorage and navigation, water quality standards, and fish and wildlife resources.[32]

The Corps' administration of the program was short-lived. On December 22, 1971, the Corps was enjoined by a federal judge in the District of Columbia from issuing Refuse Act permits under the Corps' regulations. The court held that the regulations were invalid because they authorized permits for discharges into non-navigable waters, which were not embraced by the Refuse Act, and because they were inconsistent with the National Environmental Policy Act of 1969. An appeal was filed with the Justice Department, but before the courts acted Congress cut through the legal difficulties. By the

Federal Water Pollution Control Act Amendments of 1972, enacted on October 18, 1972, the pollutant permit program was transferred to the Environmental Protection Agency.[33]

During the brief few months the program was under the jurisdiction of the Corps, the Permits Branch of the New England Division was an exceptionally busy place. Its small personnel, which early in 1971 numbered only eleven people from chief to clerks, was expanded until a staff of sixteen was employed on the discharge program alone. Launching a tremendous publicity program through the newspapers, television, radio, and notices sent to known or probable dischargers, the branch sent application forms and information about the program to approximately 3300 prospective applicants, most of whom responded cooperatively. About 1000 applications were determined not to be pertinent. Either the applicant did not have a discharge that came under the program, had ceased to discharge, was interested in the program but not discharging, or was discharging outside the area of the division and was referred to the New York District. Another 1652 applications were in the process of review, of which about 80 had reached the stage of public notices being issued, before the program was transferred to EPA. An enforcement and follow-up program was in progress in 648 more cases relating to refusals to file applications or furnish additional information, about 10 of which had already been recommended for possible legal action. When the program was transferred to EPA, 426 applications from dischargers located on navigable waterways were screened for possible applicability under Section 10 of the act of 1899, and permits under this authority were issued in 35 cases.[34]

The Corps continues to issue permits relating to dredging, filling, and construction, but decisions are made on a broader basis than envisaged or authorized when the permits program began. No longer is the protection of navigation the sole criterion. The National Environmental Policy Act and several subsequent environmental acts require the Corps to consider all factors affecting the public interest. And in the milestone test case of *Zabel* v. *Tabb*, 1970, in which the Office of the Chief of Engineers instructed the Justice Department to cite the injury to wildlife but not the obstruction to navigation that would result from a land developer's scheme, the Fifth Circuit Court of Appeals reversed the decision of a district court that a permit could be denied only to protect navigation. "Every Federal agency," said the court, "shall consider ecological factors when dealing with activities which may have an impact on man's environment."[35]

V THE CAPE COD CANAL

On March 30, 1928, Boston District Engineer Colonel Sherwood A. Cheney received the following telegram from Washington:

PAYMENT FOR CAPE COD CANAL MADE TODAY AND TITLES NOW IN UNITED STATES YOU ARE AUTHORIZED TO TAKE POSSESSION OF THE CANAL AND APPURTENANT PROPERTY ON BEHALF OF THE UNITED STATES STOP THIS SHOULD BE DONE AT NOON MARCH THIRTY-FIRST STOP[1]

Dormant since the 1820s, the idea of a canal through the cape was revived by Governor Nathaniel P. Banks of Massachusetts in 1860. Immediately the Corps of Engineers again became involved in the planning. Chief Engineer Joseph G. Totten was at this time a member, with Professor A. D. Bache, Superintendent of the United States Coast Survey, and Captain Charles H. Davis, Superintendent of the United States Naval Academy, of a special board known as the Commissioners of the United States on Boston Harbor, which was examining the harbor and advising the city concerning it. And it was to this group of engineering experts that a special committee appointed by the state legislature turned for assistance and advice.

The commissioners thought that the canal would be easy to build and comparatively inexpensive. Locks would be necessary to control the current, they advised, and the eastern, or Barnstable Bay, entrance, which was exposed to storms from the north and northwest, would have to be sheltered by breakwaters. For the assistance of the committee they had Coast Survey personnel make topographical surveys of the route and conduct studies of tides, currents, and water temperatures. They also suggested that the committee employ an engineer who "stands at the very head of his profession" to carry the project further. Accordingly, the committee appointed one George Baldwin, who drew up plans for a locked canal 18 feet deep, 120 feet wide at the bottom, and 204 feet wide at the surface, protected at its eastern end by three breakwaters.[2]

In 1870 planning seemed about to evolve into building when the Massachusetts legislature granted a construction charter to a newly organized Cape Cod Ship Canal Company. The legislature also requested the federal government to assist the canal enterprise by building a breakwater in Barnstable Bay, claiming that such work would be comparable to any other federal harbor project. The request was referred to the War Department, and the Chief of Engineers directed Boston District Engineer John Foster to furnish information relating to the construction of the canal and the breakwater.

Citing the 617 wrecks of vessels passing around the cape in the past ten years and elaborating on the commercial and military value of a canal, Foster favored its construction. He proposed a bigger waterway than had Baldwin—one "wide enough to permit vessels of all classes to pass each other''—and suggested widths of 300 feet at the high-water line and 198 feet at the bottom. The depth should be twenty-three feet, the same as the main ship channel of Boston Harbor. This would allow the heaviest vessels of the Navy to pass through at half tide. Significantly, Foster was the first engineer to discard the idea of locks, which he felt would only increase costs and contribute to shipping delays and accidents. He calculated that in a canal of the dimensions he proposed the swiftest current for mean tides would be 3.8 miles per hour, and for maximum tides, 4 miles per hour. This velocity— which would only last for a few minutes anyway—was no greater, he pointed out, than that of currents in some other navigable waterways. For the protection of the eastern entrance of the canal, Foster proposed a granite breakwater 4,000 feet long running nearly parallel to the shore, estimated to cost nearly $2 million. The total cost of the canal, including the breakwater, he figured at about $9.7 million.[3]

Foster's report established the concept of an open canal, but had no further effect, for the Ship Canal Company never started construction. In 1880 the Massachusetts legislature granted a charter to a new Cape Cod Canal Company. Again government aid was sought, and the River and Harbor Act of 1881 called for an examination and survey of Buzzards and Barnstable bays at the entrances of the proposed canal. The assignment this time went to Newport District Engineer Gouverneur Warren. Reporting the next year, Warren recommended the dredging of a 500-foot-wide, 21-foot-deep approach channel in Buzzards Bay, costing about $350,000, and the construction in Barnstable Bay of two jetties extending from the shore, rather than an offshore breakwater, which, with a small amount of dredging, would cost only about $918,000.[4]

A bill for granting this aid began its way through Congress, but was ultimately discarded, for the new company also failed to begin construction. And for the next twenty-five years the prospects for a canal remained uncertain. Petitioners scrambled for charters, several were granted, considerable land was acquired, and small starts were made at digging, but never was more than a pittance of capital raised or more than a few shovelfuls of earth turned. Almost everyone saw rosy possibilities in a canal, but practically no one was willing to risk his own money.

In 1907 August Belmont, a New York investment banker and builder of the city's first subway, agreed to buy the rights and property of the Boston, Cape Cod and New York Canal Company, chartered in 1899. Belmont formed a syndicate to underwrite the building of the canal, organized a subsidiary construction company, and retained William Barclay Parsons, a noted railroad engineer, as chief engineer. On June 22, 1909, Belmont, removing a shovelful of earth with a small silver spade from Tiffany's, proclaimed the start of the Cape Cod Canal.[5]

Five years later, on July 29, 1914, the canal was opened with great fanfare, the presence of numerous distinguished guests, and a grand procession through it of the palatial yachts of the New York Yacht Club on its annual summer cruise.[6] It was a much smaller waterway than Colonel Foster had proposed. Although its charter depth was 25 feet, its minimum bottom width was only 100 feet and its surface width 200 feet, which precluded two-way traffic. The land cut of the canal was 7.68 miles long, the dredged approach

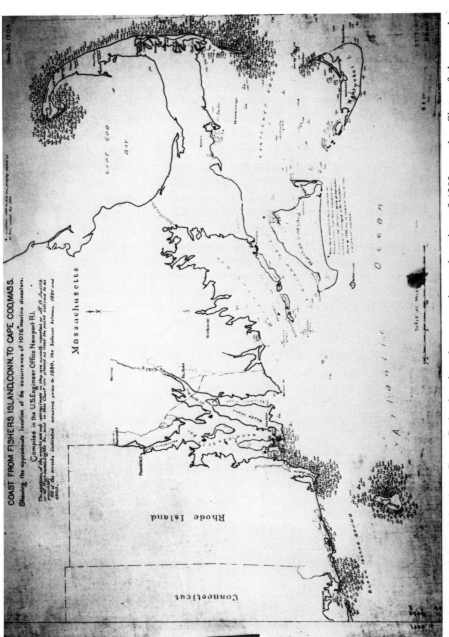

Coast from Fishers Island to Cape Cod, showing the approximate location of 1203 wrecks. Sixty of the wrecks indicated occurred prior to 1880, 1016 between 1880 and 1903, and 127 between 1903 and 1920.

in Buzzards Bay about five miles, and the approach in Barnstable Bay about one-half mile, making the total length of the passage about thirteen miles. A 3,000 foot breakwater extended into Barnstable Bay from the north side of the canal's eastern entrance, and a stone sand-catch jetty 600 feet long reached out from the opposite side. Crossing the canal were two highway bridges and one railroad bridge, each with an opening under its draw span about 140 feet wide.

After more than two hundred years of discussion and planning, the canal was a reality. Investigations, traffic analyses, and common sense had all pronounced that it would save lives, ships, and cargoes, shorten distances to southern ports, lessen freight costs, and reduce insurance rates. Yet the canal was neither a financial success nor a transportation triumph. Miscalculations had added greatly to construction time and costs. Difficulties presented by boulders scattered through the sands of the cape had been underestimated, too much digging had been done with dredges and too little by more efficient steam-shovel operation in the dry, and excavation equipment had been too antiquated and too small for the job. When finished, the canal failed to attract the traffic expected for it. The current was a major deterrent. Underpowered vessels had to await slack water or a favoring tide. Tugs towing barges could not proceed against the current, and on going with it had to take them through one at a time. And accidents occurred, giving the canal a bad reputation. Mariners complained of delays in transit through the single-track route, of the narrowness of the channel and of shoals caused by erosion of the canal's banks, of the hazards of passing through three drawbridges, and of the prevalence of ground fog. There were also skippers who avoided the canal simply because they preferred sailing wide-wayed routes they knew to trying a narrow one they not know.[7]

As early as 1915, Belmont, who formerly had been indifferent to government aid or purchase, thought that the national government "ought to really acquire the canal." The first actual step in this direction was taken in May 1917, five weeks after the United States declared war on Germany, when Senator John W. Weeks of Massachusetts introduced a bill for the purchase of the canal. Slightly amended, the bill became part of the River and Harbor Act of August 1917. The Secretaries of War, Navy, and Commerce were authorized to examine and appraise the value of the works and franchises of the canal. If all favored acquisition, the Secretary of War was to negotiate for its purchase or, if that failing, institute condemnation proceedings. The actual investigation, the act stipulated, was to "be conducted under the direction of the Secretary of War and the supervision of the Chief of Engineers in the usual manner provided by law for making preliminary examinations and surveys."[8]

The bulk of the investigative work was carried out under the direction of the engineer of the Northeast Division, Brigadier General William T. Rossell, retired, a former Chief of Engineers. Rossell hired the public accounting firm of Price, Waterhouse and Company of New York to examine the books of the canal and construction companies to determine the actual cost of the canal. The accountants reported that cash construction costs were $8,265,743.04, and if various intangible items, such as payments in stocks and bonds for rights, promotion, and services, discounts on securities, and

Old type dipper dredge chewing out the channel for the Cape Cod Canal during its construction, 1909-14.

Section of the original cut of the Cape Cod Canal showing the railroad tracks over which material excavated in the dry was carried away.

Colonel Barclay Parsons, right, congratulates August Belmont in April 1914 when the final construction gate of the Cape Cod Canal was removed, permitting the waters of the east and west excavations to meet.

The Nantasket Beach paddle-wheel steamer *Rose Standish* leads the fleet that celebrated the opening of the Cape Cod Canal on July 29, 1914.

View of the Sagamore Highway Bridge shortly after the canal was opened. The narrow passage between the abutments of the bridges crossing the canal was one reason many mariners preferred the outside route around the cape despite the dangers.

The Eastern Steamship *Belfast* rammed into Sagamore Bridge on April 16, 1919.

losses in operation, were added at their stated value, the total cost of the canal was $12,956,718.31. Rossell also requested Boston District Engineer Colonel Francis R. Shunk to investigate the value of the canal from the point of view of its use. Shunk submitted a lengthy report on the amounts and character of shipping that went around the cape or through the canal, on various aspects of the canal's operation and commercial benefit, and on why it did not carry more traffic. "On the whole I do not think that the canal can be considered a success," Shunk concluded, "nor do I believe that with its present dimensions it will be of great benefit to commerce." After considering all the data, Rossell reported that from military and commercial points of view the canal was worth to the United States its actual cash cost of construction, or $8,265,743.04.

The Board of Engineers for Rivers and Harbors held public hearings and secured additional information relating to the canal, and, shaving down the intangibles in the Price, Waterhouse audit, reached an appraisal of $10 million for the cost of constructing the passage. It did not believe, however, that the United States should pay that amount. Since the canal diverted only about one-fifth of the tonnage carried past the cape from outside routes, the savings effected to the public by making it a free waterway would not warrant an expenditure equal to the cost of construction. If commercial uses alone were considered, the board held, $2.5 million was the upper limit of any justifiable expenditure by the government. As to the military value of the canal, the board cited a memorandum from the General Board of the Navy that concluded the military advantages of the waterway were not worth the costs of enlarging and defending it. The board, therefore, simply capitalized the savings on tolls by government vessels that would use the canal, which it figured would hardly exceed $1 million. The total value of public ownership, it concluded, was thus not more than $3.5 million.

Chief of Engineers Major General William Murray Black, while recognizing the limitations on the worth of the canal, nevertheless felt that it did have commercial value and recommended its purchase. "In the existing emergency," he explained further, "war risks make continued use of the canal necessary and its improvement desirable." The channel was deteriorating, and the canal company was unable to maintain its project dimensions. Taking a different approach from either the division engineer or the Board of Engineers in determining what price should be paid, Black said it should be as nearly as practicable what it would have cost the United States to have done the work. Submitting a report to the Secretary of War in July 1918, he said that this would probably be $10 million, the amount named by the Board of Engineers as the construction costs of the canal company. In December 1918, however, Black submitted a second report containing more precise estimates that he had meantime obtained. One estimate, made by Newport District Engineer Colonel J. H. Willard, retired, set the hypothetical cost to the United States at $8 million, while another estimate made by an assistant engineer in the Office of the Chief of Engineers, M. W. Lewis, set the figure at $8,110,000.

The Cabinet secretaries subscribed to General Black's government-cost approach and offered the canal company $8,250,000 for its rights and properties. The company's response was to claim that the government could not have built the canal for that amount and to make a counterproposal of $13 million.[9]

Meantime the issue of price had become further complicated by government operation of the canal. On the morning of July 21, 1918, the German submarine *U-156* had surfaced three miles off the elbow of Cape Cod and shelled the Lehigh Valley tug *Perth Amboy* and her string of four barges until the barges sank and the tug was set afire. The next day President Wilson announced that the canal would be temporarily taken over by the government and run by the Railroad Administration, an agency set up the previous December to avert chaos in the nation's transportation system. To handle the increased traffic driven to protected waters by the submarine menace, the Railroad Administration dredged the canal, which had suffered badly from lack of routine maintenance, and made other repairs. Disputes now arose over compensation due to the government for its expenditures and compensation due the canal company for the government's use of the passage.

Since no agreement was being reached on the price of the canal, Secretary of War Newton D. Baker instituted condemnation proceedings in April 1919. The government contended that a fair price was something under $8 million; the canal company wanted $25 million. The jury, arriving at a verdict in less than a day despite extremely lengthy and complicated testimony, apparently split the difference and said that the canal was worth $16,801,201.11.[10] This award was made in November 1919. In February 1921, however, it was set aside on writ of error by the Circuit Court of Appeals, which remanded the case back to the District Court for a new trial.

Another complication from the government takeover of the canal had meanwhile arisen. When the Railroad Administration returned the country's railroads to private control on March 1, 1920, the canal was included in the transfer. But claiming that the condemnation proceedings had ended its rights and titles in the canal, the company would not accept it. Since nobody would mind the store, the canal closed down—just as a severe snowstorm paralyzed land transportation and worsened already short fuel supplies in the Boston area. Appealing to Washington with no success, Governor Calvin Coolidge of Massachusetts prevailed on the company to open the canal. This it did on March 4, but by a temporary arrangement with the canal's superintendent that did not prejudice its legal position.[11]

The condemnation proceedings and the prospect of a new trial brought the Corps of Engineers once again back into the chain of events. Upon orders from Secretary Baker, the Chief of Engineers instructed Colonel Edward Burr, a former Boston District Engineer, to undertake a thorough examination of the history and operation of the canal to assist the government in judicial proceedings and guide Congress in determining the value of the waterway. Beginning in February 1921, Burr completed his investigations in November 1922. The canal had been a failure, he reported, because of strong currents, insufficient width and depth, shoaling caused by the erosion of its banks, low and narrow bridge passages, and the psychology of mariners who felt safe only when their vessels had plenty of sea room. He did not think that tolls deterred much traffic. He dwelt at length on the reasons why the canal was of value and recommended that the government purchase it since private capital was incapable of providing necessary improvements and maintenance. The United States should pay a reasonable price for the canal, he advised, and improve it by installing a set of locks, which he saw as the only practicable solution to the problem of the current, and increasing its bottom width to 200 feet and its depth to 35 feet. This work would cost between $14 and $17 million. Without locks, the canal would have to be at least 300 feet wide to provide safe navigation, and the cost of improvement would run from $11 to $14 million.[12]

While Burr was making his study, the government and the canal company came to an agreement. Rather than face the expense, delay, and uncertainty of further condemnation proceedings, the company offered to sell its property for $11.5 million, and on July 29, 1921 a contract was signed by the Secretary of War. The government would pay the company $5.5 million in cash and assume the company's $6 million bond obligation. It was agreed that until Congress approved the contract and appropriated the money, the company would operate the canal and the government would be responsible for the interest on the bond issue.[13]

Seven more years were to pass, however, before the canal became the property of the United States. On seven occasions bills to carry out the contract were introduced in Congress, only to die in House committees, in conference committee, or in the Senate because of haggling over the terms of the sale or, more often, because of indifference or opposition. The purchase was finally authorized in Section 2a of the River and Harbor Act of January 1, 1927. Senate approval of the bill was won, however, only with an amendment providing that the government should pay interest on the canal bonds from the date of transfer of title rather than from the date of contract, which meant a loss of nearly $2 million to the canal company. An appropriation for the purchase was lost in the shuffle of that session of Congress, but was quickly passed when Congress reconvened the following December. Meantime questions arose over the validity of canal company land titles, which took a year of legal work to settle. But finally, on March 30, 1928, the Attorney General notified the Secretary of War that title to the Cape Cod Canal was vested in the United States in fee simple.[14]

The Boston Engineer Office now took over the operation of the canal. Colonel Cheney kept the old employees and retained Captain Harold L. Colbeth, who had managed the canal for the company, as superintendent. But it was quickly apparent that the canal was under new ownership. Late in July a leased dredge went to work on shoals just west of Sagamore Bridge, and in September the United States hopper dredge *Minquas* began maintenance operations that were to continue steadily for the next six years. Due to severe erosion of the canal's banks, however, it was found impracticable to maintain continuously a depth in excess of twenty-two feet. Meantime the United States seagoing dredge *Marshall* cleared out the Buzzards Bay approach channel. Hired labor was put to work repairing bulkheads, bridges, and the lighting and signal systems, and placing riprap and slope pavement on banks where it was most urgently needed. When barge companies asked for the repair of dolphins at each end of the canal, the district's response was so prompt that one company sent a letter of appreciation. Tolls were of course abolished, and cargo tonnage passing through the canal jumped from

Brig. Gen. Sherwood A. Cheney.
Courtesy of the U.S. Army Engineer
Museum, Fort Belvoir, Virginia.

894,763 in 1927 to 1,405,782 in 1928; to 2,154,465 in 1929; and to 2,498,943 in 1930. Colonel Cheney, with all the initiative of a private entrepreneur, wrote in January 1929 to some forty companies engaged in coastal shipping to impress on them that if the canal was to be really useful, it should carry still more traffic.[15]

Yet the canal could never attract the great bulk of shipping compassing the cape without major improvements. The River and Harbor Act of July 3, 1930 called for an examination and survey of the canal, the reports of which were sent to Congress the following March. District Engineer Cheney was convinced, as Colonel Burr had been, that a locked canal was the only solution to the problems of dangerous currents, constant bank erosion, and tows having to wait for the tide. He therefore recommended the construction of twin locks about midway in the land cut of the canal, each chamber to be 110 feet wide, 1,000 feet long, and 40 feet deep over the sills, which would be capacious enough to accommodate the largest ships. A single-chambered lock, Cheney contended, could not handle summer traffic and would have to be closed for maintenance for about three months every four years. Dual chambers were also a valuable precaution from the viewpoint of national defense. Cheney proposed deepening the canal to 35 feet and widening it to 300 feet at the bottom through its land cut, which would be sufficient width for safe two-way traffic in a slack-water channel. To eliminate two turns in the Buzzards Bay approach channel that mariners considered hazardous, he recommended a straight channel through the bay, 500 feet wide to Wings Neck and 700 feet wide beyond the neck to deep water. To replace the two hazardous highway lift bridges, Cheney proposed the construction about midway on the canal of a six-lane high-level bridge with a vertical clearance of 150 feet. As for a new railroad bridge, Cheney concluded that the grades of a high-level bridge would be too heavy and that some type of drawbridge with a span of at least 300 feet would have to do. Lastly, Cheney recommended the construction of a harbor of refuge at the western end of the canal. He estimated that these improvements would take seven years to complete and would cost $34,233,000.

In the process of review within the Corps, Cheney's recommendations were cut back by officers habituated to planning projects with an eye on keeping them both worthwhile and within the limits of appropriations likely to be forthcoming. Division Engineer Colonel W. J. Barden agreed with the proposals, except that he believed a channel 32 feet deep and 250 feet wide in the land cut would be ample. The Board of Engineers further reduced the depth to 30 feet, reduced the channel width in Buzzards Bay to Wings Neck to 400 feet, and recommended a single tidal lock, claiming that it would be adequate to handle the traffic. The Chief of Engineers concurred with the views of the board, whose recommendations were sent to Congress with a cost estimate of $23,250,000.[16]

The Boston District placed a model of the proposed reconstructed canal on exhibition at the Boston Army Base in May 1932 and awaited action by Congress. How long it would have waited in normal times is impossible to say. But the year 1932 was not normal. As the economic depression that began in 1929 grew worse and unemployment soared, demands for federal public-works programs became increasingly insistent. In July 1932 the Emergency Relief and Reconstruction Act appropriated over $322 million for public works, including $30 million "for the prosecution of river and harbor projects heretofore authorized." The Eastern Steamship Company, which was planning to run larger ships through the canal, suggested that Emergency Relief funds be used to improve the waterway, and Congressman Charles L. Gifford of Massachusetts requested Chief of Engineers Major General Lytle Brown to allot $500,000 for this purpose. Brown replied that while a substantial sum under the act would be applied to renewing riprap and straightening channel approaches to Sagamore Bridge, Emergency Relief funds could not be used for enlarging the canal since the project had not been approved by Congress. The National Industrial Recovery Act of June 1933 removed this obstacle. Under the public-works title of the act, river and harbor improvements could be carried out provided they had been "adopted by Congress . . . or recommended by the Chief of Engineers." On September 6, 1933 the Public Works Administration authorized the construction of three bridges over the canal and the widening of its land cut to 205 feet, allotting $5,783,500 for the work.[17]

Construction began in December, under the direction of District Engineer Colonel John J. Kingman, with contractors laying the foundations for the bridges. In accordance with PWA regulations, work was distributed as widely as possible and wherever practicable hand labor was used in lieu of machinery. The plan for erecting a single highway bridge had been altered, fortunately for future automobile traffic to the cape, because of contentions that it was inconsistent with obligations imposed on the United States in acquiring the canal. In designing and supervising the construction of two high-level highway bridges, the Boston District contracted the services of

Sagamore Bridge, Cape Cod Canal.

Bourne Bridge, Cape Cod Canal.

Railroad Bridge, Cape Cod Canal.

the engineering firm of Fay, Spofford, and Thorndike of Boston, who in turn
retained the Boston architectural firm of Cram and Ferguson to advise upon
architectural details and the appearance of the structures as a whole. The
Sagamore Bridge was constructed about two and a half miles from the eastern end of the canal, and the Bourne Bridge about one and two-thirds miles
from the western end. Identical in design, the bridges each have a main span
measuring 616 feet between centers of supports, with a vertical clearance of
135 feet above high water. Each flanking span is 396 feet long, and the road-
way width of the bridges, designed for four-lane traffic, is 40 feet between
curbs. Built more or less simultaneously, the bridges were dedicated on June
21, 1935 and opened to traffic.

The railroad bridge was constructed close to the western end of the canal,
near the site of the old bridge. A vertical-lift bridge, it has a 544-foot hori-
zontal span, at the time of its construction the longest lift span in the world,
supported by towers 210 feet high. The span is normally kept in the raised
position, 135 feet above mean high water. In preparing plans for the bridge,
the Boston District employed the engineering firm of Parsons, Klapp,
Brinckerhoff, and Douglas of New York, who were advised on architectural
matters by Mead and White of that city. Work on the bridge began on December 18, 1933, and almost exactly two years later the first train rolled
across it on December 29, 1935.[18]

Meantime, the widening of the land cut of the canal was begun. Before
work had progressed very far, however, further experience in operating and
improving the waterway forced a reconsideration of existing plans. The
winter of 1933-34 was unusually severe, choking Buzzards Bay with a mass
of ice from Wings Neck to Bourne Neck. Since even icebreakers could not
crash through the channel, shipping was interfered with for weeks at a time.
But the canal itself did not freeze. Therefore when the House Committee on
Rivers and Harbors requested the Board of Engineers, in June 1934, to review its recommendations for the improvement of the canal, Colonel
Kingman proposed modifying the existing project to provide for an open
waterway.

Motor Barge L.T.G. No. 3 frozen in the ice in Buzzards Bay, March 1934.

The ice conditions in Buzzards Bay during the past winter made it apparent, Kingman reported, that in the still waters of a locked canal there would be serious trouble with ice formations every few years. The widening of the canal to 170 feet near Sagamore Bridge the previous year, he continued, had resulted in greater current velocities, yet tugboat operators had found that most of the navigation difficulties for one-way traffic had been removed. The trouble with the canal had not been the current, but the narrow width of the channel. A 500-foot-wide channel, even with the current, Kingman figured, would be amply safe for two-way navigation. A canal this wide had not been considered earlier, he assumed, because of the high cost of earth removal. But with equipment now available, and by doing much of the work in the dry, costs would be lower. They would be considerably less than building a lock, which recent experience indicated would be a troublesome project. In driving sheet metal piling for the foundations of the new bridges, he explained, the contractors had run into serious difficulty with boulders. In view of the necessity of installing sheet piling under the walls and miter sills of a lock, so that it might be drained to make repairs, construction difficulties would be extremely expensive to overcome. The problem of bank erosion and consequent shoaling, Kingman also concluded, had not been due principally to the current but to wave wash, which would be less in a 500-foot-wide canal. These considerations, together with the hazards to vessels entering a lock during high winds and the loss of time to ships spent in lockage, made an open canal, in Kingman's view, decidedly preferable to a locked one.

Kingman presented plans for a canal 32 feet deep and 540 feet wide at the bottom through the land cut. He recommended the 540-foot width so that a channel 40 feet deep and 500 feet wide could be excavated at some future time without impairing revetments and other works on the banks of the canal. He proposed a straight channel in Buzzards Bay 500 feet wide to Wings Neck and 700 feet wide beyond the neck, mooring basins at either end of the land cut, a harbor of refuge for small vessels at the western end of the canal, an improved lighting system, and such other accessory features as might be deemed necessary. The division engineer, the Board of Engineers, and the Chief of Engineers concurred in Kingman's recommendations, which were sent to Congress on December 26, 1934. Eight months later Congress authorized the improvements in the River and Harbor Act of August 30, 1935.[19]

Work began with the construction by hydraulic engineers at the Massachusetts Institute of Technology of a 111- by 34-foot concrete model of the canal and its approaches with which to study tidal actions, currents, and erosion effects. The new straight approach channel at the head of Buzzards Bay was the subject of considerable experimentation as engineers tested ways of reducing crosscurrents and preventing erosion. They found that the gaps between Rocky Point, Hog Island, and Mashnee Island, which lay along the southern side of the proposed channel, would cause strong crosscurrents and consequent silting of the channel. The solution was to close these openings with dikes built from material excavated from the western end of Hog Island, which lay athwart the line of the new channel. To prevent the channel current from swinging too far north beyond Stony Point, on the opposite side of the passage, the district built another dike over two miles long from Stony Point to a ledge opposite Wings Neck. The construction of the dikes and dredging formed the "Hog Island Channel," a passage 500 feet wide, 32 feet deep, and 4.7 miles long. Beyond Wings Neck the "Cleveland Ledge Channel" was cut 700 feet wide to the same depth for a distance of 4.1 miles.

View of the canal during reconstruction by the Corps of Engineers, 1935-40, showing simultaneous wet and dry digging.

To enlarge the land cut of the canal, dredges worked from the existing channel into the banks, while dry excavation equipment worked from the outside of the new prism toward the center. Totally they removed some fifty-four million cubic yards of material. Because of the boulders that peppered the sands of the cape and the depth of the cut, dipper dredges did about fifty-five percent of the work. Hydraulic dredges handled about thirty percent, and the remaining fifteen percent—every bit that was possible—was done in the dry. Dry excavation had many advantages: it was cheaper, boulders could be more easily handled, riprap could be laid on dry banks more efficiently, and a larger number of unskilled workers could be employed, an important consideration during depression years. The surface width of the canal was cut to about 700 feet, but the bottom width was reduced from the proposed 540 feet to 480 feet. More gradually sloping banks, it was decided, would reduce erosion, help keep the riprap in place, and provide greater safety if a ship ran aground.[20] With a land cut about 7.7 miles long, and extended approach channels reaching to the new 32-foot depth, the total length of the canal became 17.5 miles.

Mooring basins, formed by carving elongated concaves into the sides of the channel, were constructed at either end of the land cut in case ships were delayed from making the passage and forced to tie up. At the eastern end the basin was located on the north side of the channel at Sandwich, at the western end it was on the south side between Hog Island and Rocky Neck. To provide refuge for smaller craft a harbor 13 feet deep and about 217 acres in extent—the East Boat Basin—was constructed opposite the east mooring basin, and a channel 15 feet deep and 100 feet wide was dredged into Onset Bay opposite the west mooring basin. To pierce the ground fog that had plagued the canal and permit nighttime navigation under all atmospheric conditions, experts designed a new lighting system. Sodium vapor and white lamps were installed alternately at 500-foot intervals on both sides of the passage.

By 1940, when the reconstruction of the canal was essentially completed, the government had spent $6 million of Public Works Administration funds, $4.8 million of Emergency Relief Administration funds, and about $8.8 million of regular funds for improvements. Including the original cost, improvements, and maintenance, the United States had spent about $37 million on the waterway. The improved canal was attracting shipping to the extent that in 1940 three times as many ships and over eight times as much cargo tonnage passed through it than had gone through the old canal in 1927, the last year of private ownership.

Aerial view of the Cape Cod Canal from the western approach.

Work on the canal was completed in time for the waterway to be of enormous benefit during World War II. Cargo tonnage through it doubled as convoys bound for Greenland, Iceland, and the United Kingdom assembled in Buzzards Bay and all but the deepest ships sailed through the passage. Other merchants ships, whose peacetime routes passed wide of the cape, sought the safety of the canal. Naval vessels of the lighter classes used it extensively. At the height of submarine activity in the Atlantic, as many as eighty merchantmen and warships passed through the canal in a single day. Nearly nineteen million cargo tons passed through it in the year 1944. Although during the war the Army Engineers turned the operation of the canal over to the Coast Guard, they were still responsible for its maintenance, and the increased traffic of heavily ladened ships made the preservation of the canal's project depth an absolute necessity. At first the Engineers assigned dredges temporarily to the canal, but after July 1943 they operated a dredge on it continuously.[21] How many ships, cargoes, dollars, and lives were saved by the canal during the war cannot even be guessed. It is certain, however, that government dollars and Corps of Engineer labors were well invested.

After the war, improvements of the canal's facilities were made in the interests of small boating and recreation. To provide additional anchorage space and reduce the hazards of grounding and collision in Onset Bay, which was used extensively by a sizable local recreational fleet as well as affording a harbor of refuge for the thousands of small craft that passed through the canal every year, a project for the harbor was authorized by Congress in 1945. It provided for enlarging an existing 15-foot-deep inner channel and a turning basin near the town wharf and for dredging a new 8-foot-deep anchorage area adjacent to them, for which local interests were to contribute one-half the cost. Delayed by budgetary considerations and then the Korean War, the project was begun in 1957 and completed in 1959. At the other end

East Boat Basin, Cape Cod Canal.

of the canal, local interests requested the enlargement of the East Boat Basin to relieve crowded conditions and provide a more adequate stopping place and harbor of refuge for transient craft. A project for extending the basin by several acres was authorized in 1958, with the proviso that local interests contribute twenty percent of the cost, furnish all necessary lands and easements, relocate utility lines, and build a suitable marina.[22] This work was carried out in 1962 and 1963, with the Commonwealth of Massachusetts con-

William D. Donovan (left), marine traffic controller, and Wilfred W. Norris (right), engineering equipment operator, are veteran members of the New England Division at the Cape Cod Canal. Both men were on the staff of the canal when it became the property of the U.S. Government in 1928.

structing the marina. Two years later an access road, a comfort station, and parking areas were completed by the New England Division.

By 1975 the United States had spent over $80 million on the Cape Cod Canal, including the purchase price and maintenance, making it the most expensive single civil work of the Corps in New England. The widest sea-level canal in the world, the waterway has in recent years carried an average of about 11.7 million cargo tons annually. It is also one of New England's outstanding public recreation facilities. It is acclaimed one of the best salt water fisheries per mile of shoreline in the world, and the Scusset Beach State Park Area is heavily stocked with pheasants by the Massachusetts Division of Fisheries and Game. The New England Division has provided access and parking areas throughout the length of the canal; and the Corps leases two major recreation areas, the Scusset Beach State Park and the Bourne Scenic Park, to the Massachusetts Department of Natural Resources and the Town of Bourne Recreational Authority respectively. Over a million visitors annually enjoy the opportunities offered by the canal's land and water areas for fishing and hunting, for swimming, picnicking, and camping, and for just plain relaxing and watching the ships go by.

VI

As the Civil War drew to a close, Army Engineers were examining Fort Adams, Fort Warren, Fort Knox, and all the rest of the great casemated forts of the Third System and wondering if they were useless piles of stone. The wooden sailing ships they had been designed to contest were passing from the seas, replaced by warships driven by steam and shielded with iron. For about three decades the United States and European maritime nations had been experimenting with new battlecraft, but these efforts had been desultory. It took the coming of age of the Industrial Revolution and the spur of war to alter drastically the character of naval weaponry. The Crimean War of the mid-1850s had speeded naval advances in Britain and France, and by 1861 each nation had a small fleet of armor-plated frigates in commission, though they were yet to be tested in battle. The Civil War prompted similar developments in America as both sides, served by naval secretaries of great ability, hastily fitted out ironclad vessels armed with recently developed heavy ordnance. The armored steamships of the Union were mostly John Ericsson's strange-looking monitors, class-named after the "tin can on a shingle" that had met and stopped the deadly *Merrimac*. Though small craft carrying few guns, monitors in onslaughts against casemated forts held by the Confederacy breached their walls, destroying with them prevailing concepts of seacoast fortifications. Exposed masonry scarps were now as vulnerable on sea fronts as they had been for centuries on land fronts. Meanwhile the maritime powers of Europe had continued to develop their naval weapons, and by the end of the war were equipping their sea forces with powerfully engined, iron-plated ships armed with rifled guns of greatly increased range, accuracy, and destructiveness. Almost overnight masonry seacoast defenses had become as obsolete as medieval castles.[1]

In 1864 and 1865 the Engineer Department appointed special boards to examine every permanent fortification along the coast and propose modifications. In New England, as elsewhere, the boards' recommendations resulted in few changes beyond the rebuilding of gun platforms to mount ordnance of heavier caliber. Originally designed for guns no larger than forty-two pounders with 7-inch bores, emplacements were now to take weapons no smaller than 10- to 15-inch bore. Experiments were begun on the use of iron shields to protect or replace masonry scarps, but meanwhile work on uncompleted forts in New England continued mostly according to original plans.[2]

In 1867 the Engineer Department established a new permanent Board of Engineers for Fortifications to conduct studies and experiments on the structures and weapons required for a thoroughly revised system of defense. Submitting its recommendations in 1869, the board concluded that until more could be determined about continuing rapid improvements of ordnance and armor, expensive types of defenses employing iron turrets and shields should remain on the drawing board. For the present, reliance should be placed on heavy-caliber barbette batteries shielded by massive earthen parapets, these to be so constructed as to accommodate disappearing gun carriages when they were perfected. The guns and gunners should be protected from infilading and reverse fires by traverses on either side of each gun platform and parados behind where needed, each structure being a thick, high wall of earth. Where barbette batteries were impracticable because of the configuration of the harbor or the nature of the surrounding terrain, heavy floating batteries should be employed. The board also recommended the installation of large caliber mortar batteries for shelling the vulnerable thin decks of heavily armored ships and the obstruction of harbors by submarine mines—or torpedoes, as they were then called—that could be electrically detonated by signal.[3]

The proposals of the boards were carried out in New England in the first years after the war by engineers assigned on an ad hoc basis. The engineer districts then being established were primarily for the oversight of river and harbor improvement. Although Thom at Portland and Houston at Newport directed some small amount of fortification work, most of the military construction in their districts was supervised by other officers. Foster at Boston directed no defense work in his own district, but was for several years in charge of fortifications at Portsmouth, New Hampshire.

Fortification construction in Boston Harbor was directed by Henry Benham and Major Charles E. Blunt in 1865 and 1866, and after that solely by Benham until his retirement in 1882. When Benham ended his long stint, his responsibilities, which for a half-dozen years past had been confined wholly to maintenance, were taken over by Blunt, now lieutenant colonel in charge of fortifications in Maine and New Hampshire. A few months later, upon the reopening of the Boston District Office under Major Charles E. Raymond early in 1883, defense work in the harbor was placed under district control.

Elsewhere in New England the assignment of officers to fortification work during the first half-dozen years after the war defies analysis. Occasionally one or two forts were under the charge of a single officer, but usually two or more engineers shared the supervision of several works. Yet seldom were all forts in a region under the same combination of officers. In this kaleidoscopic fashion seven officers at one time or another directed fortification work on New England's south shore until 1871. More orderly administration was then instituted by placing all military construction under the supervision of Newport District Engineer Gouverneur Warren.

In northern New England eight officers supervised fortification construction during the immediate postwar years. In 1871 all military work was placed under the direction of a single engineer, but apparently because of more extensive military and civil construction in the area than in southern New England, the supervision of defense work was entrusted to Lieutenant Colonel James C. Duane rather than to Portland District Engineer George Thom. The military and civil functions of the Corps in northern New England thus continued to be separately administered for another dozen years. They were finally fused, about the same time as at Boston, when Lieutenant Colonel Charles E. Blunt, Duane's successor in charge of military work since 1879, became the Portland District Engineer in 1883.

The new defense system elaborated by the Board of Engineers for Fortifications in 1869 meant that barbette batteries, formerly accessories of Third System forts, now became their primary elements of defense. Parapets made of sand, sodded to prevent erosion and faced inside with brick, were constructed forty feet thick—four times the dimension considered sufficient only a decade before. Guns were usually grouped in pairs, and traverses and parados were designed to afford emplacements maximum protection. Ammunition magazines with thick masonry and earth coverings were built into the traverses, nearer to gun emplacements than formerly had been the practice, to save the transportation of heavier charges. To bear the weight of the heavy ordnance with which the defenses were to be armed, old-style gun platforms of pieced granite were replaced with monolithic masses of concrete.[4]

A 15-inch Rodman gun mounted at Fort Warren, Boston Harbor, about 1863. Courtesy of Gerald Butler.

It was along these lines that Colonel Benham began reconstructing old and building new barbette batteries for Boston Harbor at Forts Warren, Winthrop, and Independence. The armament planned for these defenses was formidable. Fort Warren would mount thirty-six heavy guns—which plans usually specified as 15-inch smoothbore guns or "equivalent rifles"—and 127 10-inch guns en barbette. It would also retain considerable casemate armament. Fort Winthrop would bristle with fifty-seven heavy guns, thirty-four 10-inch guns, and six heavy mortars. Fort Independence would boast five heavy guns, twenty 12-inch rifles, and six 10-inch rifles en barbette, plus fourteen guns in casemates.

Like most pre-Civil War fortifications, whose relatively short-range guns were most effective on narrow channels, Forts Independence and Winthrop were located close to the city they were designed to protect. The increased range of naval guns, however, now made it imperative to oppose attacking ships from more advanced positions, like that of Fort Warren on Georges

Island. A temporary board of engineers examining Boston Harbor in 1865 had therefore recommended the construction of a new outer battery on Long Island, whose guns, like those of Fort Warren, could bear on all entrance channels from a position on the harbor's outer rim. This was what Major Joseph Swift had unsuccessfully urged on the War Department nearly sixty years before. The new permanent Board of Engineers endorsed the plan in 1867, title to the site was acquired, and in 1871 Benham began building the new defense. An open barbette battery protected by traverses and parados, it was designed to mount twenty-eight heavy guns.

At Portland Harbor work on Forts Gorges, Preble, and Scammell was redirected in accordance with the new defense system. Since Fort Gorges, located on a wave-washed ledge, could carry barbette batteries only above its casemates, the plans for it called for only fourteen heavy guns en barbette and the retention of all casemate ordnance. Fort Scammell was also to retain considerable casemate armament, but would mount thirty-six heavy guns and four heavy mortars en barbette. At Fort Preble, the casemate batteries were wholly dispensed with and emplacements were started for forty-one 15-inch and two 10-inch guns en barbette.[5]

Since Portland Harbor required new outer defenses, the Board of Engineers designed a battery of thirty-four heavy guns for Portland Head, a promontory three miles below the city. The battery could sweep all approaches to the main channel into the harbor and command the seaward side of a large island from behind which enemy ships might shell the city. The project was prepared in 1870, but difficulties in securing the land delayed the start of construction until 1873. The Board of Engineers also prepared plans for three more batteries on outer islands of the harbor that would guard all approaches to it and prevent enemy occupation of Casco Bay. But no appropriations were made for these defenses, and they were never begun.

North of Portland work on Forts Knox and Popham was suspended in 1869. Both forts required more extensive changes than their value to current defense plans warranted. Work was also stopped at Forts Constitution and McClary at Portsmouth Harbor. Outer defenses for Portsmouth were now more important, and in 1873 Colonel Duane began the construction of two new batteries, each for twelve heavy guns, farther down the harbor. One was on Jerrys Point on the south side of the estuary, the other on Gerrish Island across the way.

At New Bedford construction on the still unnamed fort on Clarks Point was continued until 1870, when everything was completed except the barbette emplacements over the casemates. But the fort had been outmoded almost before it was begun. The Board of Engineers recommended that nothing further be done on it and that an earthen battery of twenty-six heavy guns be placed on an elevation behind it. Plans for the battery were ready in 1875 but were never implemented.

At Narragansett Bay the Board of Engineers decided to leave the casemated portions of Fort Adams as they were and construct a new exterior battery of twelve heavy guns behind it. The board also proposed a battery of twelve heavy guns on Dumpling Rocks, which would cross fire with the guns at Fort Adams, and recommended three detached batteries for thirty guns on Dutch Island, commanding the western passage into the bay. Colonel Warren began work on the Fort Adams and Dutch Island batteries in 1871-72, but the emplacements on Dumpling Rocks never came off paper.

For New London Harbor the board prepared plans for modifying the old barbette battery at Fort Griswold to receive eight heavy guns, but these too were never implemented. Somewhat more success attended its plans for rebuilding the exterior batteries of Fort Trumbull to accommodate twelve guns. Operations begun in 1874 resulted in the near completion of one battery before funds for the project were exhausted the next year.

None of the postwar defenses planned for New England was ever completed, some were hardly begun, and several were never started at all. While Congress multiplied the civil works of the Corps with a lavish hand, it systematically pared back appropriations for seacoast fortifications. After 1875 it ceased to vote anything for new construction and provided so little for maintenance that the Engineers could do scarcely more than watch the unfinished batteries fall into decay. Even scantier provisions had been made to arm the new defenses. While European nations were arming their warships with rifled guns of from 9- to 14-inch bore, the largest gun in American service was the 15-inch Rodman smoothbore, developed in the 1850s. The most powerful service cannon in the world at that time, it was by the 1870s hopelessly outclassed. Beyond a range of 1,200 yards it was less powerful than a 9-inch rifle. "Any guns we could mount in hastily thrown up earthworks would be useless," complained the Chief of Engineers in 1876. "The projectiles from such batteries would fall harmlessly from the side of the enemy." He could lie beyond their range and destroy them. Moreover, there were only 325 of the big Rodmans available for all fortifications on American coasts. Four years later the Chief of Engineers reported that the only modern guns in the United States were 8-inch rifles, of which only 110 were on hand.[6]

Critics of defense preparations voiced a familiar litany of complaints. Permanent fortifications were quite unnecessary, they said, since defensive measures could be quickly taken when they were needed. Fortifications were also a waste of money considering the rapidity of technological change. Worst of all, they were the instruments of sinister militarists planning to use them to overawe our cities, and their construction furnished the pretext for raising a large standing army to be used to destroy the liberties of the country.

Replying to these criticisms year after year in annual reports and before committees of Congress, Chiefs of Engineers deplored the "sand hill" philosophy that lay behind some of them. Modern earthen fortifications and modern armaments were so massive, they explained, that defenses could no longer be thrown up on short notice. Before effective works could be improvised at a harbor, an enemy with his ironclads would have destroyed it and departed for some other equally vulnerable port. "Unfinished earthen batteries," Major General Andrew H. Humphreys warned in 1878, " . . . provided with a small fraction only of the number of guns for which they were designed, and those of insufficient caliber, and mortar batteries without mortars, though aided by torpedoes, will form but a feeble defense against the powerful fleets prepared and now being prepared to take the high seas." Some years later, in reply to the reckless assertions of anti-militarists that the forts would be used against the cities they were supposed to protect,

Major General John Newton painstakingly explained the nature and position of the forts and the manner in which they would be garrisoned in an emergency by militia-type gunners recruited from the local citizenry.[7] Had critics been of a different mind, his statements could have raised questions about the vulnerability of the forts on their landward sides and the efficiency with which they would be manned.

Warnings cast in vague generalizations that never identified any foe likely to ravage American coasts had little force. When congressional attitudes toward fortifications took a new turn, it was in response to currents of thought in the country that began to make themselves felt in the early 1880s. Sensing a need to protect or expand American interests abroad in the face of growing international political and economic competition, a number of vocal Americans began to clamor for a more active foreign policy. This demanded naval muscle. But after the Civil War the government had dismantled its wartime fleet with such haste and thoroughness that the American Navy had become an embarrassing collection of museum pieces. Goaded by conscientious Secretaries of the Navy and by concerned men in its own houses, Congress made its first appropriation for building modern warships in 1883. By the same act it established a joint panel of Army and Navy officers, the Gun Foundry Board, to see what could be done about the fact that American industry did not possess the facilities for producing a single modern gun or piece of armor plate. Ranging beyond this problem when it reported the next year, the board directed attention to the defenseless state of America's coastal cities and harbors where the Navy would have to be based and urged the adoption of a comprehensive scheme for their defense. In March 1885 Congress referred this question to a special civilian and military Board of Fortifications and Other Defenses, chaired by Secretary of War William C. Endicott.[8]

Submitting its report in January 1886, the Endicott Board laid down the same general principles to govern a scheme of defense that Chiefs of Engineers had been suggesting for a decade. It urged Congress to make provisions for the manufacture of modern weapons and armor plate and to authorize the immediate construction of gun emplacements so that weapons could be mounted as rapidly as they came out of the factories. The board estimated that under the most favorable conditions it would take at least five years to produce and prove the first heavy gun, and it wanted no further delay. Getting down to details, it specified the types and quantities of armament required for the protection of each of twenty-seven harbors listed in order of urgency of need. Nine were in New England. All were to be defended with modern rifled guns of from 8- to 16-inch bore shielded by earthen or armored works, all with submarine mine apparatus, most with 12-inch rifled mortar batteries, and several with fleets of torpedo boats.[9]

The recommendations of the Endicott Board were never precisely followed. The flotillas of torpedo boats were never provided, partly because of changes in naval strategy and partly because newly developed rapid-fire guns of 3- to 6-inch caliber, suited to deal with minesweepers and beach attacks, filled some of their intended functions. Advances of unpredicted magnitude in the power and range of rifled guns allowed the use of smaller calibers and reduced by nearly half the number of weapons required. The perfection of a disappearing gun carriage suitable for heavy guns permitted the substitution of open emplacements for the expensive turrets and armored casemates the board had proposed for more important harbors like Boston and Narragansett Bay. The real significance of the Endicott Report was that it constituted a statement of policy initiated by Congress itself, which that body was willing to underwrite. Although the legislature balked at the board's estimates of over $127 million, it nevertheless accepted the report as the basis for a scheme of defense followed for the next twenty years.

The Endicott Report was taken off paper in 1888. Congress established a Board of Ordnance and Fortifications to review plans of the Corps of Engineers; it voted appropriations to begin the manufacture of modern seacoast ordnance at the Watervliet Arsenal in New York and to assist steel manufacturers in procuring necessary plant equipment; and it provided for the construction of mining casemates and cable galleries at Boston, New York, and San Francisco.

Mining casemates were not really "casemates," but were apparently so called because in early experiments with mining equipment, operating rooms had been installed in casemates of old forts.[10] They were small, squat bombproof structures made of reinforced cement covered with thick layers of sand. From them submarine mines could be detonated by electric cables running through tunnels, or galleries, to the water. In 1888-89 two of these simple buildings were constructed at Fort Warren. Not a particularly dramatic beginning for a great new defense system, their construction nevertheless launched a fortification-building program in New England that was to continue until it was essentially completed about 1906.

In 1890 Congress passed its first bill for the construction of modern gun and mortar batteries. Upon the recommendation of the Corps of Engineers it authorized emplacements at Boston, New York, and San Francisco for the first high-powered breechloading rifles and mortars scheduled to come from the factories in January 1892. The Boston District thus began building emplacements for three 10-inch disappearing rifles on Long Island Head and for sixteen 12-inch rifled mortars at a new site, later named Fort Banks, perched on Winthrop Highlands on the harbor's north flank.

Gun and mortar batteries of the "Endicott period" were similar in concept to those begun after the Civil War, but more massive and complex. Gun batteries generally consisted of two or three weapons, but each gun platform was a unit in itself, enclosed on the sides as well as the front by concrete walls fifteen to twenty feet thick. These concrete emplacements were nestled into parapets of sand about forty-five feet thick, the whole structure in its resistance to the penetration of shells being designed as the equivalent of seventy feet of sand. Although the new defenses were hardly visible from the sea, with the low-lying silhouettes of the embankments blending inconspicuously into the shoreline, the interior crest of a parapet was usually about twenty feet above the general lay of the land, with the gun platform approximately ten feet below the crest. Ammunition magazines were located under the parapet adjacent to the gun platform, but sunk to a lower level to allow for a thick roofing of concrete and earth while still retaining a low profile for the whole work. Mechanical hoists hauled up the heavy charges of powder and shell stored in these vault-like rooms to waiting ammunition carts on the platform level. Galleries, guard rooms, office rooms, and other chambers were distributed in the rear of the magazines under the gun platform.

Mortar emplacements were similarly constructed, but were fully enclosed. Four mortars were grouped together in a pit, and two or four pits into a battery. This arrangement was worked out by General Henry L. Abbot of the Corps of Engineers. After an analytical study of experiments with mortars abroad, Abbot devised a system of firing four mortars simultaneously so that the high-arcing shells would form a shotgun-like pattern, increasing the chances for a hit. The best results were obtained by four pits located at the corners of a rectangle, and this type of battery was adopted whenever sites were suitable.[11]

Twelve-inch mortars installed at Fort Banks, Boston Harbor.
Courtesy of Gerald Butler.

Several of the gun and mortar batteries built in New England were located adjacent to old forts whose sites were still useful. At Fort Warren, where space on Georges Island was limited, three of the largest gun emplacements were built right over the east front of the old masonry work. Most of the batteries, however, were constructed on the new sites selected after the Civil War and at other outer positions. Commanding broad water approaches, their long-range rifles could guard harbors formerly requiring many more guns on narrower channels closer to the cities. Groups of these sprawling batteries, or even single batteries, were still designated as forts, but forts now became merely pieces of real estate over which the new defenses were scattered according to how best to obtain effective fields of fire. Simple in design and materials, the batteries took far less time and money to

Fort Warren, Boston Harbor. The outer works at the bottom of the photo were designed to protect the masonry scarps of this Third System fort from the fire of guns an enemy might mount on nearby Gallops and Lovells islands. The Endicott period barbette batteries appear at the top of the photo. Courtesy of Gerald Butler.

construct than the masonry citadels of the pre-Civil War era; it was their enormously improved guns that became comparatively more expensive and time-consuming to fabricate.[12]

For several years the new defense program, geared to the expanding but still small quantity of modern weapons coming from the government arsenal at Watervliet and the shops of private contractors, seemed hardly to move. Until 1896 the only construction started in New England was a mortar battery at Boston, four 10-inch gun emplacements at Boston and three at Portland, and three mining casemates at each of these harbors and two at Newport. Large-scale construction was finally authorized in 1896 and 1897. This work was getting under way when, on February 15, 1898, the *Maine* went down in Havana Harbor. Three weeks later a bellicose Congress unanimously voted $50 million for war preparations, part of which the War Department earmarked for a crash program of coastal battery construction. The reports of the district engineers reveal that by July, about two months after the start of the brief war with Spain, New England's major harbors were at least approaching a condition where they might put up some defense.

Lieutenant Colonel Samuel M. Mansfield at Boston had built and armed emplacements for eight 10-inch guns, two rapid-fire guns, and sixteen mortars. He also had platforms ready to receive five 12-inch, two 8-inch and two rapid-fire guns. Major Richard L. Hoxie at Portland had turned over five 10-inch rifles to the artillery and was rushing along emplacements for sixteen mortars, two 12-inch guns, six 8-inch guns, and one rapid-fire gun. At Portsmouth Hoxie had completed and armed emplacements for two 8-inch rifles. Major David Lockwood at Newport had transferred to the artillery emplacements in Narragansett Bay for three 10-inch guns and sixteen mortars. He also had platforms ready for two 12-inch guns, two 10-inch guns, one of which was mounted, and three rapid-fire guns. Lockwood had also finished platforms for two 8-inch guns at New Bedford. The ordnance for which they were designed was not yet available, but at the request of the governor of Massachusetts the Commanding General of the Department of the East had sent to New Bedford two 8-inch converted rifles on converted carriages. The converted rifles were 10-inch smoothbore guns converted into muzzle-loading rifles by sleeve insertions. The converted carriages were 15-inch smoothbore mounts strengthened to bear the additional strain imposed by rifle discharges.

No permanent batteries were constructed at harbors in Long Island Sound. Here the quick outdating of the Endicott Report was dramatically illustrated. The board had specified gun and mortar batteries for New London and New Haven and had suggested the deployment of heavily armored floating batteries at broad passages like the eastern entrance to the sound. But none of these defenses ever reached the planning stage. The rapid development of long-range rifles made it possible to mount guns at the mouth of the sound that could bring all parts of the passage under fire. Not only would the manufacturing towns along the north shore of the sound be protected, but New York City would be made secure from attack from that quarter. By July 1898 Major Smith S. Leach at New London had essentially completed emplacements on islands at the mouth of the sound for two 12-inch, four 10-inch, and two 8-inch rifles and for a rapid-fire gun. Only one 10-inch rifle and the rapid-fire gun, however, were mounted.

A few weeks before the war with Spain began New England's Engineers had also started mining harbor channels. Unlike gun and mortar batteries, which were turned over to the artillery as soon as completed, mining equipment remained under the command of the Corps of Engineers, which had developed the defense. It was not until the Army Reorganization Act of February 1901 that mining operations were transferred to the newly created Coast Artillery Corps. By 1898 bombproof mining casemates had been built at several harbors, and temporary casemates hastily constructed at others. Using specially adapted vessels, the district engineers had by early May planted mine fields at Boston, Portland, Portsmouth, New London, New Haven, and Bridgeport harbors and at the entrances to Narragansett Bay and the Penobscot and Kennebec rivers.

The moment the war began congressmen, business interests, and the public in general, after years of indifference toward coastal fortifications, set up a clamor for the immediate erection of defenses. So weak were the harbor defenses of the Atlantic coast, and so apprehensive were coastal communities of bombardment, that the North Atlantic fleet was divided: the one-half blockading Havana and the other, reassuringly called "the Flying Squadron," stationed at Hampton Roads. Against some other power such a strategy might have been disastrous; but fortunately for the United States, while the Spanish navy was believed to be formidable, it was unconceivably neglected, ill-armed, and untrained. Temporary land defenses were also thrown up at more than a dozen places on the Atlantic and Gulf coasts. Lacking enough modern rifles to arm even the permanent fortifications being hurriedly prepared, the War Department provided comfort, if little actual protection, to the citizenry of a number of localities by ordering old-style armament pressed into service.

At Bar Harbor, Maine, Major Hoxie set up on temporary wooden platforms two 10-inch Rodman smoothbores and two 8-inch converted rifles. He overhauled old guns at Fort Knox and mounted four 15-inch Rodmans and an 8-inch breechloading rifle on a converted carriage at Fort Popham. At Portsmouth Harbor he supplemented the single modern 8-inch battery, located at Fort Constitution, with three 15-inch Rodmans at Fort McClary and two 8-inch breechloading rifles on converted carriages at Jerrys Point. At Portland he supported the skimpy modern armament in the harbor with two 8-inch converted rifles on Great Diamond Island and two 15-inch Rodmans at Fort Scammell. Meantime Major Leach erected temporary batteries at communities on Long Island Sound, caught nearly defenseless with its single modern rifle. He mounted three 15-inch Rodmans at Fort Trumbull at New London, two of which were shipped in from Fort Washington in Maryland. To defend other towns along the sound, he stripped the old battery at Fort Griswold of eleven 10-inch Rodmans, mounted six at New Haven, four at Bridgeport, and one at Stonington. Hardly did Hoxie and Leach have these weapons in place, than the ten-weeks' war was over. The temporary defenses were soon dismantled, and the smoothbores, already relics of another military age, were stored or sold.

Unlike after the Civil War the construction of permanent seacoast defenses, however, did not slacken. New sites were acquired at Boston, Portland, Narragansett Bay, and the eastern end of Long Island Sound, and guns and mortars for them continued to pour from private factories and government arsenals. By 1906 most of the batteries contemplated for New England under the Endicott program were completed, and by 1910 the last of them were transferred to the Coast Artillery. Once more American coasts were protected by a vast body of fortifications, and again New England had the heaviest concentration of defenses. Of eighteen fortified positions on the Atlantic coast, seven were within the jurisdiction of the New England districts.[13]

Boston Harbor lay behind the guns of seven forts. Fort Banks and Fort Heath occupied Winthrop Highlands on the northern flank of the harbor, and Fort Revere lay on Nantasket Head on the southern flank. Between them, scattered across the harbor's broad opening to the sea, were Fort Strong on Long Island, Fort Standish on Lovells Island, Fort Warren on Georges Island, and Fort Andrews on Peddocks Island. Castle and Governors islands, by congressional resolutions of 1890 and 1902, had been turned over to the city of Boston for park purposes. The city did nothing to improve or protect these historic sites, and while Fort Independence was retained for some years by the War Department as a storage place for the mine defenses of the harbor, Fort Winthrop soon fell prey to vandals and thieves. Totally the forts of Boston Harbor contained thirty-one batteries housing thirty-two mortars and seven 12-inch, fourteen 10-inch, thirteen 6-inch, and thirty 3- to 5-inch guns.

Portland Harbor was defended by five forts. Fort Preble on Spring Point, whose primary batteries were mortars, was the only older work incorporated

Twelve-inch disappearing guns installed at Fort Warren, Boston Harbor.
Courtesy of Gerald Butler.

Fort Standish, Lovells Island, Boston Harbor, as it appeared in 1934.

into the new system. Fort Lyon on Cow Island, Fort McKinley on Great Diamond Island, Fort Levett on Cushing Island, and Fort Williams on Portland Head formed an almost straight north-south line separating Portland Harbor from Casco Bay. Obsolete Fort Gorges was utilized as a mining equipment storehouse. The harbor's armament consisted of twenty-five batteries containing twenty-four mortars and seven 12-inch, seven 10-inch, eight 8-inch, fourteen 6-inch, and thirteen 3-inch guns.

North of Portland, light defenses were placed at the mouth of the Kennebec River, on which ten miles upstream lay the Bath Iron Works where warships were built for the United States Navy. In 1902 the government had purchased a tract of land on Sabino Hill, an elevation behind Fort Popham, as the site for Fort Baldwin. Construction began in 1905, and in 1908 three batteries housing three 6-inch guns and two 3-inch guns were transferred to the artillery. At Fort Knox on the Penobscot River nothing was done except build a storehouse for mining materials.

Pointing down Portsmouth Harbor were the rifles of eight batteries at three forts. Fort Constitution on Newcastle Island on the New Hampshire side of the estuary was armed with two 8-inch and two 3-inch guns. Fort Stark on Jerrys Point at the southern extremity of the island was provided with two 12-inch, two 6-inch, and four 3-inch guns. Fort Foster on Gerrish Island on the Maine side of the harbor's mouth boasted three 10-inch and two 3-inch guns.

At New Bedford, where the military reservation on Clarks Point had finally been named Fort Rodman in 1893, five batteries flanking the old masonry fort contained two 8-inch, two 5-inch, and four 3-inch guns.

The entrances to Narragansett Bay were commanded by five forts. Fort Adams, with a half dozen new gun and mortar batteries behind the old fort, and Fort Wetherill, across the way on Conanicut Island near Dumpling Rocks, guarded the eastern passage. Blocking the western passage was Fort Greble on Dutch Island, flanked on the east by Fort Getty on Conanicut Island and on the west by Fort Philip Kearny on the mainland. Mounted in the twenty-three batteries of the five forts were twenty-four mortars and seven 12-inch, ten 10-inch, sixteen 6-inch, four 4.7-inch, and twelve 3-inch guns.

Five forts also covered the eastern entrance to Long Island Sound. Four were strung on a direct line extending southwesterly across the mouth of the sound: Fort Mansfield on Napatree Point, Rhode Island; Fort H. G. Wright on the western end of Fishers Island; Fort Michie on Great Gull Island; and Fort Terry on Plum Island, just off Orient Point, Long Island. Fort Tyler was located on Gardiners Point, actually a small island, a few miles southeast of Fort Terry. Along this line of defense were twenty-nine batteries with sixteen mortars and four 12-inch, six 10-inch, four 8-inch, seventeen 6-inch, eight 5-inch, and sixteen 3-inch guns.[14]

Within two decades New England's Engineers had built 27 forts containing 124 batteries with emplacements for 96 mortars and 247 guns. By 1906 the great surge of fortification building was about over. Military construction still continued on a limited scale, but now centered mainly on providing the batteries with various accessory equipment. Already under way for some time, this work was accelerated for a few years by the recommendations of a new coast defense board.

At the suggestion of Chief of Engineers Major General George L. Gillespie that it was time to create another panel similar to the Endicott Board to review defense projects for the United States and its new insular possessions, President Theodore Roosevelt, in January 1905, appointed a National Coast Defense Board of army and navy officers chaired by Secretary of War William Howard Taft. Reporting in February 1906, the Taft Board recommended the construction of insular defenses, which was done, and the installation of additional guns and mortars on continental coasts, including seventy-one new weapons in New England, which was not done. More important to continued defense construction in New England were the board's proposals for further developing the adjuncts of coastal batteries, which included fire control systems, submarine mine defenses, searchlights, power plants, and lighting systems. The Endicott Board had contemplated only mine defenses and searchlights to cover the mine fields, but by the turn of the century other accessories, and especially fire control systems, were regarded as equally necessary elements of a modern and adequate defense system.[15]

References to fire control systems first appear in the reports of New England district engineers between 1900 and 1902, when the districts built twenty or more fire control stations for the precision aiming of guns and mortars. Prior to this time guns had been aimed individually with elementary sighting instruments, and accuracy of fire against moving targets had been largely a matter of experience and educated guessing. The new aiming system, in contrast, employed sighting with precise optical instruments, the rapid calculation of mathematical data, and the electrical communication of target-sighting and gun-pointing information. The installations of the first systems, however, were quickly called to a halt. Many details of fire control had not yet been worked out by the artillery, and a vertical method of sighting was used that required high towers near the batteries, furnishing perfect targets for enemy fire. In 1904 the Coast Artillery adopted a horizontal-base system of position finding. This employed two or more "base-end" stations off a considerable distance on either side of a battery, from which simultaneous optical bearings were continuously taken on a moving target. The angles of sight were constantly communicated by telephone and telautograph to a battery plotting room, which computed the target's position at the moment a projectile would reach it and transmitted aiming directions electrically to each gun emplacement or mortar pit.[16]

In 1905 the Engineer and Ordnance departments selected Boston, Portland, and New York for the first installations of this system. A special army board planned the fire control stations for Boston, which the district had ready for operation in December 1907. Forty-eight base-end stations, with generally two to four stations serving different batteries housed in a single building, were precisely positioned on fort sites and on new military reservations on either side of the harbor. Small, simple structures of wood or brick, the stations contained only observation rooms and spartan living quarters. During the next half-dozen years fire-control systems were installed at all New England fortifications.

Mining casemate at Fort Constitution, Portsmouth Harbor. The addition on the left is a harbor defense telephone switchboard room constructed in 1942. Courtesy of Gerald Butler.

The New England districts had been constructing mining casemates and appurtenances such as mine storehouses, cable tanks, and loading wharves since 1888. This construction continued on a small scale after 1906, with one new component of the mine defense system added. This was the mine observing or control station, used like the fire-control stations to get better fixings on ships entering harbors. At Boston Harbor six of these small, box-like structures were built and turned over to the Coast Artillery in 1907.

References to equipping batteries with electric power plants and lighting systems first appear in the reports of the New England districts in 1898. The first installation of searchlights took place in 1901 and 1902, when several lights were set up at the entrance to Long Island Sound. Experiments had been made off and on with searchlights since 1872, but among the most significant were a series of tests conducted in the Portland District in the summer of 1904. The major recommendations coming from the Portland experiments were that no useful purpose was served by illuminating a water area much beyond the maximum range of fire, and that to put lights so far to the front of fortifications that they could not be defended was to waste them. These findings were quite the opposite of ideas held at that time by prominent artillery officers.

Other work by the New England districts on the auxiliaries of the defense system included the construction of tide observing stations, the installation of improved mechanical ammunition hoists in gun emplacements, and the building of district wireless stations, the first of which were constructed at Fort Andrews at Boston and Fort Levett at Portland in 1908. Related also to the Taft Board Report was the responsibility given to the Boston Engineer Office to purchase materials for fortifications under construction in the Philippine Islands.[17]

Defense preparations of the "Taft period" involved New England districts in still other activities. By order of the War Department in 1907, boards of officers were appointed to meet in the Artillery Districts of New England to consider the protection of seacoast forts from attack on their landward sides. The upshot of this was the planning of land defenses around Boston, between May and November 1909, by Captain Gilbert A. Youngberg and troops of Company B, Corps of Engineers, in consultation with Boston District Engineer Edward Burr. Plotting a vast semicircle around the city and harbor, the Engineers established a defense line more than seventy miles long. Touching the sea at Lynn on the north and Hingham on the south, it extended inland at its farthest point about twenty miles. Earthen fieldworks were designed for strategic places along the line, to be raised by local citizens if ever needed. Three thousand soldiers, it was figured, could hold this defense perimeter against any force an enemy would be likely to land.[18]

During wartime the seacoast forts would have to be garrisoned by reserve army units as well as by the regular Coast Artillery. Therefore between 1911 and 1914 Congress provided over a half million dollars for the installation of equipment in state armories for the instruction of Coast Artillery militia companies. Six of the nine cities in which these funds were expended were in New England. At the South Armory in Boston the Boston District set up a 10-inch gun on a disappearing carriage, a 12-inch mortar, a 3-inch rapid-fire gun, two sets of fire-control stations, and a thirty-inch searchlight. Similar training equipment was installed by the other New England districts in armories at Portland, Bridgeport, Providence, Pawtucket, and Woonsocket.[19]

The forts built on American coasts at the turn of the twentieth century were unexcelled anywhere in the world. Their batteries were mostly widely spaced and carefully hidden. Most of their heavy guns were exposed above their protective parapets only for the brief moment of firing. Their heavy mortars were totally invisible from the sea. Moreover, their fire control systems were more accurate than those of ships, giving the shore batteries a huge edge in long-range duels. So not only were guns and gun crews almost invulnerable because of their concealed and protected positions, but it was unlikely that any ship could fight its way close enough to be effective.

But the years of the Endicott period forts were numbered. Around the beginning of World War I great advances were made in naval weapons and tactics. Accurate shipboard ranges increased with better fire-control techniques. Improved battleship turrets permitted ships to fire at higher angles, greatly extending maximum ranges and making it possible, by curved trajectory fire, to drop shells behind parapets. Overhead bursts, a minor danger before the war, became a serious threat. Shore guns mounted on disappearing carriages, as seven out of every eight American heavy seacoast guns were mounted, in contrast, were limited to about twenty degrees elevation, with consequent restriction in range. Outranged and lacking overhead cover,

Endicott batteries were already obsolescent almost before some of them were finished. "When designed and constructed our seacoast batteries were thoroughly modern and fully adequate for the purpose for which they were intended," reported Chief of Engineers Brigadier General Dan C. Kingman in 1915, "but the work of battery construction has in the past few years been allowed to practically cease and has not kept pace with recent progress in naval development."[20]

The question of what should be done prompted the War Department to convene a special Board of Review in February 1915. The board's major proposal was to increase the effective range of harbor defenses by the installation of a considerable number of 12- and 16-inch guns. Although planning in cooperation with district engineers began immediately, the United States entered the war in Europe before any construction was started. Its attention was then directed primarily to matters more urgent than defending shores that were never seriously threatened. Nevertheless, the construction of a few new batteries was begun during or immediately after the war. Of the ten localities on continental coasts where new batteries were erected, four were in New England.

Batteries were constructed at Boston, Portland, New Bedford, and Long Island Sound. Except at Long Island Sound, the fortification works were of new and extremely simple design. The guns were not provided with cover of any sort, but relied for protection against naval fire solely on wide separation of the emplacements and concealment from sea-level observation. The emplacements were merely large circular platforms of concrete, designed to permit the guns at their centers to turn a full 360 degrees. Ammunition was stored in underground concrete magazines between them.

Two batteries were erected at Boston. One was on Nahant, a boot-like peninsula jutting into Massachusetts Bay a few miles northeast of Winthrop Highlands. The site had been acquired in 1904 for mortar batteries, a project that was later eliminated from Boston defense plans. Fire control stations were erected there in 1907, and in 1915 a sixty-inch searchlight was installed. The construction of the battery began in November 1918. It was for two 12-inch guns mounted on newly designed high-angle barbette carriages that increased the range of existing model Endicott period 12-inch rifles from about eight miles to more than seventeen miles. The battery was completed in December 1921, and a new fort, Fort Ruckman, was added to the roster of Boston's defenses.[21]

Boston's second new battery was constructed on Hog Island, a small spot of land concealed from the sea behind Nantasket Head. Purchased in 1917, the island was originally slated for two 12-inch guns. Work on the emplacements began in April 1920, but before the armament for them was supplied, the project was revised and the platforms were modified to accommodate 16-inch guns. Hog Island was the third site in Boston Harbor to be selected for this size armament. Great Brewster Island, lying about a mile and a half seaward of Georges Island, had been purchased in 1917 as the site for two 16-inch guns mounted in a naval turret. Nothing more was done to further the project, and in 1920 it was abandoned in favor of locating the guns on Calf Island. Lying a quarter-mile north of Great Brewster, Calf Island had also been selected in 1917 for the location of two 16-inch guns. In 1922 this

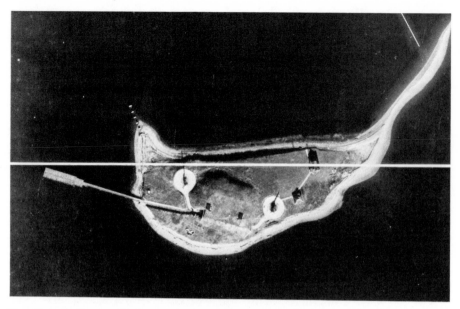

Fort Duvall, Boston Harbor. A harbor defense of the post-World War I generation, its two 16-inch rifles were not provided with any material cover.

One of the pair of Army Model 1919 rifles installed at Fort Duvall.
Courtesy of Gerald Butler.

site was in turn discarded in favor of Hog Island, which lay protected behind Nantasket Head. The 16-inch rifles that were finally mounted in 1925 were Army Model 1919 weapons, the most powerful service cannon ever produced in the United States. Fort Duvall, with weapons capable of hurling projectiles weighing more than a ton for about twenty-eight miles, was thus also added to Boston's defenses.[22]

At Portland the Board of Review's recommendation for the installation of two 12-inch rifles on barbette carriages resulted in the construction of a battery of the new type at Fort Levett on Cushing Island. Provided for in 1917 estimates, the battery was completed and turned over to the artillery in January 1921. A similar recommendation for New Bedford was implemented by the construction of another two-gun 12-inch barbette battery at Fort Rodman, transferred to the artillery in May 1921.

To cover the broad entrance to Long Island Sound the Board of Review proposed six 16-inch guns, with batteries at Forts Wright, Michie, and Terry. The only battery constructed, however, was at Fort Michie on Great Gull Island, nearest the center of the passage. During the war plans were adopted for mounting two 16-inch guns in a naval turret at Fort Michie, but the war ended before work had progressed beyond the blueprint stage. In July 1919 the project was modified to provide for the installation of one 16-inch gun mounted on a disappearing carriage. This work was completed in March 1922. Meantime Forts Mansfield and Tyler, located on the edges of the sound and armed with only a few small guns, were abandoned and their ordnance removed.[23]

The airplane, although still in a primitive stage of development, was a weapon that had to be reckoned with in World War I. American coastal defenses and cities could conceivably be subject to aerial observation or attack. The United States itself had pioneered in naval aviation and shown that it was possible. On January 18, 1911, in San Francisco Bay, a daring civilian pilot flying a Curtiss biplane had made the first landing and take-off from a warship, the U.S.S. *Pennsylvania*, fitted out with a rickety wooden platform on her afterdeck. The next year a naval aviator flew a plane shot from a compressed-air catapult, and the year after that an aviator made the first scouting flight for the fleet and the Navy established an aviation station and school.[24] Since other navies could use airplanes as well, the coastal defense plans drawn up in 1915 included antiaircraft batteries. When the United States entered the war in 1917 the New England districts began installing two 3-inch antiaircraft guns at almost every fort. But since the guns were in short supply the last of the batteries were not transferred to the artillery until October 1921. The districts also built emplacements for antiaircraft guns in and around the major cities of New England. Boston, for example, was ringed with pairs of concrete foundations at Lynn, Cambridge, Brighton, and Braintree; and platforms were built on Castle Island and Boston Common. Guns had been mounted, however, only on the Common and at Brighton before work was stopped by a telegram from the Chief of Engineers five days after the signing of the armistice.[25]

It soon became apparent after the United States entered the war that its coasts were not likely to be attacked and that some seacoast guns could be put to better use elsewhere. Therefore the New England districts dismounted a number of weapons designated for arming transports or mounting on railroad carriages for service abroad. Boston Harbor was stripped of nine 10-inch guns, thirteen rapid-fire guns, and ten mortars; and other harbors were similarly pruned of a portion of their armament. Few weapons, however, were actually shipped away before the war ended.

During and after the war the districts also carried out renewed programs of modernizing and improving the auxiliaries of fortifications. Powerful sixty-inch searchlights were installed, some temporarily on private property, as on the estate of Senator Henry Cabot Lodge at Nahant. New mining casemates were built. Ammunition hoists were modernized. Post telephone systems were installed. New fire-control stations were erected, and fire-control systems were improved by the construction of protected switchboard and plotting rooms and the installation of new communications equipment.[26]

In 1923 the War Department, recognizing that its harbor defenses offered no protection against aerial bombardment and that most seacoast guns were outranged by naval armament, made another study of coastal defense requirements. It recommended the abandonment of a number of works that were no longer of military value and concentration on improving the remaining defenses, particularly by providing them with new long-range guns and more antiaircraft protection. It designated eighteen coastal areas where permanent defenses should be retained, including Portland, Portsmouth, Boston, New Bedford, the entrances to Narragansett Bay, and the eastern entrance of Long Island Sound. The most important factor determining this selection was the insistence of the Navy on the defense of its shore installations and fleet anchorages.

Between 1930 and 1932 the Army drafted new defense projects for each of the eighteen harbor areas and established a Harbor Defense Board to supervise the execution of the projects. During the 1930s, however, funds voted for harbor protection were meager, and the growing tension between the United States and Japan determined that what little was available would be spent mostly on improvements along the Pacific coast. Not until the threat of war in Europe was imminent in 1939 were larger appropriations forthcoming and was work resumed on gun installations along the Atlantic front. In March 1940 the Harbor Defense Board began a resurvey of harbor defense needs, which soon took on new urgency with the downfall of France in June. Naval attacks on American coasts had until then been only a remote possibility, but with the fate of the French and British fleets suddenly made uncertain and serious American naval inferiority in either the Atlantic or Pacific a disquieting prospect, the danger took on new dimensions. The survey of the Harbor Defense Board broadened into a complete reassessment of harbor defenses.

Reporting on July 27, 1940, the board recommended the replacement of practically all pre-World War I heavy armament with 16-inch guns. These weapons, already available, were Mark II naval guns originally intended for capital ships whose construction had been cancelled by the Washington Naval Treaty of 1922. Almost as powerful as the Army's Model 1919, only a few of which had been produced, they had a range of about twenty-six miles. The board proposed the construction within the continental United States of twenty-seven two-gun 16-inch batteries, all to be emplaced in casemates. It recommended similar air cover for ten 16-inch and thirteen 12-inch batteries that had been installed since World War I or were already approved for construction. It also proposed the construction of fifty twin-gun 6-inch batteries. With ranges of about fifteen miles, they could deal with cruisers and other light ships and would reinforce sixty-three existing secondary batteries of small caliber that were to be retained in the defense system.[27]

This modernization program had to compete from the beginning with other and more pressing requirements of the Army and Navy. Moreover as American air and sea power expanded, the less likely it seemed that coastal defense guns would ever be used. Consequently in each of the next three years the program was cut back, especially as it related to the primary batteries. By the end of the war nineteen 16-inch and forty-eight 6-inch batteries had been installed.[28] Eight of the 16-inch and sixteen of the 6-inch batteries were constructed by the New England districts.

The newly installed 16-inch guns and the heavy batteries retained from the interwar period were emplaced within casemates from which only the gun barrels protruded. Twenty- to twenty-five-feet-thick coverings of concrete, steel, and earth protected the guns and carriages from direct hits. Thick canopies of reinforced concrete projected over the front openings of the casemates, and in some instances the forward part of the carriage was surrounded by a four-inch steel shield that almost completely closed the casemate opening. The guns of a battery were generally spaced about five hundred feet apart, and between them, also protected by reinforced concrete and earth, were strung chambers housing the battery's magazines, power generators, air conditioners, communications equipment, and storage and service facilities. To transport the one-half or one ton shells along galleries to the guns, overhead trolleys ran on tracks suspended from the ceiling. The 6-inch guns were not casemated but were enclosed in cast-steel shields four to six inches thick. The guns of a battery were spaced about two hundred feet apart, and between and slightly behind them was constructed an earth-covered, reinforced-concrete magazine complex similar to those that serviced the big guns.[29]

Batteries of these types were built by the Boston District at Boston, Portland, and Portsmouth. For the defense of Boston Harbor, the district placed a 16-inch battery on East Point, Nahant, and another on Deer Island, the harbor's northern chop. The latter site, purchased from the city in 1907 for the installation of fire-control stations, was now christened Fort Dawes. The district casemated the 16-inch battery at Fort Duvall and the 12-inch battery at Fort Ruckman. To supplement this heavy artillery it built 6-inch batteries on East Point, Nahant; on Outer Brewster Island; at Fort Dawes; and at Fourth Cliff, a new military reservation established at Scituate on the harbor's south flank. At Portland Harbor it constructed a 16-inch battery on Peak Island, casemated the 12-inch battery at Fort Levett on Cushing Island, and built 6-inch batteries on Cape Elizabeth and Jewell Island. At Portsmouth it erected a 16-inch battery at new Fort Dearborn, just outside the harbor in Rye, New Hampshire, and built 6-inch batteries at Fort Dearborn and Fort Foster.[30]

The Providence District was equally busy in southern New England. At Narragansett Bay it installed 16-inch batteries at Fort Church on Sakonnet

Point and at Fort Greene on Point Judith. Located about sixteen miles apart on the outermost edges of the bay, these four guns practically supplanted the five forts within the bay once armed with nearly sixty 6- to 12-inch rifles and heavy mortars. The big guns were supported by three 6-inch batteries constructed at Fort Church, Fort Greene, and Fort Burnside, the last located on Beavertail Point on the southern tip of Conanicut Island. The district also built, at Fort Church, the only modern 8-inch battery constructed within the continental United States. A smaller version of the 16-inch casemated batteries, even to its guns being surplus Navy pieces transferred to the Army after the Washington Naval Treaty, it was completed before the war began when defense work was first resumed on the Atlantic coast.[31] At the eastern end of Long Island Sound the district constructed a 16-inch battery at Fort Wright on Fishers Island and another at Fort Hero on Montauk Point, Long Island. It also built 6-inch batteries at Fort Wright and at Wilderness Point on Fishers Island, at Fort Hero, and at Fort Terry on Plum Island. Additional coastal defense construction by the district consisted of casemating the open 12-inch battery at Fort Rodman, New Bedford, and erecting a 6-inch battery on Mishaum Point in South Dartmouth, Massachusetts, to command the entrance to Buzzards Bay and the western end of the Cape Cod Canal.

A 155-mm. gun on a Panama mount at the Salisbury Beach, Massachusetts, Military Reservation. Courtesy of Gerald Butler.

At a number of forts and military reservations the districts also built concrete platforms for lighter artillery: 3-inch antiaircraft guns, 90 millimeter anti-torpedo boat batteries, and 155 millimeter field pieces. The latter weapons, which had a range of about fifteen miles, were provided with the scope of traverse required of seacoast guns firing at moving targets by mounting them on circular platforms with steel rails around the rims, along which the guns' trails could easily be moved. Such "Panama" mounts were constructed at several places, including four at the Salisbury Beach Military

Reservation, two at Sagamore Hill at the eastern end of the Cape Cod Canal, and two at East Point, Nahant.

Each of the larger gun installations was served by a network of up to a dozen fire-control stations strung along the coast for miles in either direction of a battery. The base-end stations for the harbor defenses of Boston, for example, stretched from Gurnet Point in Plymouth Bay to Plum Island on the south side of the Merrimack River, a straight-line distance of about sixty miles. A station on the Salisbury Beach Military Reservation on the north side of the Merrimack began a series of sighting posts serving the batteries at Portsmouth that extended to York, Maine. From there base-end stations for

Fire-control stations of the Boston Harbor defenses

Emerson Point, Rockport, Massachusetts. Courtesy of Gerald Butler.

Fire-control tower camouflaged to resemble a church tower. Halibut Point, Cape Ann, Massachusetts. Courtesy of Gerald Butler.

Strawberry Point, Scituate, Massachusetts. Courtesy of Gerald Butler.

Point Allerton, Hull, Massachusetts. Courtesy of Gerald Butler.

the Portland Harbor defenses spread along the coast to the Kennebec River. Existing base-end stations were retained, and many new ones were constructed, each serving three or four batteries and most of them disguised. For the Boston Harbor defenses the Boston District built over twenty stations made to look like beachfront cottages and about a dozen steel or cement towers, some camouflaged to resemble church towers and one a windmill.

The artillery installations themselves were also camouflaged. Although both the Endicott period batteries, some of which were retained in service until 1943, and the batteries completed after World War I were well concealed against observation from ships at sea, their gun emplacements in the center of well-groomed grass areas and slopes distinctively marked by roadways presented perfect bull's-eyes for modern aircraft whose observation and attack capabilities were being dramatically illustrated in the war theaters abroad. To reduce their vulnerability through disguise, the Army General Staff in 1941 directed the Corps of Engineers to conduct camouflage training schools in each Coast Artillery District. The school for the First Coast Artillery District was held from September to November that year at Fort Heath in Winthrop. The instructor was First Lieutenant Walter Krotee, sent from the faculty of the Engineer School at Fort Belvoir, Virginia. The students, about thirty in number, were Coast Artillery officers with engineer training and noncommissioned officers selected from the harbor defense units. The officer assigned from the Harbor Defense of Portsmouth was First Lieutenant Wilbar M. Hoxie, now Safety Engineer of the New England Division.

Learning by experimentation and the development of new techniques, the school concealed the three 12-inch disappearing guns of Fort Heath and distorted the distinctive outlines of the whole fort by means of removable netting, painting, and landscaping, and by remodeling structures to create the illusion of an area of private homes and commercial properties. Extensive use was made of nonreflective paints, including formulas designed to reduce reflectivity to infra-red light by which photography could penetrate some camouflage techniques.[32]

Returning to their duty stations, the students of the school camouflaged the older batteries, procuring supplies and equipment from the Boston and Providence engineer districts. Meantime the engineers of the districts were themselves camouflaging the new gun installations they were constructing. The earthen blankets of the casemates were somewhat irregularly shaped and planted with grasses and shrubs to blend in with natural surroundings. At Fourth Cliff all the barracks and other structures were constructed so as to present the appearance of a typical seaside resort community, and similar techniques were employed at other military reservations.

Along with the gun batteries and fire-control stations, the New England districts constructed the various ancillaries of a coastal defense system, such as up-to-date reinforced concrete mining casemates and harbor entrance command posts that were both bombproof and gasproof. Some of these installations represented sizable projects. The placing of an extremely sophisticated mining casemate on Great Brewster Island required the additional construction of barracks, quarters, and messes, a reservoir, and platforms for 90 millimeter rapid-fire anti-torpedo boat batteries. The installation of the

A 6-inch barbette battery at Fort Standish, Boston Harbor, camouflaged with netting.
Courtesy of Gerald Butler.

The military installation at Fourth Cliff, Scituate, Massachusetts,
disguised to resemble a seaside resort community.
Courtesy of Gerald Butler.

Harbor Entrance Command Post at Fort Stark, Portsmouth, New Hampshire.
Courtesy of Wilbur Hoxie.

6-inch battery and a searchlight on Outer Brewster Island similarly necessitated the construction of living accommodations and a desalination plant.

With far fewer but far more powerful guns, the New England districts had by the close of World War II armed the region's harbors more formidably than ever in their history. Within three years of the war's end, however, the entire concept of harbor defense by long-range artillery was abandoned. The technology of amphibious invasion had been developed during the war to the point where whole armies could be landed without the use of port facilities, and if heavy shipboard guns were used at all in another war, they would be used to support such open-beach landings rather than to bomb coastal cities or naval bases, which could more easily be attacked from the air.[33] Moreover, the era of missiles had begun. Therefore, when Army Engineers within a few short years again turned their skills to defense construction, it was to be of a much different character.

The Battle of Bunker Hill.

Bunker Hill Monument.

Colebrook flood control and water supply reservoir, Connecticut.

Local flood protection, Woonsocket, Rhode Island.

Fox Point Hurricane Barrier, Providence, Rhode Island.

Charles River Dam under construction.

Cape Cod Canal.

Bourne Bridge, Cape Cod Canal.

Improved small boat harbor, Scituate, Massachusetts.

Cliff Walk Restoration, Newport, Rhode Island.

Transportation Systems Center, Cambridge, Massachusetts.

Chapel at Fort Devens, Massachusetts.

North Hartland Dam, Vermont.

Townshend flood control reservoir, Vermont.

Profile Falls, Franklin Falls flood control project.

White water canoe race at Knightville Dam, Massachusetts.

VII A LARGER MILITARY MISSION

On November 27, 1940 the Boston Engineer District took over from the Army Quartermaster Corps the construction of Grenier Air Force Base in Manchester, New Hampshire. The transfer marked the beginning of a new military mission for the Corps of Engineers and the abandonment of a military practice dating back to colonial times. In the tradition of the British, the Corps of Engineers had customarily built fortifications and military roads and bridges, while the Quartermaster Corps had erected the camps, depots, and other facilities that sheltered and supplied the Army. Even at seacoast fortifications, the Engineers had built the batteries and Quartermasters had put up the barracks. The one corps took care of combat construction, the other quartered the Army.

Although the Quartermaster Corps was essentially a supply rather than a construction agency, this division of responsibility raised no great problems throughout the nineteenth century, for not much construction was required. Peacetime armies were insignificant, and wartime armies were mustered in small units and almost immediately sent into the field. World War I, however, relegated militia methods to history. The mobilization and training of large armies and the mass production of war matériel required the building of training camps, munitions plants, supply depots, and other facilities on a vast scale and at breakneck speed. A Cantonment (later, Construction) Division, nominally a part of the Quartermaster Corps but for all practical purposes an independent unit within the War Department, was hastily established, and, heavily staffed by bigwigs from the country's leading construction firms, it got the huge job done. But the agency also drew criticism for inefficiency, waste, and corruption. And throughout the war, a struggle went on within the Army and Congress over whether to transfer the Construction Division to the Corps of Engineers, create a permanent Army Construction Division that would absorb the civil function of the Corps of Engineers, consolidate all federal construction into a new federal department of public works, or, after the war, return the division's function to the Quartermaster Corps. With army officers, contractors' associations, and congressmen tugging in all directions, the issue was papered over in 1920 by the compromise of establishing a Construction Service as a separate branch of the Quartermaster Corps.

Between World Wars it again did not matter much where responsibility for military construction lay. The Army was as usual pared to a token force, and most of the huge wartime military plant was sold or allowed to decay. But when the realities of events unfolding in Europe and Asia in the 1930s were finally faced and the United States belatedly began to rearm in 1939, it geared up a military construction program that was to dwarf the efforts of 1917-18. The Construction Division of the Quartermaster Corps, despite a high level of competence and extraordinary achievements, soon began to stagger under the strain. Twenty years of national inattention to considerations of security and the makeshift character of a hastily assembled and understaffed organization were handicaps not easily overcome. Once more the question of the proper agency for military construction was debated, and this time the logic of the Corps of Engineers' unique technical competence, established nationwide field organization, and long experience in directing large construction enterprises prevailed. In September 1940 Congress authorized the Secretary of War to transfer any part of defense construction to the Engineers, and in November the Chief of Staff assigned to them all Army Air Force work. A year later, by a measure put into effect December 16, 1941, Congress placed all Army construction, and responsibility for maintenance and real estate as well, under the Corps of Engineers.[1]

In addition to Grenier Field in Manchester, the first project in the country to pass from the Quartermasters to the Engineers, Air Force construction by the Corps in New England included a half-dozen other major air bases. At Bangor, Maine, the Boston District transformed the municipal airport into the Dow Air Force Base. More than a hundred miles north of Bangor, in the northeastern corner of the United States, it built two more fields at Presque Isle and Houlton. These were western terminals of the North Atlantic route of the Air Transport Command. Construction of the fields was authorized in August 1941, and by October the Presque Isle base was ready for limited operations. It became the main point of departure for the thousands of American aircraft ferried over the Atlantic to Britain, either directly across Newfoundland or by the stepping-stone route of Labrador, Greenland, and Iceland. Houlton became an alternate landing field. At Falmouth on Cape Cod, the Boston District turned Otis Field, a former Massachusetts National Guard installation with two turf airstrips, into another large Air Force base. In 1940 the Army leased the National Guard property for the construction of Camp Edwards, and in the fall of 1942 the district laid the first concrete runways on the portion retained for an airfield. During the war Otis was used successively by the 14th Antisubmarine Patrol, the Civilian Air Patrol, and the Naval Air Force. In the Connecticut River Valley, the Providence District built Westover Field in Chicopee, Massachusetts, and Bradley Field at Windsor Locks, Connecticut. Westover Field, planned in 1939 and begun early in 1940 by the Constructing Quartermaster, was the first Air Corps base located in New England. Bradley Field, together with Grenier Field, was part of an accelerated Air Force program drawn up in 1940.[2]

When taken over by the Engineers, the airfield construction program was in chaotic condition. In selecting sites the Air Corps had followed the easy path of accepting tracts donated by communites, and they frequently turned out to be soggy or subject to flooding or in some other way unsuitable. No basic data necessary for proper design had been collected, no criteria existed for constructing paved runways, and not much information was available on airfield drainage. Plans for buildings had been drawn with insufficient clarity and detail, and no attention had been paid to passive defense measures of camouflage and dispersion.

One of the toughest nuts to crack was designing runways that could stand up under the great weight and pounding vibrations of the heavy bombers developed during the war. Before the emergency, commercial planes of 25,000 pounds gross weight, with wheel loads of 12,500 pounds, were the heaviest in use. Now runways had to be constructed for superbombers weighing as much as 140,000 pounds, and no precedents for such loads existed in either airport or highway engineering. To push research on both rigid cement and flexible asphalt pavements, the Corps assembled a crack team of specialists, including two experienced soils men, Reuben M. Haines and D. Dana Leslie, from the New England Division. Assisted by personnel in many districts, the researchers within two years designed airfields capable of handling the heaviest planes of World War II and developed methods for meeting the challenge of much heavier planes in the future. Among the many experiments conducted were those at Bradley Field, where deflection tests were made on asphalt pavements with static loads ranging from 20 to 112.5 tons, and at Grenier Field, where data was collected relating to pavements laid on sand.[3]

The Quartermaster Corps had prepared standard plans and specifications for the barracks, mess halls, and numerous other structures that make up a military base. But when the Engineers unrolled them at the airfields, complaints came in thick and fast. They were "too general" and therefore "ambiguous and confusing," reported the acting district engineer at Providence, Lieutenant Colonel Harley Latson. They were poorly prepared, improperly organized, and difficult to read, he continued. Both he and Lieutenant Colonel Leonard B. Gallagher at Boston were among the district engineers who compiled long lists of recommended changes in response to the request of the Chief of Engineers to review the plans and offer suggestions for revision.[4]

Another feature of the bases that bothered the Engineers was their high visibility from the air. Westover Field, for example, stood out starkly from the surrounding tobacco farmland that characterized much of the lower Connecticut River Valley. Construction forces, tackling a tract of 5,000 acres in April 1940, had bulldozed away all vegetation and proceeded to labor in great clouds of dust. The buildings of the base were crowded into about one-third the space available, their close, regular formations unmistakably those of a military post. In the same way other bases along the Atlantic, Gulf, and Pacific coasts stood out in bold relief, offering splendid targets for possible enemy air strikes.

Less than three weeks after taking over the Air Force projects, the Engineers started blocking out plans for a comprehensive program of camouflage and concealment. But they were soon drawn up short by the War Department, which took a cool attitude toward the additional expense involved. Without increased allotments district engineers were unable to employ dispersed layouts or expensive camouflage measures. Generally the best they could do was preserve vegetation at the fields.

Bradley Field, some twenty miles down the Connecticut River Valley from Westover, was the one notable exception. Providence District Engineer Lieutenant Colonel John S. Bragdon, upon taking over the project in December 1940, discarded an unsatisfactory site at Hartford selected by the Air Corps and chose one near Windsor Locks. The new location was ideal for an airport, and Bragdon wanted to make the most of it. With the help of the Assistant Chief of Engineers in charge of construction, he persuaded the Air Corps' Chief of Buildings and Grounds Division to agree to a dispersed and camouflaged layout, even though longer utility lines would add some $500,000 to costs. The General Staff was reluctant to spend the money, but finally consented on the basis that the scheme was experimental. With advice from the Engineer Board, Bragdon blended Bradley Field into its tobacco-farming environment. He scattered the buildings for housing personnel and equipment over the entire reservation, concealing some in heavy woods and gullies; and by such expedients as butting regulation army barracks buildings end to end and painting them a dark reddish-brown, made larger buildings out in the open look like the tobacco sheds that dotted the countryside. He allowed no unnecessary clearing, grading, or cutting of trees, left all existing paths and roads intact, and designed most new roads to follow the general contour of the ground. Bradley Field was about as invisible from the air as it could be made, and on the day of Pearl Harbor it was the only field in the United States built on a dispersed layout. When, a few days after the attack, the Air Corps prescribed passive protection for all air stations, Bragdon's plan was reproduced and distributed as a model.[5]

Bradley Field as it appeared from the air in the 1950s. The landing strips are visible at the upper right.

Concurrently with taking over Air Corps work, Army Engineers also began constructing civilian airfields. When Hitler's blitzkrieg across Western Europe in the spring of 1940 heightened apprehensions in the United States over its own vulnerability to attack, Air Corps bases were few and widely scattered, and not many municipal airports in the country were suitable for the use of air combat groups. Therefore in October 1940 Congress appropriated $40 million for the improvement by the Civil Aeronautics Authority of airports designated by the War and Navy departments as important to national defense. A list of these airports was worked out in joint conferences, and the Secretary of Commerce arranged with the Secretary of War for the Corps of Engineers to do the survey and construction work. Congress later appropriated almost $295 million more for this upgrading of civilian airfields.[6] Under this program, which was nearly completed by the end of 1943, the Boston and Providence districts built twenty airstrips in Maine, New Hampshire, Vermont, and Massachusetts. The work consisted mostly of laying paved runways of about 5,000-foot length. At Eastport and Bar Harbor, Maine, the airfields included seaplane ramps used by the Navy.

CIVIL AERONAUTICS AUTHORITY AIRFIELDS

Boston District

Augusta, Maine	Concord, New Hampshire
Bar Harbor, Maine	Laconia, New Hampshire
Eastport, Maine	Portsmouth, New Hampshire
Greenville, Maine	
Norridgewock, Maine	Beverly, Massachusetts
Oldtown, Maine	Norwood, Massachusetts
Sanford, Maine	
Winterport, Maine	

Providence District

Burlington, Vermont	Claremont, New Hampshire
Coventry, Vermont	Keene, New Hampshire
Rutland, Vermont	Lebanon, New Hampshire

Athol-Orange, Massachusetts[7]

Early in 1942 the New England districts prepared civilian airports at Groton and Bridgeport, Connecticut, and at Boston for immediate occupation by fighter squadrons. At the same time they constructed several aircraft warning radar stations for the I Fighter Command. These installations, which included access roads, power facilities, and housing, were part of an initial Atlantic coast radar net of fifteen stations from Maine to Virginia designed to cover vital industrial centers.[8]

When all military construction was transferred to the Corps of Engineers on December 16, 1941, the office of the Constructing Quartermaster for the New England zone was incorporated into the Boston Engineer District, and the workloads of both New England districts were further enlarged. Cantonment work accounted for a large measure of the new activity. The Engineers continued construction at New England's two large Army camps—Fort Devens in Ayer, Massachusetts, built in World War I, and Camp Edwards on Cape Cod, begun in September 1940—both of which had been scenes of large-scale building by the Quartermaster Corps. In Taunton, Massachusetts, they constructed Camp Myles Standish, the Boston Staging Area for troops departing overseas. Begun early in 1942, the camp was in operation within a few months. With large railroad yards and seven cantonment areas, it accommodated up to 50,000 soldiers at a time as they poured in from all over the country on their way to Europe. The Engineers also built Camp Wellfleet on the Atlantic shore of Cape Cod, an adjunct of Camp Edwards used for gunnery practice; they rehabilitated Fort Ethan Allen in Colchester, Vermont, an old Field Artillery post called into service for training purposes; and they performed cantonment work at each of the harbor defense areas, where sizable camps were necessary for the crews manning around the clock the installations scattered all along the coast.

Other military work involved a variety of facilities. The Engineers made renovations and alterations at the Watertown Arsenal and the Springfield Armory, remodeled mill buildings in Lowell, Massachusetts, for an ordnance plant, and constructed an ordnance depot of igloo-type magazines at Maynard, Massachusetts, for storing ammunition for Fort Devens. They repaired the Boston Army Base, a shipping terminal constructed during World War I; and since the base could not handle all the shipping scheduled from Boston, they constructed a new terminal at nearby Castle Island. The biggest port facility in New England, the Castle Island Terminal involved the construction of thousands of feet of wharfage, the laying of miles of railroad track, and the erection of numerous warehouses, barracks, and other buildings. The districts constructed several prisoner of war camps, built temporary structures or converted buildings in most major cities for use by the United Services Organization, and converted civilian buildings in numerous places for Army occupation.[9]

Castle Island Terminal. Fort Independence appears on the lower left and the Boston Army Base on the upper right.

The construction of military facilities in the United States peaked in 1942 and then rapidly declined as men, resources, and equipment were shifted from homefront preparations to supporting combat operations in the war theaters. The New England districts continued to shoulder heavy workloads, but there was greater concentration on improving existing facilities than building new ones. Notable exceptions, however, were several large hospitals constructed to care for the sick and wounded returning from overseas. In addition to station hospitals at the air bases and army camps, the districts constructed a general, two regional, and two convalescent hospitals. The hospitals were of the cantonment type. The wards, clinical rooms, quarters, messes, and other components of a plant were separate one-story buildings, with all except utility buildings joined by covered corridors. Hospitals constructed on this plan reduced fire hazards and were safer for patients, more efficient for arranging clinical facilities, more easily expandable, and less costly than conventional multistoried plants.

Although constructed on an emergency timetable, some hospitals were planned with an eye to postwar use by the Veterans Administration and were therefore of semipermanent type. Such was the Cushing General Hospital in Framingham, Massachusetts, completed by the Boston District in February 1944. Located on 110 acres of rolling countryside carved from two private estates, it was a complex of seventy-nine buildings. It had an authorized bed capacity of 1,800 and cost $5 million. "It is the finest physical layout of any hospital of its kind in the country," was the opinion of Colonel Edward A. Noyes, its commanding officer, after completing an inspection of hospitals for the Surgeon General. The project set the standards thereafter demanded by the Office of the Chief of Engineers for similar hospitals built throughout the United States. After the war it was transferred to the Veterans Administration. The Waltham Regional Hospital in Waltham, Massachusetts, was also a Type A hospital, as plants of this semipermanent design were called. Completed late in 1944, it was a 950-bed unit costing $2 million. Later it was converted into a general hospital—the Murphy Army Hospital—and in 1958 it became the headquarters of the New England En-

View of the Murphy Army Hospital, Waltham, Massachusetts, shortly after it became the headquarters of the New England Division in 1958.

140

Veterans Administration Hospitals constructed at the close of World War II

West Haven V.A. Hospital.

Manchester V.A. Hospital

Providence V.A. Hospital.

Boston V.A. Hospital

gineer Division. Both hospitals were constructed of red brick and were designed by consulting architects from plans from the Surgeon General's Office to conform to New England colonial-type architecture.[10]

When the war came to an end, the New England Division settled back to major concentration on its normal peacetime mission of navigation improvement and flood control work. Yet a healthy percentage of its workload continued to be military-related construction. Hospitals were the largest projects. In February 1946 the Veterans Administration requested the Corps of Engineers to design and construct some seventy hospitals with a capacity of about 40,000 beds. The criteria for the hospitals were worked out jointly by the Corps and the Veterans Administration, and design work was delegated to selected architect-engineer firms. In September 1946 construction began on the first hospital, a 418 bed, multistoried unit at Providence, Rhode Island. This was followed by further construction by the New England Division of 1,000-bed hospitals at Boston and at West Haven, Connecticut, and a 150-bed plant at Manchester, New Hampshire.[11] Construction for the National Guard and the Air National Guard also contributed importantly to the division's military workload in the late 1940s. It built armories for the National Guard at a number of cities throughout New England and installed facilities for the Air National Guard at Air Force fields and at the Burlington, Vermont, Airport, Barnes Field located near Westover Air Base, and Thomas Greene Field at Providence, Rhode Island.

By June 1950, while military projects continued to comprise nearly 40 percent of the workload of the division, few were of any significant size. Twenty military construction contracts and three architect-engineer contracts for the military program were in force, with a value of $3,974,687 and $901,292 respectively. In contrast, nine flood control contracts, valued at $4,287,153, and eighteen river and harbor projects, valued at $3,468,550, were in effect. The large organization that had functioned during the war had shrunk to 556 people, only 95 of whom were on military work.[12]

This pattern of activity, almost somnolent by war-year standards, was suddenly shattered when North Korean forces struck across the 38th parallel in the early morning hours of June 25, 1950, in a well-organized surprise attack on the Korean republic to the south. Within hours President Truman called for action by the United Nations Security Council, and within days the President ordered United States naval, air, and ground forces into Korea. Intelligence reports over the next few months reinforced suspicions that the attack in Korea was part of a broader Soviet plan of pressure on the West, and on December 15 Truman declared a national emergency and a program of national preparedness. The Congress and the nation were shocked into reversing the policy of hasty and severe military retrenchment that had been demanded at the close of the war and galvanized into supporting defense measures recommended by the National Security Council to balance the still growing military might of the USSR.

In the new age of long-range aircraft and missiles, New England was of prime strategic importance. Its harbors, naval stations, industries, and centers of dense population had in the past merited the heaviest concentration of coastal fortifications in the country. Now a new strategic element was added. Air attacks and retaliations, if they should come, would be made over the arctic circle, which pinpointed New England as a key area for measures both of defense and deterrence. The workload of the New England Division quickly reflected the new situation. By September 1951 the number of military construction contracts had jumped to fifty-six and their value to $55,420,174, and the number of architect-engineer contracts for military projects had increased to thirty-three, with a value of $2,169,495. Conversely, contracts for flood control and river and harbor work had dropped from twenty-seven to twenty-two, with a value of $3,673,506 and $1,832,097 respectively. The personnel of the division had been nearly doubled in size, with two-thirds of a force of 1065 people employed on military projects.

The Cold War building program so hastily put into force continued without letup for nearly a decade, during which the New England Division constructed a congeries of military installations and allied facilities the magnitude of which could not have been visualized even in the years of World War II.

The urgency of the enlarged military program meant putting new policies into effect, many of which were established by the Office of the Chief of Engineers. Reverting to practice followed during the war, the division began to use negotiated contracts on large military jobs in order to minimize the risk of unsatisfactory performances at a time when speed and successful prosecution of projects was essential. Competition was still maintained by soliciting proposals from a number of carefully selected contractors whose capabilities and resources made it reasonably certain that they could finish their projects within specified time limits. The New England Division Engineer could select contractors without reference to the Chief of Engineers and could award contracts up to $15 million. This greatly exceeded even the decentralized practices followed at the height of wartime building activity, when division engineers had been empowered to approve negotiated contracts up to $5 million. To limit as much as possible the expansion of the normal engineering organization of the division in the new burst of military construction, greater use was made of architect-engineer firms, with whom the division engineer could negotiate contracts up to $500,000.[13]

In the selection of architect-engineers and contractors, New England firms were chosen whenever possible, and efforts were made to give contracts to firms in the general vicinity of a project. Since jobs were often larger than local contractors could handle, the policy could not be rigidly applied, but this fact did not prevent complaints about the use of out-of-state contractors. A case in point was the Loring Air Force Base in Limestone, Maine, the largest single project of the New England Division. Maine officials were openly critical of the award of multimillion-dollar contracts on the base to firms from Massachusetts and other states. Writing to the governor of Maine, Division Engineer Colonel Henry J. Woodbury pointed out that if all Maine contractors registered with the division devoted their entire construction potential to nothing but Corps projects, they would be capable of accomplishing only about 25 percent of the Corps' program in that state. Moreover, Woodbury continued, Maine contractors, singly or in combination, were invariably invited to submit proposals for work in the state and were awarded contracts when they submitted the lowest proposals. The governor, at least, was apparently convinced that Maine contractors were not being shortchanged.[14]

A major component of the defense program in New England was the construction of Air Force bases. The heart of each base was its long runway, but it took a gigantic framework of support facilities to make it operational. Control towers, hangars, hardstands, taxiways, communications equipment, airfield lighting, maintenance shops, warehouses, fuel storage areas, and numerous other structures were necessary to operate and service airplanes. Barracks, quarters, mess halls, family housing, hospitals, dental clinics, administration buildings, readiness rooms, and training facilities were required for base personnel. The amenities of civilized living demanded chapels, libraries, laundries, commissaries, recreational facilities, and water-supply, heating, and sewage-treatment plants.

Five New England airfields were constructed or almost wholly rebuilt for the Strategic Air Command, whose long-range planes capable of delivering nuclear bombs were for some time the nation's principal weapons of deterrence. Loring Air Force Base in Limestone, Maine, was the first and largest of the bases constructed. Located at the northeasternmost point of the United States, it was started in May 1947, before the emergency program was inaugurated, and was the first air base in the country designed for the B-36 bomber, a plane of 12,000-mile range and a gross weight of 300,000 pounds.

Loring was constructed on 9,000 acres of scrub woodland previously intruded upon only by a few scattered potato farms and two dirt roads. The project was far from labor markets, and it was necessary for contractors to import practically all the skilled mechanics and much of the common labor employed. To house at least a portion of the work force, barracks, mess halls, and recreation buildings were moved from the abandoned wartime air base at Houlton, sixty-five miles away. Because of Limestone's remote location and severe winter climate, many workers were reluctant to accept jobs there, and of all projects of the division, it was Loring which suffered the most severe manpower shortages. When the military construction program was accelerated in 1951, efforts to recruit engineers and inspectors in the vicinity of Boston resulted in eight out of ten prospects declining to work at Limestone. A recruiting officer of the division, whose trip was preceded by a campaign of newspaper publicity, spent two weeks in Maine trying to hire construction inspectors. Since most employees had to find living accommodations off the base, the shortage and quality of rooms for rent in the nearby small towns did not ease the task of recruiting. In March 1951 a single room could be obtained in Limestone for $5 a week. In September the same room cost $15.[15]

The runway at Loring, a strip more than two miles long and one hundred yards wide, was designed for wheel loads of 150,000 pounds. This normally would have required the most careful construction, with top quality materials, of a pavement and subgrades over two feet deep. But conditions at Limestone necessitated a runway depth three times greater. Much of the soil in New England is glacial till. It is subject to frost action, which heaves pavements and greatly weakens bearing capacities during spring thaws. The average annual snowfall in the area of Limestone is over ninety inches, and the temperature drops to minus thirty degrees. The freezing period normally extends from November to April, with the destructive frost melting period ending about the middle of May. These conditions meant that the average frost penetration was about seventy inches. Therefore in building the runway, aprons, and taxiways of the base, earth was removed to a depth of six feet, entailing more than two million cubic yards of excavation, and replaced with a base course of gravel. Explorations turned up an adequate source of aggregates about two miles from the base, which could be procured without excessive costs. The gravel had to be washed to reduce fines smaller than .02 millimeter, which would be subject to frost action. But it was physically

Washing the face of gravel deposits before excavating to reduce fines subject to frost action in materials used in the base courses of the runway, taxiway, and aprons of the Loring Air Force Base.

impossible to wash in commercial gravel treatment plants, in one working season of five months, the huge amount of gravel required. Yankee ingenuity solved the problem. A beaver pond in a nearby stream was enlarged to supply water, which was directed by hydraulic jets against the face of the deposits before excavating, thus washing the gravel to a gradation within allowable limits. The gravel was laid in approximately twelve-inch layers and compacted with rollers. Over this was laid nine inches of crushed stone topped by three inches of hot asphalt pavement. Perforated pipe drains were laid in the subgrade under both edges of the pavement for the length of the runway to provide an outlet for any possible seepage, thereby insuring a dry base course.

The main hangar at Loring is a mammoth arch-ribbed monolithic structure of reinforced concrete, with an unobstructed interior 300 feet square. When completed in 1949, it was one of the largest hangars in the world, big enough to accommodate two B-36s. The design was adopted to provide maximum

Aerial view of the runway and taxiway, Loring Air Force Base, October 1950.

Arch-ribbed concrete hangar at Loring Air Force Base under construction, September 1948.

fire resistance and minimum form cost. Its huge ribs, 5 to 7 feet deep and 20 to 24 inches wide, are spaced 25 feet on center and have a clear span of 240 feet and a clear height of 90 feet. They were poured one after another in a single form mounted on tracks and jacks, which was slid down the length of the hangar, with a pour being made about every three weeks.

Eventually twenty-six steel-shelled multipurpose hangars were also built at Loring, each large enough to enclose the nose and wings of a big bomber needing maintenance or repair. To supply the base with fuel, a 200-mile-long pipeline was laid to Searsport, Maine, where a tank farm was constructed to receive oil from tankers. Other buildings and utilities made the field a self-

146

sufficient community. Barracks were constructed for 4,600 airmen and housing for 1,750 families. A 100-bed hospital, a dental clinic, a grade school for 1,750 pupils, a community center, a commissary, a 1,000-seat theater, a gymnasium, and various other facilities provide essential services. Heating is supplied through a unique high-pressure hot water system by which water of

New England Division personnel on an inspection tour of Loring Air Force Base, 1951. Left to right: (front) John Wm. Leslie, Chief, Military Branch; Christopher Murray, Chief, Construction Division; Eugene Groden, Chief, Design Branch; John Allen, Chief, Engineering Division; (behind, clockwise) Ralph Hitchings, Mechanical Engineer; Leonard H. Foley, Mechanical Engineer; John Eklund, Chief, Supervision and Inspection Branch; Donald Mills, Resident Engineer; Lt. Col. E. Flanders, Area Engineer; William Smith, Jr., Construction Division; Richard Payzant, Construction Division. Eklund, Smith, and Payzant (in uniform) were on active duty with the U.S. Army Reserve. Courtesy of William Smith, Jr.

A double cantilever hangar of the type first constructed at Pease Air Force Base, Portsmouth, New Hampshire, dwarfs the original main hangar at Loring Air Force Base, September 1956.

Laying concrete pavement at Loring Air Force Base, August 1958.

temperatures to 400 degrees Fahrenheit is pumped from a central heating plant to the buildings, where it passes through heat exchangers that reduce its pressure and can adjust its temperature for heating or convert it to steam for cooking and other uses. Water is furnished by deep wells capable of supplying 1.8 million gallons a day. It is pumped from the wells through carbon purifying tanks into an underground reservoir of one million gallon capacity and from the reservoir by booster pumps into the distribution system. These and other facilities, including an Air Force communications center, Globecom, located offsite, represented a government investment of more than $100 million.[16]

At Bangor, Maine, New England Division engineers rebuilt Dow Field into another massive SAC base for modern jet aircraft. After World War II the base had been returned to the City of Bangor, but the exigencies of the Cold War caused the Air Force to take it over again. The division strengthened its runway and lengthened it to 13,500 feet, constructed new buildings, and in other ways carried out a multimillion-dollar project of enlargement and modernization. Westover Field, which became the headquarters of SAC's 8th Air Force, was similarly modernized by the rebuilding of runways and the construction of giant hangars, reconnaissance technical laboratories, and other facilities. Nearby, as an adjunct to the command headquarters, the division installed an underground combat operations center. At Presque Isle, the division transformed the World War II airfield into a modern SAC fighter support base.[17]

Pease Air Force Base at Portsmouth, New Hampshire, started in 1954, was the fifth base constructed by the division for the Strategic Air Command. Located only three miles from the heart of the city, it was built on the site of the municipal airport and adjacent farmland. The base boasts a runway 11,320 feet long and 300 feet wide, a main parking apron 8,800 feet long and 1,100 feet wide, and smaller hangar aprons covering 120,000 square yards. Including 1,000-foot-long warm-up pads at each end of the runway, parking areas for planes at Pease cover 1.5 million square yards. In keeping with latest Air Force criteria, they were constructed with fourteen-inch-thick portland cement concrete pavements. Because of the large spillage of fuel and oil on aprons, bituminous concrete did not stand up as well as portland cement, and the Air Force was willing to pay the extra cost of construction, which the Engineers had determined would be less than five percent.

View of Pease Air Force Base under construction, June 1956, showing the enormous size of the main parking apron. Automobiles are parked on the far end.

The project at Pease included the numerous buildings and utilities required for operating scores of airplanes and quartering thousands of airmen. But the most impressive structure of the base is its 600-by-250-foot double cantilever hangar. The vertical supports of the hangar are four steel-frame towers, each about 60 feet square, located along the center line of the building. From the tops of the towers, cantilever trusses jut out 93.5 feet on either side. Connecting the cantilever trusses are longitudinal arch trusses, each spanning 120 feet. A roof of steel decking, steel siding, and six electrically operated sliding steel doors, each 65 feet high, enclose the hangar. The concrete arch hangar completed at Limestone a half-dozen years before was at that time considered huge because it could accommodate three medium or two heavy bombers. The double cantilever hangar at Portsmouth can house six medium or five heavy bombers.[18]

The SAC bases constructed by the New England Division were instruments in that command's mission of posing the primary deterrent to enemy aggression through retaliatory strike capability. For more purely defensive measures, the division constructed three major types of installations. These were airfields for the Air Defense Command and other air units, aircraft warning stations, and missile batteries.

Otis Field on Cape Cod, Laurence G. Hanscom Field at Bedford, Massa-

chusetts, and Ethan Allen Field at Burlington, Vermont, were the major installations of the Air Defense Command. At each field the division constructed runways and hangars, administration buildings and maintenance
shops, airmen's dormitories and family housing, and all the other operational
and living facilities that make up a large air base. At Ethan Allan Field the
operational facilities of the fighter base were built across the runway from
the Burlington Airport buildings, while the housing area was located at Fort
Ethan Allen, about four miles away in Colchester. Of nineteenth century
vintage, the former Field Artillery post possessed substantial brick buildings
that were renovated, and new structures, including a modern hospital, were
added. At Grenier Air Force Base, and at a number of Air National Guard
installations, the division carried out similar but less extensive projects of
modernization.[19]

Alert Hangars for fighter planes at Ethan Allen Field, Burlington, Vermont.

Air National Guard facilities at Barnes Field, Massachusetts.

The aircraft warning stations were elements in the first and southernmost of three radar lines constructed across the continent—the Pine Tree Line, lying wholly within the United States, the Mid-Canada Line, and the Distant Early Warning (DEW) Line. Construction on the Pine Tree Line began before the outbreak of hostilities in Korea and was accelerated in the fall of 1950 on instructions from the Office of the Chief of Engineers. The stations built by the New England Division looped around the eastern and northern perimeters of New England from North Truro on Cape Cod to Saint Albans on Lake Champlain, with intermediate stations at Charleston, Bucks Harbor, and Caswell, Maine, and at North Concord, Vermont. At Topsham, Maine, the division constructed a large control center that tied together the eastern stations of the Pine Tree Line. Each station, in addition to its search and tracking radar towers, was equipped with various buildings and utilities to accommodate about one hundred airmen. Between the manned stations and at several interior locations, the division later constructed "gap fillers."

Aircraft warning station, North Truro, Massachusetts.

These were remote-controlled installations consisting of a radar tower and a small cement equipment building, positioned so as to detect planes that might penetrate under the radar sweeps of the main stations by coming in low from the sea or along major river valleys. In 1957 the aircraft warning stations became part of the defense mechanism of the North American Air Defense Command (NORAD), when that command was created to combine United States and Canadian defense units into a single system.[20]

Early in the 1950s the New England Division constructed emplacements for radar-controlled 75 millimeter antiaircraft batteries, called Skysweeps, near Loring and Dow Air Force bases; and it strung facilities for 90 millimeter antiaircraft guns in a ring around Boston extending from Lynn on the north to Hull on the south. These defenses were soon succeeded by Nike Ajax missiles. The first surface-to-air guided missile to go into service in the United States, the Nike Ajax became operational in 1953. Named after Nike, the Greek Goddess of Victory, and Ajax, a fleet-footed hero of the Trojan

War, the missile was a finned cylinder twelve inches in diameter and twenty feet long, fired by a booster rocket, that could travel at supersonic speed for a range of approximately twenty-five miles.

Each Nike battery had its own acquisition and tracking radar facilities for picking up a target, locking on it, and guiding the missile designated to destroy it. While each battery could thus operate independently, and battery commanders were responsible for the decision to launch a missile, all battery capabilities were normally coordinated through a fire direction system known as "Missile Master." This was a command installation with an electronic brain for integrating the fire of Nike missiles throughout an extensive defense area. Its computers collected and stored and instantaneously evaluated and transmitted essential target data to consoles manned by battery commanders.

Nike Ajax missiles guarding the Boston Defense Area poised on a launching rack at Nahant, Massachusetts.

During the mid-1950s the New England Division constructed thirty-five Nike Ajax batteries that encircled the strategic military or industrial areas of Limestone, Boston, Providence, Hartford, and Bridgeport. Each battery consisted of a launcher site and a control site, located about a mile apart on high ground to provide uninterrupted radar sweeps and a direct line of sight between them. Facilities at the launcher site included underground storage pits with elevators to lift missiles onto launching racks, towers for acquisition and tracking radars, a fallout shelter, and various service buildings. The control site contained operational and living facilities for the battery's eight officers and 101 enlisted men. At Quincy, Massachusetts, and New Britain, Connecticut, the division constructed Battalion and Group Headquarters for the Boston and Bridgeport-Hartford defense areas respectively. At Fort

Heath in Winthrop, Massachusetts, it built a bombproof, fallout-proof Missile Master unit for coordinating all Nike batteries in the Northeast.

In 1960 the New England Division, because it had already assembled considerable data on the subject, was selected by the Office of the Chief of Engineers to propose measures for controlling hazards to construction posed by the electromagnetic radiation emitters of the Nike sites and aircraft

The control area for the Hull-Weymouth Nike installation was built on the World War II casemates of Fort Duvall in Boston Harbor. Courtesy of Gerald Butler.

Missile Master at Fort Heath, Winthrop, Massachusetts.

warning stations. In the same year the division began converting some ten Ajax sites to accommodate the more potent Nike Hercules, a missile that could carry a nuclear warhead and had more than triple the range and altitude capabilities of its predecessor. Since the Hercules was larger than the Ajax and had an improved guidance system, modifications were made on both launcher and radar facilities.[21] Both generations of Nike missiles, however, soon became obsolete as the threat from air strikes shifted in the mid-1960s from aircraft to intercontinental ballistic missiles.

The Nikes were weapons of the Army Air Defense Command. The Air Force also developed missiles, its first surface-to-air weapon, the Bomarc, becoming operational in 1959. Forty-seven feet long, with a wing span of eighteen feet, and propelled by twin ram-jet engines, the Bomarc could attain an altitude of 60,000 feet and strike at incoming aircraft at distances of over 200 miles. Believing it vital to national defense, the Air Force urged installation of the weapon at top speed. Accordingly, the New England Division rushed construction of Bomarc batteries at Dow and Otis fields, turning them over to the Air Force late in 1959 and early in 1960. At Otis Field the Air Force immediately converted the Bomarcs from liquid to solid fuel propulsion, entailing additional work on the launcher facilities that was completed in February 1962.[22] Twenty-eight launcher shelters were constructed at each field, and each battery was equipped with a power, heating, and air-conditioning plant and other service buildings. The shelters, measuring about sixty feet long, twenty-four feet wide, and twelve feet high, were made

Bomarc launcher shelters nearing completion at Otis Air Force Base, July 1959.

of reinforced concrete and fitted on top with massive steel biparting doors. The doors were opened and the big missile was raised into firing position in about ten seconds by a mechanism of watchmaker's precision, powered by hydraulic rams, designed by the Boeing Aircraft Company, which developed the Bomarc. Not all engineering problems, however, had been fully solved. Getting the mechanism to work properly, and making the doors weathertight, essential to maintaining a precise air-conditioned environment for the missiles, required considerable cooperative effort by division engineers and Boeing representatives. Among the most hastily constructed projects, the Bomarcs were also among the most ephemeral of Cold War installations.

They were hardly completed when, like the Nike batteries, they were made obsolete by ICBMs.

At the same time the division was installing Bomarcs at Dow and Otis fields, it was constructing facilities for Snark missiles at Presque Isle Air Force Base. The first American intercontinental missile, the Snark was a weapon of the Strategic Air Command. Over sixty-seven feet long, with a diameter of fifteen feet and a wing span of forty-two feet, it had a range of about 5,000 miles. The Snark installation at Presque Isle, the only one constructed in the country, consisted essentially of several assembly and maintenance buildings with nearby launcher pads from which missiles mounted on mobile launchers could be fired. The Snark, however, was a guided missile with limited speed and capabilities, and in the rapid evolution of missile technology it was outmoded almost before the Presque Isle installation was completed.

Artist's rendering of the Snark Missile Facility, Presque Isle Air Force Base, Maine.

The airfields, the aircraft warning stations, and the missile batteries built in the 1950s attested to the highly technical nature of modern military establishments. Not only did the armed services rely on sophisticated weaponry and equipment, they had to be prepared to operate in climates and under conditions in which their experience was limited. Consequently, a large part of the military program of the New England Division after 1950 was the construction of research facilities for the Air Force and the Army. Even before this, however, New England engineers had themselves become engaged in a vital research activity.

At airfields constructed in northern states during the war, Army Engineers had combatted frost action by highway methods of insulating subgrades with blankets of well-drained sand and gravel. Sometimes this worked and sometimes not, and no one knew for certain why. Upon building roads and airfields in northwestern Canada and Alaska, the Engineers encountered a phenomenon new to their experience—permanently frozen ground, or "permafrost." Permafrost carries over it a thin layer of soil that thaws in the summer and freezes again in the winter. Construction operations disturbed the delicate natural thermal regime of the annual freeze and thaw cycle, which triggered actions and reactions that were complex and unpredictable. The Engineers were beset by mudflows, landslides, cave-ins, gullies, cracks, and blisters, which they overcame only by the hard way of trial and error. The first Corps studies of frost and permafrost began on a small scale in 1943, when the Missouri River Division investigated several airfield failures caused by heaving and thawing and the Office of the Chief of Engineers produced a primer on permafrost compiled from Russian sources. The next year the Corps launched a vigorous effort to find out how to build on permafrost.

Early in 1944 General Henry H. Arnold, Chief of the Army Air Corps, forecast the North Pole as the future center of strategy and declared cold regions research "most important and urgent." The response of the Corps of Engineers was immediate. Beginning with frost investigations at Dow Field in Bangor, Corps research activity quickly mushroomed to include observations and tests at ten northern air bases, experiments at Harvard University, and various theoretical studies—all under the direction of the chief of the Boston District Soils Laboratory, Harvard-trained soils engineer William L. Shannon. Continuing to expand, Corps efforts soon included wholesale translations of Soviet publications on permafrost, the collection of soils and meteorological data at Alaskan air bases and subarctic weather stations, geological explorations north of the arctic circle, attempts to locate permafrost by aerial photography and geophysical methods, and soils studies at Purdue University and the University of Minnesota.[23]

By the end of 1944 what had begun as a crash program of investigation was metamorphasizing into permanent institutions of research. A Soils, Foundation and Frost Effects Laboratory, headed by Shannon, was established at Boston, and the next year the Corps set up a Permafrost Division in the St. Paul District. In 1953 the two research centers were consolidated into the Artic Construction Frost Effects Laboratory (ACFEL), located in the Boston District. ACFEL's mission, like that of the earlier laboratory at Boston, was to conduct investigations relating to the design, construction, operation, and maintenance of installations on frozen ground and ice.[24]

At airfields in northern states, in Greenland, Alaska, and other regions of the arctic and subarctic, members of the Boston-based laboratories carried out studies on the properties and behavior of frost, frozen soils, snow, and ice. They experimented with the construction of airfields, roads, and buildings on ice and permafrost, and they developed an arctic construction manual for the guidance of engineers tackling jobs in cold regions. Putting their know-how directly to use, they advised the North Atlantic Division on construction problems at Thule Air Force Base, built in the early 1950s in northern Greenland, nine hundred miles from the North Pole. Buildings at Thule, to prevent their thawing the permafrost beneath them and sinking into the ground, were insulated from the soil by air. The lighter buildings were erected on wooden, non-heat-conducting stilts, and were anchored with concrete weights to prevent their being blown away by the region's hurricane winds. Heavier steel-framed structures like hangars and machine shops were also built on wooden pilings, and their floors were further insulated by thousands of feet of twelve-inch pipe, which was closed in the summer to keep the warm air out and opened in the winter to let the cold air in.[25] The New England Division's cold region specialists also advised the North Atlantic Division on the installation of DEW Line aircraft warning stations on the Greenland icecap and contributed to the design of an experimental nuclear-powered undersnow city constructed by the Corps on the icecap 138 miles from Thule.

In 1951, when the threat of attack over the North Pole came even more to the forefront of concern after the invasion of South Korea, the Corps of Engineers created another research organization, the Snow, Ice, and Permafrost Research Establishment (SIPRE) at Wilmette, Illinois. SPIRE's mission was research in the mechanical and physical properties of snow and ice. In 1963 SIPRE and ACFEL were combined into a single research center known as the Cold Regions Research and Engineering Laboratory, or CRREL, located at Hanover, New Hampshire.

Construction of the new laboratory for the CRREL team at Hanover was begun by the division in April 1960 and completed in June 1963. Conspicuous among the laboratory's furnishings is a series of cold rooms for testing military materials in which temperatures can be lowered to -58 degrees Fehrenheit by an environmental system containing 175 tons of refrigerant.[26]

Although costing $3 million, the CRREL laboratory was a small project compared to the Quartermaster Research and Engineering Center at Natick, Massachusetts, built by the division for the Army Materiel Command. The original installation, begun in 1952, was a group of laboratories designed for developing clothing, equipment, and materials suitable for worldwide military operations. Included in the facilities was a Climatic Research Chamber consisting of experiment rooms and living quarters equipped with air conditioning systems that could simulate either arctic or tropic conditions. In 1963 the center was expanded to include laboratory facilities for the Chicago Food and Container Institute, which developed and tested food and packaging materials for military use and space explorations. Continuing to add research tools to the center, the division had by 1970 constructed an animal laboratory, a heavy equipment laboratory and development building, a blast freeze facility, a microbiology laboratory, an environmental medicine laboratory, and a solar furnace, the last being a system of mirrors for concentrating the sun's rays to produce tremendously high temperatures.[27]

Other laboratories for the Army were constructed at the Watertown Arsenal. The division remodeled buildings of the ordnance plant, which was wholly phased out in 1967, and installed facilities for basic metalurgical research. An important aspect of this work was the construction of a nuclear reactor for utilizing neutrons in investigations of the prime structure of matter.[28]

Construction of research facilities for the Army was more than matched by the kindred program carried out for the Air Force. The division's initial project was a Climatic Projects Research Laboratory on the summit of Mount Washington, New Hampshire, built for the Air Force Research and Development Command. Its purpose was to test jet engines under icy storm conditions. Planning for the laboratory began in fiscal year 1951, and workmen started construction on the windy mountaintop in June 1953. The laboratory and an accompanying two-story dormitory to house its personnel

Cold Regions Research and Engineering Laboratory (CRREL) at Hanover, New Hampshire.

This photo gives an idea of the size and complexity of CRREL's main refrigeration unit.

A laboratory of the Army Quartermaster Research and Engineering Center, Natick, Massachusetts.

Nuclear reactor under construction at the
Watertown Arsenal, November 1959.

were designed to withstand winds up to two hundred miles an hour and temperatures that fall far below zero. Concrete foundations two feet thick were anchored to rock by steel rods, and metal-covered panels of corrugated insulating material were welded to steel frames to form the walls and roofs of the buildings. Doors thirty feet square on either side of the laboratory allowed test engines to be exposed to the icy blasts generally prevailing on the barren summit. In addition to the construction of the laboratory and dormitory, the project required the rehabilitation of the famous Mount Washington cog railroad and the automobile road to the summit in order to carry up materials, the erection of temporary barracks on the top for workmen, and the construction of base operations buildings at the foot of the mountain.[29]

In fiscal year 1952 the division began work on a very much larger Air Force research center at Hanscom Field in Bedford, Massachusetts. Enlarged upon several times in succeeding years, the center consists of two groups of geophysics and electronics laboratories. One complex of laboratories, libraries, shops, and administration buildings became the permanent home of the Air Force Cambridge Research Center, which probes into such areas as meteorological and astronomical phenomena and optical and solid-state physics. The other group of laboratories and ancillary facilities, known as the Lincoln Laboratory, was constructed for use by the Massachusetts Institute of Technology, which under contract to the Air Force conducts basic and applied research in radar and electronics.

The Bedford Research Center was nearly matched in size by the Connecticut Aircraft Nuclear Engine Laboratory (CANEL), constructed between 1955 and 1957 in Middletown, Connecticut. A complex of over a dozen laboratory, service, administration, and utility buildings, the facility was designed for use by the Pratt & Whitney Aircraft Corporation for developing nuclear aircraft propulsion plants. Since research was to focus heavily on liquid-metal circulating systems, several laboratories were equipped with large liquid-metal furnaces and with special apparatus for testing, under a large range of simulated conditions, liquid-metal to air radiators and liquid-metal to liquid-metal heat exchangers.[30]

Another research facility constructed by the New England Division for the Air Force was the New Boston Tracking Station, designed to receive information from satellites. Located in a small town in rural New Hampshire, the installation included both sophisticated radar equipment and dining accommodations for a sizable contingent of Air Force personnel. Provisions for quartering the station's personnel were made by renovating buildings at Grenier Field in Manchester, some fifteen miles away.

Huge airfields, missile batteries, and research laboratories were among the more notable military projects of the 1950s and 1960s, but the New England Division also busied itself extensively with renovating and improving more commonplace Army installations. Soon after the outbreak of hostilities in Korea, the division constructed emergency-type infantry training facilities at Camp Edwards and Camp Wellfleet, while at Fort Devens it built rail training facilities for personnel of the Transportation Corps. At Camp Myles Standish it constructed new warehouses, shops, and other buildings in addition to rehabilitating the camp's utility systems, roads, and railroads. At the Springfield Armory it built new test ranges, constructed a new railhead, and

Research Library of the Air Force Cambridge Research Center, Hanscom Air Force Base.

Plasma Laboratory of the Air Force Cambridge Research Center, Hanscom Air Force Base.

A radome under construction at the New Boston,
New Hampshire, Tracking Station, May 1961.

rebuilt structures to adapt them to new production methods. It constructed
NCO family quarters and four new Type A wards at the Murphy General
Hospital in Waltham.[31] At Fort Banks in Winthrop, Massachusetts, it constructed administrative, housing, and other buildings necessary to headquar-
ter the region's Army Defense Command.

Fort Devens became the scene of a large amount of work by the division.
Almost every year of the 1950s and 1960s saw new construction to imple-
ment an Army plan for replacing the hastily built facilities of the two World
Wars with improved permanent structures. Every type of post facility, from
barracks to fire stations, from commissaries to hospitals, was included in the
program. This upgrading of facilities was motivated in part by a desire to
encourage longer careers in a service becoming increasingly technical and
specialized. Indicative of this aspect of the program was the supersedure of
traditional sixty-three-man open barracks by dormitory-style buildings. The
first of the new type quarters accommodate eight men to a room; later dormitories constructed at Devens house only two men to a room. Air Force
bases saw the same changes. Dormitories constructed by the division at
Hanscom Field house two enlisted men to a room and provide a fully
equipped tile bath and shower for every four men.

Longer careers did become more common as the military became more
challenging and rewarding, which increased the need for family housing at
military posts. At Fort Devens the division provided accommodations for
2,400 families. Half of these homes were so-called "Capehart Housing"
units. In 1955 Congress extensively amended the National Housing Act of
1943. Under one section of the act, drafted by Senator Homer E. Capehart
of Indiana, the Secretary of Defense was authorized to enter into contracts
with eligible builders for the construction of urgently needed housing on or

A Chapel at Fort Devens.

Enlisted men's barracks at Fort Devens.

near military reservations. To finance this construction of large but uncertain size without direct federal appropriations, the law provided for the negotiation by the builders of private loans guaranteed by the government. As in other projects, the Corps was responsible for designing the houses and acting as the supervisory agent between the builder and the Army command receiving the Capehart units. The 1,200 units built at Fort Devens were turned over to the Army in April 1962. The division also supervised the construction of 540 Capehart units at twenty-six locations for personnel assigned to Nike batteries, and another 35 units at Hudson, Massachusetts, for soldiers attached to the Quartermaster Laboratory at Natick.[32]

Capehart housing units at Fort Devens.

Another aspect of the preparedness program launched in the early 1950s was the construction of Army Reserve Training Centers. The division built them in some twenty-eight towns and cities, in all six New England states. Most of the centers, which were designed to accommodate from 200 to 1,000 reservists, were substantial brick-faced edifices equipped in the manner of school buildings with classrooms, auditoriums, gymnasiums, and other facilities. In some instances large buildings, such as former automobile dealers garages, were leased and renovated. The division also continued improving National Guard installations by constructing headquarters, renovating armories, and adding service buildings, motor pools, and utilities.[33]

A project more challenging from an engineering point of view was the rehabilitation of the Boston Army Base in 1955-56. Built during World War I as a storage and shipping terminal, it consisted of an eight-story warehouse 1,638 feet long and 126 feet wide, a two-story wharf shed the same length and 100 feet wide, a pier shed 924 feet long and 100 feet wide, a four-story administration building, a powerhouse, and a wharf and pier that stretched along the Reserved Channel of Boston Harbor for 5,400 feet. Its construction had been an engineering marvel of speedy accomplishment. Begun in April 1918, it was more than 90 percent completed by December.

While most of the buildings of the base rested on cement caissons or concrete piles sunk into fill on reclaimed flats, the wharf and pier, because of the need for haste, were built on wooden piles. Oak piles were usually used

Boston Army Base under construction, 1918.

in Boston Harbor, but because they could not be obtained in sufficient quantity—30,000 were needed—piles of untreated southern pine were employed.[34] The piles might still have lasted for years had not a crustacean borer, whose activity had been at a low level for some time, moved back into Boston Harbor in force. By 1935 the piles had been so badly attacked that the wharf was repaired as a WPA project under direction of the Constructing Quartermaster. Hundreds of piles were replaced or repaired, a steel sheet pile bulkhead was placed along the whole 5,600-foot perimeter of the wharf and pier, and the enclosed area was packed with sand. In 1945-46 further repairs were made; but in 1953 trouble was again discovered. The sheet piling had corroded, sand was washing out through holes, and marine borers were again attacking the wooden piles. Investigations by the New England Division revealed that corrosion of the bulkhead was progressing too rapidly to be halted by any stopgap method, and rehabilitation would be expensive. Since the base had been leased at the close of World War II to private parties and was not considered necessary for government use, the Army considered abandoning it. Thereupon Boston interests, faced with the loss of a major shipping facility, hastened to Washington. Their entreaties, the fact that repairs were necessary in any case since the base could not be left to fall into the channel, and the possibility that it might again be useful in a national emergency, prompted Congress to take action. The Army was authorized to rehabilitate the wharf and pier structures at a cost not to exceed $11 million and lease the facilities to the Commonwealth of Massachusetts, which was to bear 10 percent of the expense.

Division engineers explored a number of rehabilitation schemes, boiled them down to four for further study, and finally decided upon a concrete gravity-type seawall placed against the existing steel sheet pile bulkhead.

The wall, more than a mile long and fifty-two feet high, rises from thirty-five feet below mean low water to seventeen feet above that mark. Supported by steel H piles driven into rock, it measures twenty-seven feet wide at the base, slopes back on its front face to a thickness of eight feet at the mean high water line, and then juts back out for twenty-seven feet to form a cantilever deck. According to the chief engineer of the contractor for the job, the physical proportions of the wall and the problems involved in building the underwater molded form made the project a unique construction "first" in terms of underwater concreting.[35]

Throughout the 1950s the New England Division expended an average of about $100 million annually on military and civil work. From $25 million in FY 1950, the annual workload rose to a peak of $137 million for FY 1956. Military work that year accounted for $105 million, while civil work, which took a big leap with the revival of flood control and navigation projects, ran to $32 million. Military construction then began to shrink; first that for the Army, which reached its maximum in 1956 at the height of the Nike program, followed in the next few years by drastic drops in the Air Force program, which had been over three times as large. In April 1960 Division Engineer Alden K. Sibley wrote to the Chief of Engineers: "For the first time in many years my civil works personnel requirement exceeds the military personnel requirement."[36]

Except for the installation of ICBM facilities in certain areas, the military building program in the United States was tapering down, and the workload of the New England Division inevitably declined with it. By FY 1964 the workload had dropped to $44 million. Civil work, representing $29.2 million, had remained fairly steady; but military work was down to $14.8 million. The next year the military workload was only $10 million; and in FY 1966, because of a sudden cancellation of work by the Department of Defense in December 1965, it dropped to about $5 million.[37]

The division's personnel had by 1964 been trimmed from the 1958 peak of 1,750 people to 945, and further reductions in force had to follow. Worried over loss in capability in its Engineering Division, the division sought work in and from other engineering districts. In April 1965 Acting Division Engineer Colonel Edward J. Ribbs reported to the Chief of Engineers that twelve of his people had spent ninety days at the San Francisco District helping with post flood work, three had been in Alaska for ninety days, and one was currently in Okinawa investigating a proposed water supply dam, for which the division would prepare the survey report for the Okinawa District. Engineers had also been sent on short periods of duty to Somalia and to Korea to give engineering assistance in construction, Ribbs further reported, and ten engineers were reviewing the design of the Keban Dam in Turkey for the Agency for International Development. When the dam in Okinawa was constructed, the resident engineer was assigned from the New England Division. The division also designed the Bloomington Dam on the upper Potomac River for the Baltimore District and planned the underground electrical distribution system for the Smithsonian Astrophysical Observatory at Mount Hopkins, Arizona.[38]

More important in offsetting the losses in Army and Air Force construction were two large projects taking shape at home. One was an Emergency

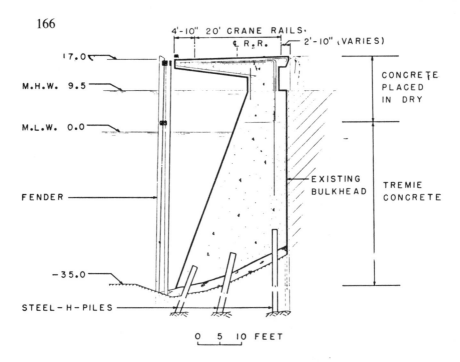

CAST - IN - PLACE GRAVITY WALL

ARMY BASE - SOUTH BOSTON , MASS.

FAY, SPOFFORD & THORNDIKE - ENGINEERS

FIG. 3.

Cross section of the gravity seawall constructed at the Boston Army Base.

Aerial view of the Boston Army Base, May 1960.

Operating Center for the Office of Civil Defense, Region I; the other was an Electronics Research Center for the National Aeronautics and Space Administration.

Construction of the Emergency Operating Center began in October 1966 and was completed in March 1968.[39] Located underground in Maynard, Massachusetts, the center was built by cutting away the side of a hill, constructing a two-story reinforced concrete building, and moving earth back over the structure. One of ten such centers in the United States, it was designed to become the headquarters of civil defense, military, and governmental operations throughout the Northeast and Caribbean territories in the event of an extreme military emergency. Fitted with all necessities from its own power source and water supply to dormitories and a kitchen, and equipped with communications systems supported by multiple back-up units to guard against failures, the Emergency Operating Center can provide living and working facilities for three hundred people.

The Electronics Research Center was a far bigger project, with promise of becoming one of the largest in the division's history. Preconstruction planning on the center began in the summer of 1963, when NASA requested the division to conduct studies of eighty-nine suggested sites for a location in the Boston area. For a few months, however, the studies remained in low gear until a political storm in Congress over the center subsided. Since millions would be spent on constructing the center and more millions annually on research, and because questions arose as to why NASA was doing so much for Massachusetts, Congress ordered NASA to justify the undertaking and the choice of Boston. When NASA stuck to its position that "no place was equal to Boston" for a research center and gave assurances that the center would farm out research projects to universities around the country, Congress gave its nod to go ahead with the project.[40]

Throughout 1964 the division continued investigating proposed sites, bringing the number surveyed up to 160; and it explored the feasibility of obtaining a twenty-nine acre site in Cambridge, close by Harvard University and the Massachusetts Institute of Technology. Finally in December it awarded an architect-engineer contract for master planning at the Cambridge location.

Then came "aches and pains," as Division Engineer Remi O. Renier put it. Clearing the site involved the relocation by the City of Cambridge Redevelopment Authority of ninety-four industries, mostly of minuscule size, and the inevitable strong opposition developed. Further problems arose over proper appraisals and relocation arrangements, and for some time the availability of all land for the site remained uncertain.

Problems also arose over design. The preliminary master plan submitted by the architect-engineer in the spring of 1965 was an impressive concept featuring two high towers enclosed in a rectangular plaza bounded by several three story buildings, with the whole complex underlaid by an expansive ground floor. Although the plan presented several alternative variations in design, all cost between $46 and $52 million, while the division's budget for basic construction was $32 million. The master plan was quickly revised to more modest proportions, but design problems nevertheless continued. Detailed planning for the center led to endless debate within NASA, and to

Emergency Operating Center for the Office of Civil Defense, Region I, Maynard, Massachusetts.

Communications room of the Emergency Operating Center, Maynard, Massachusetts.

frequent directives for extensive criteria changes. The upshot was uncertainty over the division's yearly workloads, delays, cost overruns, and contractual difficulties with the architect-engineer. "My Chief of Engineering and myself," Renier reported, "spend much of our time in conference with the ERC staff to resolve problems and offer guidance to them."[41]

Revised plans called for a thirteen-story edifice of considerably less height than the towers of the original design, flanked by several one- to three-story buildings also of less ambitious dimensions. Longer-range plans provided for the expansion of the center in stages until it comprised eighteen buildings housing laboratories, offices, and other facilities. Foundation work for the high-rise program management building, two low-rise laboratories, a personnel services building, a power plant, and a warehouse began in October 1966, and by December 1967 superstructures were under way. By early 1970

Transportation Systems Center, Cambridge, Massachusetts. This building complex was originally constructed to house an Electronics Research Center of the National Aeronautics and Space Administration.

the buildings were nearing completion. Then it was suddenly announced that authorization for the Electronics Research Center would be terminated on June 30. Designs had been completed for another building to contain a computer facility, and the division was about to request bids for the job, when prospects of further NASA construction thus evaporated. Remaining work on the project, with some deletions, was finished, the division's NASA area office was phased out by the deadline date, and the buildings of the center were transferred to the United States Department of Transportation.[42]

Meantime the division's military construction program, after continuing at rock-bottom level through FY 1967, began to revive. Major projects in the next two years included a barracks complex, a 116-bed hospital, and a water-treatment plant at Fort Devens; officers quarters, cold storage facilities, and an emergency electric power plant at Westover Field; an Air National Guard squadron operations building at Burlington Airport; remodeling at the Watertown Arsenal for the Army Materials Research Agency; a laboratory support building at Natick; and a computation laboratory at Hanscom Field. One of the largest projects, code-named GRAVEL, was a crash operation carried out for the Army Ammunition Procurement and Supply Agency. Awarding cost-plus-a-fixed-fee contracts, which were frequently used by the Engineers for urgent projects during World War II but almost never employed since, the division renovated old buildings, constructed new ones, and rebuilt railroad facilities at the Hingham Naval Annex, located south of Boston, for the installation of a government-owned, contractor-operated munitions plant. Initially estimated to cost about $1 million, GRAVEL grew through modifications requested by the Army into a project valued at over $3 million.[43]

Another large military project—potentially the largest since the mid-1950s—died aborning. This was the construction of a Sentinel Ballistic Missile Defense System for the protection of Boston and its environs, the location of the heaviest concentration in the country of vital electronics and other highly technical industries. Work on a Sentinel emplacement, the first started in the country, began late in 1967 when soils and water supply investigations at possible sites were carried out for the Army Ballistic Missile Agency headquartered at Huntsville, Alabama. Like a Nike battery, each Sentinel facility would normally occupy two sites. By 1969 sites had been acquired at North Andover and on the Reading-Wakefield line; division engineers were designing support facilities for both installations on the basis of standard plans developed at Huntsville; and excavation and foundation work had been started.

The decision by the government to proceed with antiballistic missile defenses, however, had from the beginning come under fierce attack from groups opposed to the program. And in January 1969 the Department of Defense suspended construction at the New England sites pending high-level review of policy. Locally, smouldering opposition to missile deployment broke out into full flame at a public meeting held in Reading on January 29. The meeting was held to discuss matters relating to construction, but the audience, mostly composed of protesters from all over the Boston area, insisted on discussing the justification for the entire ABM program—a matter of government policy beyond the authority of the Engineers. The following May word was received from Washington that the Sentinel project was terminated.[44]

After the very lean years of 1966 and 1967, the military workload of the New England Division had taken a decided upturn. For FY 1968 military construction, including the NASA project, accounted for $18.4 million out of a total workload of $40.9 million. For FY 1969 expenditures on military construction, exclusive of NASA, came to $17 million; NASA added $9 million and civil works $21 million for a total workload of $47 million. And for FY 1970 the military program contributed $25.4 million to a total workload of $47.9 million. Yet the volume of defense work was insufficient to insure retention by the division of its military mission. Military construction throughout the country was at a low level, and as part of an economy reorganization measure affecting ten other divisions and districts, the Department of the Army on June 30, 1970 transferred military work in New England to the New York Engineer District.[45] After two hundred years of notable achievement in constructing military defenses for New England—from the earthen redoubts of Colonel Gridley to the airfields and missile batteries of the New England Division—New England's Army Engineers would, until perhaps another military emergency, concentrate almost exclusively on the civil functions of the Corps.

VIII FLOOD CONTROL

The winter of 1935-36 was one of the most severe New England had ever seen. Snow piled high on the northern hills, and rivers and streams were choked with ice. Early in March came a week of unseasonably warm weather, melting snow on the hillsides and thawing ice in the rivers. On March 13 a torrential rainstorm worsened the sudden runoff, and a second pelting rain followed a few days later. New England's rivers became swollen and then leapt their banks, forcing two hundred thousand workers from closed factories and thousands more from their homes. By March 19 life in the Connecticut River Valley, where the floodwaters raged the highest, was virtually paralyzed. Not a railroad was running, the Coast Guard, the Boston Navy Yard, and Gloucester fishermen sent flotillas of boats to rescue the flood's victims, and the National Guard moved into almost every major town. Hartford was practically in a state of siege: a curfew was imposed and everyone entering the area had to be inoculated. In Massachusetts a Flood Relief Administrator was given dictatorial powers to seize food, clothing, and medical supplies. By the time the floodwaters subsided they had taken twenty-four lives and left 77,000 people homeless.[1]

It was the worst flood in at least three centuries, and most of the eastern and central sections of the United States were lashed by the same storms and suffered similar devastation. The damage and disruption was more widespread than the country had ever experienced, and for the first time demands for aggressive federal action to prevent such tragedies reached nationwide dimensions. The upshot was the Flood Control Act of 1936, which assigned new responsibilities to the federal government and new duties to the Corps of Engineers. The measure established a national policy of flood control, to be carried out by the Engineers, and authorized some 220 flood control works and an additional 220 flood control surveys.[2]

The interest of the Corps of Engineers in flood control was by no means new. But prior to 1936 the Corps' authority had been limited, and there had been little public or congressional sentiment to extend it. Federal concern with flood control had been restricted almost wholly to the Mississippi River and the Sacramento River of California, where protective work had developed out of interest in navigation and debris control.

It was not until 1927 that Congress authorized surveys of most of the nation's major rivers and streams for purposes that included flood control. One of the most important acts relating to water resources in the nation's history, this legislation was inspired less by specific congressional interest in flood control than by concern with hydroelectric power development during a decade when the electric power industry was doubling in size and output. The River and Harbor Act of March 3, 1925 had directed the Corps of Engineers and the Federal Power Commission to prepare an estimate of the cost of making surveys of those navigable streams and their tributaries on which power development appeared feasible, with a view to formulating general plans for improving navigation, developing power, controlling floods, and

March 1936 flood

Chicopee Falls, Massachusetts.

Manchester, New Hampshire.

providing irrigation. The next year the estimates were presented for the consideration of Congress in House Document No. 308. The River and Harbor Act of January 21, 1927 authorized the surveys, and over the next decade the Corps completed comprehensive studies of nearly two hundred rivers and streams, including seventeen in New England. The resulting "308" reports were not prepared as recommendations for specific projects, but were basically inventories of the water-resource potentialities and problems of the river basins, with broad comprehensive plans of improvement. Nevertheless they formed the bases for subsequent congressional authorization of flood control work, they provided a valuable reservoir of emergency relief projects during the depression of the 1930s, and they remained for years the major source of information for all public and private agencies concerned with the nation's water resources.[3]

Hardly had the surveys been started when the rivers of the Mississippi Valley badly flooded, and a few months later, in November 1927, the streams of New England went on a disastrous rampage. For a time Congress appeared about to enact nationwide flood control measures, but all that finally resulted was authorization for more protective works in the Mississippi Valley. To this, no spokesman for New England objected. The region regarded flood control wholly as a matter of state concern and indeed viewed federal intervention as intolerable. The most popular solution for flooding was to encourage private power companies to build more storage reservoirs, and no one suggested that perhaps the federal government should build multipurpose dams for power generation and flood control.[4] Meantime the Boston and Providence districts went ahead with their "308" surveys, completing most of them in 1929 and 1930. The survey of the Housatonic River was finished in 1932, and the survey of the Connecticut—the most extensive and the most handicapped by inadequate funds—was wrapped up in February 1936, just before the valley was again inundated by raging waters.[5]

As New Englanders dug out from the debris of a second major flood within a decade, hands-off attitudes toward the federal government were for the moment overwhelmed by spontaneous demands from the afflicted valleys for federal action. And seeking assistance for their region, New England congressmen joined in the general cry for national flood control legislation. The Flood Control Act of 1936, drawing on the "308" reports, authorized the construction of ten flood control reservoirs in Vermont and New Hampshire on tributaries of the Connecticut River and "a system of flood control reservoirs" in the Merrimack River Basin. The act stipulated that states or other local agencies must provide the lands, easements, and rights-of-way necessary for the projects, hold the United States free from damages due to construction, and maintain and operate the completed works. Since river basins were no respecters of state lines, states were permitted to enter into compacts to allocate these local costs.[6] These provisions of local cooperation were to delay construction on the first of the reservoirs for at least two years. The compacts had to be drafted before the districts could start work, and this proved to be a troublesome business.

Meantime, since interstate relationships were not involved, the Engineers had a freer hand to begin the construction of local flood protection works to help safeguard individual communities where flood hazards were most se-

NEW ENGLAND "308" SURVEYS

RIVER BASIN	STATES	COMPLETED
Kennebunk	Maine	June 18, 1930
Salmon Falls	Maine	June 19, 1930
Androscoggin	Maine, New Hampshire	December 2, 1930
Kennebec	Maine	December 2, 1930
Machias	Maine	December 2, 1930
Penobscot	Maine	December 2, 1930
Presumpscot	Maine	December 2, 1930
Union	Maine	December 2, 1930
St. Croix	Maine, New Brunswick, Canada	December 2, 1930
Saco	Maine, New Hampshire	December 4, 1930
Merrimack	New Hampshire, Massachusetts	December 2, 1930
Pawtucket (Seekonk)	Rhode Island	November 26, 1929
Pawcatuck	Rhode Island, Connecticut	November 26, 1929
Taunton	Massachusetts	November 26, 1929
Thames	Connecticut, Massachusetts, Rhode Island	December 2, 1930
Housatonic	Connecticut, Massachusetts, New York	February 9, 1932
Connecticut	Connecticut, Massachusetts, New Hampshire, Vermont	February 11, 1936

vere. Under authority of the Emergency Relief Appropriation Acts of 1935 to 1938, the districts built or improved local protection works on the Merrimack River at Lowell and Haverhill, Massachusetts; on the Nashua River, a tributary of the Merrimack, at Fitchburg, Massachusetts; and on the Connecticut River at Hadley, Hatfield, Springfield, West Springfield, Chicopee, and Holyoke, Massachusetts, and Hartford and East Hartford, Connecticut. The districts enlarged channel capacities to prevent flooding of adjacent properties, riprapped river banks, constructed earth levees and concrete floodwalls, repaired and enlarged existing dikes built by local authorities, laid out drainage systems, and installed conduits and pumping plants to carry sanitary and storm water through the protective barriers. At Lowell, where several of the largest of these emergency relief projects were carried out, the river channel was widened or deepened at several places, almost a mile of earth dike and concrete wall was erected to protect 930 acres of urban land, and two pumping stations were constructed. The communities fulfilled the

Floodwall along the Merrimack River at Haverhill, Massachusetts, was one of the first local protection works constructed by the Corps in New England.

same conditions of local cooperation as prescribed in the 1936 Flood Control Act, and practically all work was done by government plant and hired labor.

While this work was going on, Massachusetts, Connecticut, New Hampshire, and Vermont appointed commissioners to draft the interstate flood control compacts for the Connecticut and Merrimack river valleys. Disagreements immediately arose. The major problem was that while most of the flood damage would occur in Massachusetts and Connecticut, the reservoirs would be built in Vermont and New Hampshire. The governor of Vermont stated flatly that he was not interested in flooding good Vermont land merely to benefit other states of the Connecticut Valley. By March 1937 the commissioners were no nearer to forming compacts than when they started. Secretary of War Harry Woodring thereupon bluntly informed the states that they must "put up or shut up" if they wanted federal flood control projects. The needs of the Mississippi Basin were more pressing than those of New England, he warned, and unless the states produced compacts within ten days he would be happy to forget about them. Somewhat jolted, the commissioners hammered out compacts before the month was over, which the states ratified early in July. The compacts settled the issue of local costs by Massachusetts and Connecticut agreeing to shoulder most of them. Then going beyond this problem, they vested ownership of all lands, easements, and rights-of-way, in effect title to the dams and reservoirs, with the states and reserved to the states all rights of power development.

These last provisions were bound to be troublemakers. Yet a poorly drafted and ambiguous section of the Flood Control Act was in part responsible. The act did not specify where title to the properties would lie, and could reasonably be interpreted to substantiate state ownership; it was almost exclusively concerned with flood control, with broader reference restricted to the provision that penstocks and other facilities for the possible future development of power might be installed on dams; and it required the states to maintain and operate the projects. In the bitter debates that ensued over whether the compacts violated the Flood Control Act of 1936 and federal waterpower legislation, both logic and casuistry were evident on each side of the argument. The Federal Power Commission and the President opposed the compacts, and Congress refused to approve them. Although some New England congressmen charged that the compacts were written by private power interests heavily represented on the commissions, the region's congressional delegation on the whole supported the agreements. Congressmen and other New England officials warned of federal domination of state resources, of invasion of the rights of states, and of violation of American standards. The chairman of the Massachusetts Planning Board solemnly told a congressional committee that if the compacts were not approved, "then government of the people, by the people and for the people shall have perished from the earth." Flood control was no longer the main concern. Currently before Congress were several proposals, one an administration measure, for the creation of a number of regional power and planning authorities modeled on the Tennessee Valley Authority. To opponents of such New Deal schemes, the compacts were the barriers to the intrusion of this type of federal authority in New England.[7]

While political dificulties held up the construction of flood control dams and reservoirs authorized in 1936, the New England districts carried out tests and experimental work on earthfill dams. Here the Boston District is conducting compaction tests at the site of the Franklin Falls Dam.

The debate was finally cut short by the Flood Control Act of June 28, 1938, which stipulated that dams and reservoirs, unless otherwise provided by law, would be constructed entirely at federal cost and would be owned, maintained, and operated by the federal government. The act also approved new general comprehensive plans for "flood control and other purposes" that had been drawn up by the Boston and Providence districts in accordance with directives for further surveys in the act of 1936. Authorized for construction were twenty reservoirs and seven local protection works in the Connecticut River Basin and four reservoirs in the Merrimack watershed.[8]

During the two-year hiatus between the flood control acts, the districts had been carrying out extensive field surveys, foundation investigations, and

September 1938 flood

Providence, Rhode Island.

Fitchburg, Massachusetts.

planning work on reservoirs with funds allotted from the 1936 Emergency Relief Appropriation Act. Now they could go ahead with the usual procedures of holding hearings, working out necessary arrangements with other federal, state, and local authorities, and completing designs. Before any of these activities had progressed very far, however, New England reeled from another flood disaster. Four days of rain in mid-September 1938 were already threatening floods as bad as those of 1936 when a tropical hurricane moving up the Atlantic failed to follow its curve out to sea and raged northward through the New England states. Winds reached up to 186 miles an hour and mountainous waves battered the coast. The main square of Providence was dry one moment and flooded ten feet deep the next, the tidal waves tossing huge oil barges onto the city's downtown streets. The property damage was devastating. Buildings were wrecked, boats were splintered into driftwood all along the coast—three hundred fifty in Boston Harbor alone—crops were destroyed, and two hundred fifty million trees were blown down. The damage was in excess of $120 million. Beyond measurement was the loss of 488 lives.

Rather than hastening reservoir construction, the disaster led instead to further delay. The elections of 1938 were only weeks away, and the floods offered an irresistible issue. Though no reservoirs authorized in 1936 could have been completed in any event, Republican candidates blamed the delay in giving New England flood protection on the New Deal generally and on the region's Democratic congressional opponents of the interstate compacts in particular. This was deadly campaign stuff at a time when thousands of people were still reckoning their losses, and Democratic leaders in Connecticut, New Hampshire and Massachusetts made desperate appeals to Roosevelt for help. On the President's order, Harry Hopkins of the Federal Emergency Relief Administration, Paul Seavey of the Federal Power Commission, and Brigadier General John J. Kingman of the Corps of Engineers met to work out an emergency program of flood control aid for New England. The conferees found that they could scrape together $11 million from War Department, WPA, and PWA funds, and recommended the immediate construction of the local protection works in the Connecticut Valley and reservoirs at Knightville and Birch Hill, Massachusetts; Union Village, Vermont; and Surry Mountain, New Hampshire. On October 4 Roosevelt ordered Hopkins to go ahead with construction. The announcement, however, failed to bolster the New Deal in New England. In the November elections every state went Rupublican. Only one of the region's congressional opponents of the compacts survived, and state offices were filled with men who for the most part opposed federal power programs and the federal-ownership provisions of the 1938 Flood Control Act. Further delay in building reservoirs was inevitable.[9]

Since neither power generation nor federal land-taking was involved in the local protection works authorized for the Connecticut Valley, they were never at issue. As soon as funds for them were made available early in October, the Providence District under Lieutenant Colonel John S. Bragdon swung into operation at Hartford, East Hartford, Springfield, West Springfield, Chicopee, Holyoke, and Northampton with plans already drafted. These projects, most of which were later extended, were sizable

Pumping station, gate structure, and flood wall along the Connecticut River at Chicopee, Massachusetts.

Floodwalls and gate structure along the Connecticut River at Holyoke, Massachusetts.

works with final costs ranging from about $1 million to nearly $9 million. At Springfield, earth dikes and concrete floodwalls were strung along about five miles of the east bank of the Connecticut; five stoplog structures, or removable wooden sections, were placed in the protective barriers where they crossed highways or railroads; several wingwalls were built on tributary Mill River; and seven pumping stations (six built by the city) were constructed to remove interior drainage. Across the river at West Springfield, the district built more than seven miles of earth dikes and concrete walls studded with six stoplog structures and seven pumping stations. At Hartford it put up over seven and a half miles of dikes and floodwalls, punctured them with six stoplog structures, laid more than two miles of pressure conduits, and constructed three pumping stations to supplement three others built by the city. Complex works at Holyoke included nearly five miles of dikes and floodwalls along the Connecticut and both banks of a power canal, seven pumping stations, eighteen stoplog structures, and thirty-six gates at power plant conduits to prevent high water from backing into mills.

Reservoir construction was less easy to get under way. With preparatory work on the storage projects well along, the districts were by October 1938 ready to acquire land. But the states, still digging in their heels against the possibility of federal power projects, insisted upon putting restrictions on federal authority over properties that would limit them to flood control purposes only. During complicated negotiations to work out arrangements, issues sometimes shifted, but behind the stance of the states there was always apparent a mixture of genuine if vague sentiments of state sovereignty, hostility toward federal planning authorities, and the influence of power companies. The federal government could have exercised its unquestioned power of eminent domain and taken land without the consent of the states, but it was normal government procedure to work out agreements with states wherever possible rather than employ this right crudely. The Engineers repeatedly indicated that they would not built a dam anywhere in New England, even with congressional authority, if a state objected. The Roosevelt administration, moreover, preferred to avoid arousing more hostility and bitterness at a time when the New Deal was already under heavy political fire.

Early in 1939 the administration finally announced that it would build no reservoirs within a state unless the state consented to exclusive federal jurisdiction over the works. Funds could be used in other states that wanted protection. Since it appeared that New England might end up with nothing at all, New Hampshire and Massachusetts moderated their stands. On May 31, 1939 the governor of New Hampshire signed a bill that granted exclusive federal jurisdiction over six reservoir projects. The bill represented a compromise. Of six projects submitted by the Engineers, the New Hampshire Flood Control Commission had objected to two in the Merrimack Valley and one in the Connecticut Valley, and three other projects had been substituted. On June 14 the governor of Massachusetts signed a similar bill granting the federal government exclusive jurisdiction over four reservoir sites. Vermont, however, refused to budge, and no reservoir construction was to take place in the state until 1947.[10]

Ironically, the issue of power development that had delayed the start of reservoir construction had little substance. The Engineers were aware of this, but few others seem to have been. Power development can be incorporated into a flood control reservoir project only if a valley is sufficiently extensive and unsettled to permit the building of a dam and reservoir large enough to provide head and storage for power development and still have storage space above the power pool for flood runoff. In New England's populated main river valleys, already saturated with reservoirs constructed by power and other industries, this was manifestly out of the question. In its narrow and steep tributary valleys, available flood control space is limited, which means that a reservoir has to be kept nearly empty in readiness for a major flood to strike. Suitable conditions for dual purpose projects exist in very few places, and in fewer still was the development of hydroelectric power economically feasible. In the early 1950s a New England-New York Interagency Committee, which made a comprehensive survey of water resources in the New England-New York region, found only two sites, one in northern Maine and the other in Connecticut, where hydroelectric power could be generated in competition with steam plants.[11]

Between August 1939 and June 1940 the districts at last began the construction of five reservoirs: Knightville, Surry Mountain, and Birch Hill in the Connecticut Basin by the Providence District, and Franklin Falls and Blackwater in the Merrimack Basin by the Boston District. In their general design and structural features the dams are typical of all Corps of Engineer dams built in New England. Since settlement and industrial development preclude the construction of reservoirs on main river stems, river basin protective systems must rely on numerous smaller flood storage areas in the narrow feeder tributaries, and therefore the dams are generally small in comparison to those in other parts of the country. Of rolled earthfill type, the dams are built up in layers of twelve inches or less, with each layer thoroughly compacted by tractors and rollers. They have cores of impervious material to minimize seepage and blankets of dumped rock to prevent erosion. All have spillways, usually on or in bedrock immediately beyond one end of the dam, to prevent excessive floodwaters from overtopping the embankments, and all except a few with small drainage areas have gated outlet works, also usually located on or in bedrock.[12] Water releases at the ungated dams are automatically controlled by designed conduit restrictions. About a third of the projects also have earth dikes closing off saddles along the perimeters of the reservoirs.

Knightville Dam on the Westfield River, Huntington, Massachusetts, was one of the first to be placed in operation late in 1941. One thousand two hundred feet across at the top, it rises 160 feet above streambed. Water is released through a 280-foot intake channel and a 605-foot tunnel cut through rock. The tunnel is 16 feet in diameter and controlled by three gates operated from a control tower above. During time of flood the reservoir has a storage capacity of 49,000 acre-feet, equivalent to 5.6 inches of runoff from its drainage area of 164 square miles. Completely full, it covers 960 acres and extends about five miles upstream. Since the project was completed at a cost of $3.22 million, there have been more than sixty significant reservoir operations, preventing damages of over $19 million. The most important operations were in January 1949, when the entire storage capacity of the reservoir was utilized, and in August and October 1955, when 58 and 96 percent of storage capacity was used.

Franklin Falls Dam on the Pemigewasset River, Franklin, New Hampshire, completed in October 1943, is a key unit in the flood protection system of the Merrimack Valley. Its embankment, containing three million cubic yards of rock and earth, is 1,740 feet long and 140 feet high. It has two 22-foot-diameter horseshoe-shaped conduits, each 542 feet long and con-

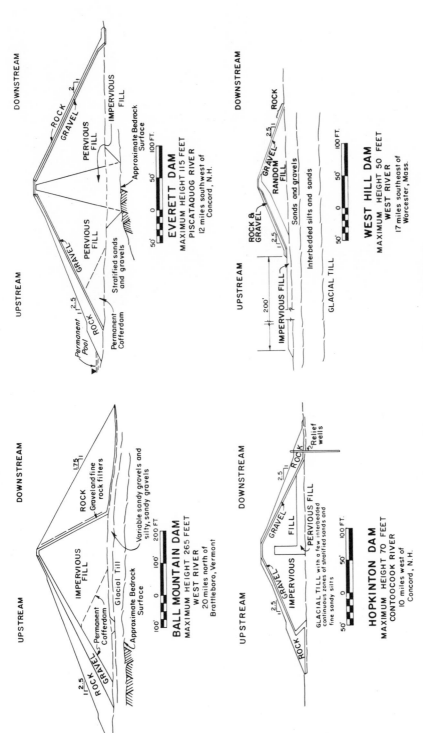

TYPICAL SECTIONS OF FOUR NEW ENGLAND DAMS

Knightville Dam on the Westfield River, Huntington, Massachusetts.

trolled by four gates. The dam can impound 154,000 acre-feet of water, which would form a 2,800-acre lake extending upstream about twelve and a half miles. Its drainage area is 1,000 square miles. Located on the main tributary of the Merrimack River, the project provides protection along its entire length. Costing about $8 million, it prevented damages of $8.8 million during the single flood of March 1953, when the reservoir reached 76 percent of capacity. Since its completion it has prevented $20,162,000 in flood damages, and with a recurrence of the 1936 basin flood of record would prevent $120.6 million in damages.

The construction of these and the other reservoirs involved a raft of related activities. Many individual parcels of land had to be purchased; highways, bridges, and utility lines had to be relocated; access roads and operators' quarters had to be built; and power and lighting systems had to be installed. Sometimes properties had to be replaced and cemeteries and historic buildings moved to new locations. At Blackwater Reservoir, for instance, the Boston District built new, modern buildings to replace a school and a garage that had to be torn down. It relocated the Old Meeting House Cemetery of Webster Village, moving it to the top of a hill over a mile away. It also moved the Town Meeting House, a white frame structure over two hundred years old, through a mile and a half of woods to a new site. Making minor repairs and giving the building a new coat of paint, the district turned it over to the townspeople again as good as ever.[13]

With the completion of the Franklin Falls Dam in 1943, work on reservoirs temporarily came to a stop as civil projects not directly related to the war effort gave way to more urgent World War II military construction. The districts continued field surveys, foundation investigations and planning, however, so that work could get under way again as soon as the war ended.

Franklin Falls Dam on the Pemigewasset River, Franklin, New Hampshire, shown holding back floodwaters in October 1959 when heavy rains posed flood threats throughout New England.

Efforts to reach agreements with the states also went on—with little abatement of former difficulties. Nearly every proposed project on upriver tributaries raised protests in villages of Vermont and New Hampshire, residents formed organizations to fight construction, and several newspapers mounted opposition crusades. Controversies raged in Congress over the purpose, the location, and the size and number of dams that should be constructed, with New England upriver and downriver interests generally at odds. In the Flood Control Act of June 30, 1944, Congress laid down the policy that all proposals and plans for flood control and the improvement of navigation must be approved by the states concerned. Trying to reach a solution that would satisfy conflicting interests in New England and still provide adequate flood control, the Engineers studied the merits of numerous alternative schemes and several times proposed new plans.[14]

Consequently it was not until 1947 that the New England Division—now the operating unit in the region—initiated construction on two more reservoirs, both in the Connecticut Basin. The next year it began work on a dam in the Merrimack Basin, and in 1949 it got under way the first reservoir outside these two watersheds. Flood control planning for the Thames, Blackstone, Pawtuxet, and Housatonic river basins of southern New England had begun in 1938 with funds allotted from the Emergency Relief Appropriation Act of that year for examination and surveys. Several projects were authorized in the Flood Control Acts of 1941 and 1944, and in 1949 the division began construction on Mansfield Hollow Dam on the Natchaug River, a tributary of the Thames. A sinuous structure 12,422 feet long supplemented by 2,507 feet of dikes, it was completed in 1952.

Reservoir construction now came to a halt for a second time as the mili-

Intake works of the Blackwater Dam on the Blackwater River, New Hampshire.

Spillway of the Blackwater Dam on the Blackwater River, New Hampshire.

Mansfield Hollow Dam on the Natchaug River, Connecticut. The spillway and outlet works are in the foreground.

tary building programs of the early 1950s again took priority over the Corps' civil works. In the immediate postwar years four reservoirs had been constructed. The number of local protection works initiated was five, four of which were channel improvement. Thus by 1955, nineteen years after the landmark 1936 Flood Control Act, only nine reservoirs and fifteen local protection works had been constructed in New England, almost all in two river basins. The authorized flood control program for the region was only twenty percent completed, compared to the national average of about fifty percent. The delays occasioned by opposition groups, suspicions of the motives of the federal government, and the urgencies of military construction had apparently not disturbed too many people—if indeed many were even aware of them. Then suddenly the need for flood protection was again tragically demonstrated.

In mid-August 1955 the third tropical hurricane of the season, code-named "Connie," passed over New England, seemingly with little damage. Although six to nine inches of rain fell on western Connecticut and Massachusetts, the soil was dry and runoff was too small to cause serious flooding. The ground was left saturated, however, and streams were raised to high levels. About midnight on Wednesday, August 17, heavy rains again began to fall in Massachusetts, Connecticut, and Rhode Island. As routine procedure, the Reservoir Regulation Branch of the New England Division was alerted to the possibility of flash floods in the upper tributaries of major rivers, which would be the early indications of serious trouble. The first warning of flooding came by telephone at 9:30 the next morning, and immediately a Flood Emergency Mobilization Plan was put into action. Dam tenders in the rainfall area were ordered to close the flood-control gates and

188

Hurricane Diane, August 1955

Putnam, Connecticut.

Southbridge, Massachusetts.

Putnam, Connecticut.

Winsted, Connecticut.

begin storing water, and liaison was established with federal, state, and town officials to coordinate flood-fighting efforts.[15]

Torrential rains continued throughout August 18 and 19. During those two days the storm center of a second hurricane, Hurricane Diane, traveled eastward across Pennsylvania and New Jersey and then turned northward to cross the eastern end of Long Island and rampage along the southern New England coast. More than twelve inches of rain, and in places up to eighteen and twenty inches, fell across southern New England from the Berkshires to the Atlantic. Pouring off the already soggy soil and surging down river valleys, it produced flash floods that in many places were two to four times greater than anything on record. As upstream runoff increased, the velocity of streams doubled and trebled. Sweeping over their banks, rivers cut new courses, sometimes through the streets of cities and towns. The Mad River of Connecticut cut a mile-long channel six to eight feet deep along the main street of Winsted; and in Waterbury, Torrington, Naugatuck, and other cities, water surged into the second stories of homes and factories. Building foundations were undercut, bridges were torn out, pavements were uprooted, and blocks of concrete, railroad cars, bridges, and buildings were tossed about like cardboard toys. Miles of water supply lines, sewer lines, electrical conduits, and railroad tracks were ripped out like string. In dozens of towns tumbled buildings, bridges, trucks, and automobiles were piled into masses of twisted and battered junk.

Land and rail transportation was brought to a standstill by highway washouts and bridge failures, and hundreds of people were left homeless. Units of the National Guard moved into heavily damaged communities to enforce martial law. Municipal departments, the armed services, and volunteers rescued trapped flood victims with boats, helicopters, and breeches buoys. The Red Cross, churches, and other organizations set up relief centers, and the Salvation Army sent in mobile feeding units as soon as they could get through. Helicopters brought casualties, doctors, nurses, and supplies to hospitals, and typhoid inoculations were administered on a voluntary basis. In Waterbury alone, more than eighty thousand people took advantage of this protection.

Diane's sock at southern New England caused damages of $540 million and took ninety lives. Losses were particularly heavy in the highly industrialized and densely populated Naugatuck Valley in the Housatonic watershed, where nearly half the dollar damage and the heaviest cost in lives occurred. Devastation in the Connecticut, Thames, and Blackstone river basins was milder only by comparison. Less than two months later, on October 15 and 16, heavy rains again fell over western Massachusetts and Connecticut, causing additional damage in excess of $50 million and claiming seventeen more lives.

The New England Division, under the direction of Brigadier General Robert J. Fleming, Jr., had immediately sent field personnel to disaster areas to assist local and state authorities in rescue work and give technical assistance. Military equipment, including portable electric generators, water purifiers, and communication apparatus, was rapidly installed in critical areas. Bailey bridges—prefabricated and quickly assembled trussed structures developed by British Engineers during World War II—were obtained from supply depots and turned over to state highway departments for installation under Corps supervision on state and national highways. Where town bridges were destroyed, Bailey bridges were erected directly by the Corps.

This relief work was soon dramatically expanded. On August 20 President Eisenhower declared disaster areas in Massachusetts, Connecticut, Rhode Island, New York, Pennsylvania, and New Jersey. He authorized the Federal Civil Defense Administrator to provide federal relief assistance, an assignment that on August 23 was delegated to the Corps of Engineers and transmitted to the New England and North Atlantic divisions.[16] On that same day officers from the advanced class of the Army Engineer School at Fort Belvoir, Virginia, were flown to Boston to assist the New England Division, and Chief of Engineers Lieutenant General Samuel D. Sturgis, Jr., arrived to survey the situation. Within a few more days experienced disaster teams from Omaha, Vicksburg, and Kansas City and Corps of Engineer specialists from forty-three districts throughout the country were also flown in. More sets of Bailey bridges and engineering teams experienced in their swift erection soon arrived. The First Army Command provided seventy jeeps, sedans, and carryalls and arranged for the loan of a helicopter and other aircraft from other army areas. Personnel of the New England Division, now armed with greater authority, got in touch with contractors carrying out division military projects and soon had their equipment and operators at work in devasted areas. By contract, loan, or rent, they obtained all types of heavy equipment from governmental agencies and from private industry for coordinated relief efforts. "Operation Noah" had begun.

A force of 253 Corps personnel, supported by additional personnel at the division office, directed Operation Noah. A central Disaster Relief Office was established at 224 Albany St., Cambridge, Massachusetts, and Strategic Area Offices were set up at Waterbury, Connecticut, and Worcester, Massachusetts. Strategic Area Suboffices were opened in Norwalk, Torrington, Washington, Winsted, and Putnam, Connecticut; Chicopee, Massachusetts; and Woonsocket, Rhode Island. The demanding task of coordinating the relief efforts of numerous governmental and private agencies was carried out largely by the officers from the Engineer School. Cutting red tape to a minimum, they maintained close liaison with state governors, army headquarters, public works commissioners, civil defense directors, local authorities, and Red Cross and other organization officials.

By order of the Chief of Engineers the responsibilities assigned to the division were "protective work," "debris and wreckage clearance," and "repair and replacement of public facilities." These deceptively simple designations covered a broad spectrum of operations. Protective work ranged from reinforcing river channels with dikes, ditches, sandbags, and riprap to evacuating flood victims; from protecting dams, bridges, roads, and buildings by sandbagging and other measures to protecting public health by spraying polluted waters and infected land areas and covering city dumps. Debris and wreckage clearance involved clearing streets, rivers, dams, bridge abutments, culverts, and public buildings of debris; cleaning reservoirs, lakes, and sewer lines; removing damaged bridges; and demolishing buildings in danger of collapse. Repair and replacement of public facilities encompassed work on dams, bridges, dikes, culverts, streets, public buildings,

Military Engineers from the Army Engineer School at Fort Belvoir, Virginia, get a final briefing before starting supervisory duties in "Operation Noah." Standing left to right: Brig. Gen. Robert J. Fleming, Jr., New England Division Engineer, and Lt. Col. Byron G. Belote, Assistant Division Engineer in charge of disaster relief operations. Captain John P. Chandler, seated second to the right of Col. Belote, became New England Division Engineer in 1976.

reservoirs, wells, water mains, sewer lines, water filtration plants, sewage disposal plants, and electric utilities. It included the restoration of river channels, the erection of Bailey bridges, the maintenance of emergency municipal dumps, and the provision of sites and utilities for emergency housing. The cost of work performed by the Corps during Operation Noah was nearly $20.8 million. Work done by local interests reimbursed by the federal government came to over $6.6 million.

"This storm did as much damage in areas of southern New England as three years of warfare had done to the Ruhr," commented Division Engineer Robert Fleming, who had been with the army corps given the mission of mopping up the Rhineland and the Ruhr after the American Army had crossed the Rhine River. Had the dams and reservoirs authorized by Congress years ago been constructed, Fleming contended, there would still have been a flood and some losses, but those losses would have been cut by seventy to eighty percent.[17]

As it was, the two reservoirs in the storm area—Knightville in the Connecticut watershed and Mansfield Hollow in the Thames—together with the local protection works on the rivers, prevented damages estimated at nearly $40 million. The reservoirs reduced flood stages in communities immediately downstream by as much as four to six feet; and with the exception of the work at Winsted, where channel improvement had been limited by building foundations and other congestion along the river, the protection projects prevented any local damage from river flooding.

WORK PERFORMED IN OPERATION NOAH

Type of Work	Corps of Engineers	Reimb.	Total
Bridges repaired, replaced, salvaged, or removed	213	67	280
Dams repaired or reinforced	35	4	39
Channels cleared and restored	278	26	304
Debris cleared			
Roads	68	57	125
Buildings	278	4	282
Other	5	-	5
Utilities cleaned or repaired			
Water lines or plants	36	19	55
Sewer systems or plants	91	28	119
Other	-	6	6
Roads repaired	182	1668	1850
Culverts repaired	110	72	182
Public Buildings repaired	32	41	73

Cost of work performed by the Corps of Engineers	$20,796,081
Cost of reimbursable work performed by local interests	6,670,624
	$27,466,705

Along with property and life, Diane swept away complacent attitudes toward flood control. A few weeks after the flood, the entire Massachusetts congressional delegation met at Boston to name a committee on flood prevention and relief. The congressional delegations of Connecticut and Rhode Island similarly ignored party ranks to conduct a vigorous campaign for authorization and construction of an adequate flood protection system in New England. Other state leaders, including Governor Abraham Ribicoff of Connecticut, and members of business communities joined in demanding action on projects recommended by the Corps of Engineers. Some seventy-five business concerns in communities in southern Massachusetts and northern Connecticut banded into an association to whip up support for the construction of the five dams and reservoirs proposed by the Engineers for the upper tributaries of the Thames River. Similar cries for protection came from other areas of the ravaged states.[18]

Interest in flood control was reawakened in northern New England too, even though Diane left most of the area untouched. In 1953 the states of New Hampshire, Vermont, Massachusetts, and Connecticut had ratified, and Congress had approved, a compact covering the Connecticut River Valley under which the downstream states benefiting from flood protection agreed to recompense the upstream states for tax and economic losses resulting from setting aside lands for the construction of reservoirs. But neither New Hampshire nor Massachusetts had shown much disposition to ratify a similar compact for the Merrimack Valley that would have permitted the construction in the basin of a major twin-dam project authorized nearly two decades before. In 1953 and again in 1955 only fifteen of the 360-member New Hampshire House of Representatives voted in favor of the compact.

In 1956 Massachusetts ratified the agreement. New Hampshire still spent more time considering the matter, but support for the compact rapidly developed. The threat of another flood disaster was no doubt a major motivating force. In the spring of 1956 the entire Merrimack Basin had between two to three times the normal water content in its snow cover. The spring season came late, and if the weather had turned warm and the area had received a moderately heavy rain, the Merrimack, to quote Division Engineer Fleming, "would have gone down the drain." For three weeks Fleming had his fingers crossed so hard they hurt. He kept state officials continually advised of the situation; and residents of New Hampshire probably noticed more army jeeps than usual on their roads, for troops from Fort Devens were reconnoitering to figure out where they would move men and equipment in an emergency. Fleming also had some of the contractors at the Pease Air Force Base standing by, prepared to rush in equipment where needed. Support for the Merrimack River Flood Control Compact culminated early in 1957 when Fleming addressed a joint session of the New Hampshire legislature by request. Shortly afterwards the agreement was ratified by a vote of 286 to 11.[19]

The actions of New Englanders had their effect in Washington. In response to public demands Congress instructed the Corps to review flood control plans for all rivers in the Northeast and appropriated funds to begin the construction of a number of badly needed works already authorized. In 1956 the New England Division began three new reservoirs and a local protection work; and every year for the next decade it continued to start new flood control projects.

Among them was the twin-dam project in the Merrimack Basin, the Hopkinton-Everett dams and reservoirs, on which construction began in 1959. Planning for the project had begun in the early 1940s under the personal direction of Boston District Engineer Leonard B. Gallagher. Hydrologic studies determined that the Contoocook River, which enters the Merrimack five miles above Concord, New Hampshire, was a heavy contributor to flooding on the main river. Dozens of sites were investigated on the Contoocook to find a suitable location for a reservoir, but they were all

Hopkinton-Everett Flood Control Project. Hopkinton Dam on the Contoocook River. The reservoir area is connected to the river by a short canal. Another 13,900-foot canal connects this reservoir to the Everett Reservoir.

Hopkinton-Everett Flood Control Project. Everett Dam on the Piscataquog River.

too small for the storage required for the river's 426-square-mile drainage area. The solution was to divert part of the storage of the Contoocook to the adjoining subbasin of the Piscataquog River, with a drainage area of 64 square miles, by means of a canal through a low point in the divide. Thus two reservoirs were constructed: Hopkinton Lake in the Contoocook watershed having a capacity of 70,800 acre-feet, and Everett Lake in the Piscataquog watershed with 86,500 acre-feet. The canal between the lakes, 13,900 feet in length, permits the two storage areas to function as a single unit during major floods. Together they provide the largest storage capacity of any reservoir project in New England, exceeding that of Franklin Falls in the upper reaches of the Merrimack Basin by some 3,000 acre-feet.[20]

By the spring of 1960 the New England Division had fifteen new flood control projects in operation, eleven more under construction, and five more almost ready to start. Then came a test of what had been done. In March 1960 an unusually heavy storm dumped eighteen or more inches of snow on New England. This was followed the first week in April by warm rains, and as the annual spring runoff accelerated, floodwaters swept down the Connecticut and Merrimack rivers. On the Connecticut, the flood was the seventh largest on record. But it caused little harm. Seven completed and four nearly completed reservoirs and the local protection works in the basin prevented damages of $27.3 million. In the Merrimack Valley, damages of $5.4 million were averted. "The Governors and members of Congress," reported Division Engineer Alden K. Sibley to the Chief of Engineers, "said this was the first time they had received negligible complaints during a major flood and were surprised that it attracted so little public attention."[21] Not expecting and seldom getting public kudos, the division continued its work, and by 1970 it had constructed sixteen reservoirs in the Connecticut Basin, five in the Merrimack, seven in the Housatonic, six in the Thames, and one in the Blackstone—a total of thirty five. By 1973 it had brought the total number of local protection works completed to thirty-seven.

Hurricane Diane had wrought its destruction by the greatest and most intense rains ever recorded in New England. But to communities on New England's southern coast, hurricanes had more often brought trouble by tidal flooding. The enormous damage caused by the September 1938 hurricane resulted in large part from high tides and intense winds that caused record tidal surges. Flooding in the Buzzards Bay area was more than fourteen feet above mean sea level. A hurricane of September 1944 caused flood levels along the south shore of Cape Cod ranging as high as eleven feet above mean sea level. In August and September 1954, disastrous losses were experienced along the Connecticut, Rhode Island, and southern Massachusetts coasts from near-record tidal flooding caused by Hurricanes Carol and Edna. Carol put downtown Providence under eight feet of water, causing damages of over $40 million. The New England Division's response to this recurring danger was to design a new type of local protection work, the hurricane barrier, four of which were constructed between 1961 and 1969.

Work on the barriers began at Providence, where storm waves driven up V-shaped Narrangansett Bay can pile to extraordinary heights. Located about a mile south of the heart of the city on the east side of the estuary, the Fox Point Barrier extends across the Providence River just above its conflu-

North Hartland Dam on the Ottauquechee River, Vermont. View of the intake tower, looking upstream to the reservoir area.

Ball Mountain Dam on the West River, Vermont.

Constructing the spillway discharge channel walls of the North Hartland Dam on the Ottauquechee River, Vermont.

Intake to the Worcester Diversion Channel. A 4,205-foot tunnel and an 11,300-foot open channel bypass flood flows from Kettle Brook, Middle River, and Blackstone River past Worcester, Massachusetts.

Flood control dam of the Woonsocket Local Protection Project. Designed to protect the industrial area of Woonsocket, Rhode Island, the project also includes a flood-wall, four dikes, a pumping station, channel improvement, and the relocation and modification of bridges on the Blackstone River.

Local protection works at Hartford, Connecticut. The extensive works protecting the city include about 35,000 feet of dikes, 4,400 feet of concrete floodwalls, 10,900 feet of pressure conduits, six stoplog structures, and six pumping stations.

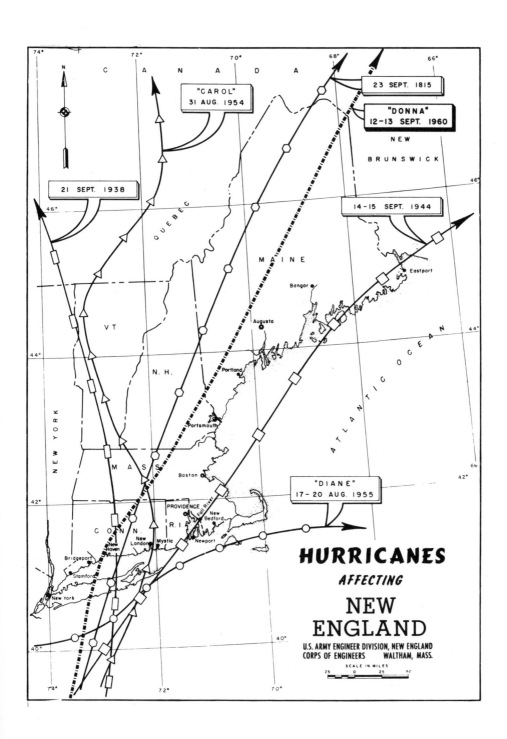

"CAROL"
31 AUG. 1954

23 SEPT. 1815

"DONNA"
12-13 SEPT. 1960

21 SEPT. 1938

14-15 SEPT. 1944

"DIANE"
17-20 AUG. 1955

HURRICANES
AFFECTING
NEW
ENGLAND

U.S. ARMY ENGINEER DIVISION, NEW ENGLAND
CORPS OF ENGINEERS   WALTHAM, MASS.

SCALE IN MILES
25   0   25   50

ence with the Seekonk River. It protects the commercial and industrial center of the city, extensive transportation facilities, public utilities, and many homes. Consisting of a concrete dam about 700 feet long flanked by rock-faced earth dikes 2,200 feet long, the barrier includes three 40-foot-wide tainter gates and a pumping station. When raised the gates allow normal river and tidal flow and the passage of small boats and barges; when closed they prevent tidal floodwaters from surging up the river. The pumping station houses five pumps with a combined discharge of 7,000 cubic feet per minute to expel flood runoff when the gates are closed. It also contains intake gates to admit condenser cooling water to a thermal-electric power plant located just behind the barrier. Construction costs were $15,844,500, to which local interests contributed 30 percent, a requirement applied in all barrier projects. In a recurrence of the record September 1938 hurricane flood stages, the barrier would prevent damages estimated at $74.9 million. Its maintenance and operation are local responsibilities. [22]

Started in the spring of 1961, the Fox Point Barrier was completed in 1966, considerably behind schedule. Delays caused by contractors running into difficulties, or by strikes tying up artisans or supplies, was an old story with the Corps, but to Division Engineer Seymour A. Potter, Jr., and to his successor, Peter Hyzer, the Fox Point Barrier was their "number one civil problem." Hyzer was further exasperated when a strike at the Tower Iron Works delayed fabrication of the barrier's third tainter gate for several months. "So we are not making up any time," he commented rather resignedly to the Chief of Engineers. [23]

Hyzer had quite the opposite experience in the construction of a much lengthier hurricane barrier at New Bedford-Fairhaven, started in 1962 and completed in 1966. The contractor tended to proceed at a faster pace than the project schedule, leaving Hyzer with the "continual problem" of funding his work. Not all Hyzer's concerns over the project, however, were that preferable. The day before the main channel into New Bedford-Fairhaven Harbor was to be temporarily closed and a bypass channel put into use, the pilots of the harbor suddenly decided that the bypass was too narrow. Hastily meeting with all interested parties in the mayor's office, Hyzer agreed to provide a wider channel. "This is still a touchy problem," he reported to the Chief of Engineers, "but I think that local interests are now convinced that the Corps of Engineers is not trying to destroy New Bedford as a port." [24]

The New Bedford-Fairhaven Barrier consists of three massive, rockfaced earthfill dikes. The main barrier extends 4,500 feet across New Bedford-Fairhaven Harbor, runs southward 3,600 feet along the New Bedford side of the outer harbor, then turns westward for 1,000 feet to high ground. A 150-foot-wide opening in the barrier, equipped with sector gates, accommodates harbor traffic. At Clarks Cove in New Bedford a supplementary dike extends 5,800 feet along the head and east shore of the cove, tying to high ground at both ends. In Fairhaven a similar dike about 3,100 feet long protects another low shore area. The project includes two gated conduits in the main barrier to permit emergency release of water, a gated conduit in the Fairhaven dike, a street gate in the west extension of the main barrier, and two street gates and a pumping station in the Clarks Cove dike. The barriers protect thickly settled industrial and commercial areas of about 1,400 acres,

Fox Point Hurricane Barrier. Dam, gates, and pump house viewed from the sea side.

Pumping Station, Fox Point Hurricane Barrier.

Aerial view of the New Bedford-Fairhaven Hurricane Barrier.

Sector gates of the New Bedford-Fairhaven Hurricane Barrier.

representing about 80 percent of the area flooded in the 1938 and 1954 hurricanes. Costing $18,614,000, the project has since its completion prevented damages of $1,245,000, and in recurrence of 1938 flood stages would prevent damages of $61.6 million. The division operates and maintains the main harbor barrier with funds provided by local interests.

A somewhat smaller barrier was completed by the division at Stamford, Connecticut, in 1969. Constructed mostly of earth dike with short sections of concrete wall and sheet pile bulkhead, the Stamford Barrier extends across the East Branch of Stamford Harbor and the low ground on either side for a distance of about 11,700 feet. It is equipped with a 90-foot-wide navigation opening with a single gate that swings up from the bottom of the channel, four pumping stations for handling storm runoff, gated openings for utility lines and drainage systems, and access ramps where the barrier crosses streets. Two months before the barrier was completely finished, it received its baptismal test. On November 12, 1968 the fourth highest tide in a century was generated by one of the "northeaster" storms that strike New England in the fall and winter. The 220-ton flap gate was raised and kept in position for seven hours, shutting out water that rose four feet higher outside the barrier than inside. Preventing damages of $750,000, this first operation of the barrier was the front page story of the *Stamford Advocate*.[25] Costing about $10.7 million, the barrier had by 1975 prevented damages of $2.5 million, and in a recurrence of 1938 flood levels would prevent damages of $9.3 million. The navigation gate is operated by the division.

The fourth barrier built by the division is a small work located on the west bank of the Pawcatuck River in Stonington, Connecticut. Costing $920,000, it consists of 1,915 feet of earth dike, 940 feet of concrete wall, two street gates, and a pumping station. In a single flood of 1938 stages it would prevent damages more than double its cost. Its maintenance is a local responsibility.

The key to optimum efficiency in regulating the division's twenty-eight gated reservoirs and two Corps-manned hurricane barriers is the rapid collection and analysis of essential hydrological and meteorological data. This is the primary function of a Reservoir Control Center established at the New England Division headquarters at Waltham in 1969. Formerly the compilation and analysis of data collected by field observation and transmitted by telephone or voice radio took several hours. Through a computerized radio reporting system the center now collects and processes information more reliably in a matter of minutes. The brainchild of Saul Cooper, chief of the division's Water Control Branch, the Automatic Hydrologic Reporting Network was developed by the Motorola Corporation and placed in operation in 1970.

The system consists essentially of forty-one centrally controlled remote reporting stations strategically located in the five river basins served by reservoirs and at two key coastal points. To safeguard against communication failures during major storms or floods, the stations transmit by radio signal, using batteries as their primary source of power. Repeater stations and relay centers pass the signals along to the Reservoir Control Center. The river basin stations send vital data on rainfall and on river and reservoir stages, while the coastal stations transmit tide, wind, and barometric conditions.

Aerial view of the Stamford Hurricane Barrier.

Stamford Hurricane Barrier with navigation gate nearly closed. Viewed from the ocean side.

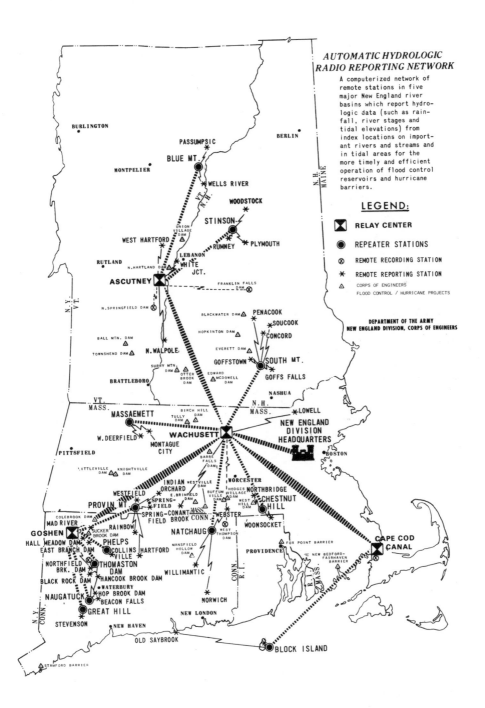

AUTOMATIC HYDROLOGIC
RADIO REPORTING NETWORK

A computerized network of remote stations in five major New England river basins which report hydrologic data (such as rainfall, river stages and tidal elevations) from index locations on important rivers and streams and in tidal areas for the more timely and efficient operation of flood control reservoirs and hurricane barriers.

LEGEND:

RELAY CENTER

REPEATER STATIONS

REMOTE RECORDING STATION

REMOTE REPORTING STATION

CORPS OF ENGINEERS
FLOOD CONTROL / HURRICANE PROJECTS

DEPARTMENT OF THE ARMY
NEW ENGLAND DIVISION, CORPS OF ENGINEERS

The computerized equipment at the center interrogates the entire network at six hour intervals and provides complete printouts in about four minutes. Whenever stations transmit flood warnings or barometric pressure drops, the network automatically reports every three hours. Manual interrogation also may be made at any time. Early warnings of high stream flows or tidal surges are assured, and the center's personnel, rapidly analyzing the data stored in the computer and information from other sources such as the National Weather Service and the U.S. Geological Survey, can issue timely operating instructions by telephone or voice radio to the managers of the dams and hurricane barriers.

Remote reporting station on the French River in Webster, Massachusetts.

Lighthouse at Old Saybrook, Connecticut, houses the hydrologic measuring equipment of a coastal remote reporting station.

With a view to developing a less expensive and possibly more reliable and effective method of data collection than by ground-station radio signal relay, the New England Division soon began experimenting with satellite data relay, using the Data Collection System of the Earth Resources Technology Satellite (ERTS, later renamed LANDSAT-1), launched by the National Aeronautics and Space Administration in July 1972, and that of its successor, LANDSAT-2, put in orbit in August 1974. Through a network of twenty-seven data collection platforms located throughout New England, information about river stages, rainfall, wind, and water quality is relayed by LANDSAT to the Goddard Space Flight Center at Greenbelt, Maryland, and from there by teletype to the Reservoir Control Center. Continuing its study in order to develop and test a direct readout system that would eliminate time delays and safeguard against communication breakdowns, the division constructed a computer-controlled satellite ground receiving station at its headquarters in Waltham, which was placed in operation in September 1975.

The successful testing of the LANDSAT Data Collection System by the New England Division has helped to determine the feasibility of the estab-

LANDSAT–2 DATA REPORTING STATIONS

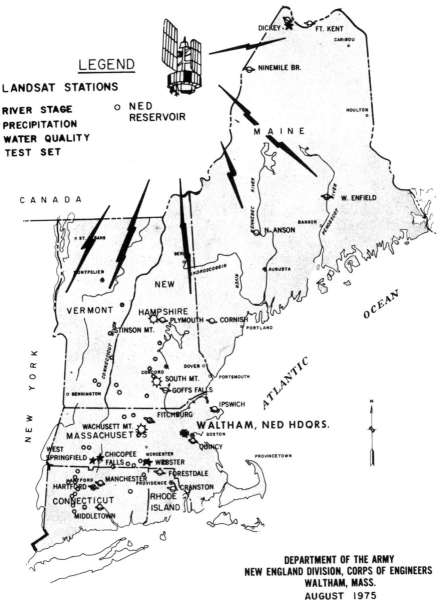

LEGEND

LANDSAT STATIONS

RIVER STAGE
PRECIPITATION
WATER QUALITY
TEST SET

o NED
RESERVOIR

DEPARTMENT OF THE ARMY
NEW ENGLAND DIVISION, CORPS OF ENGINEERS
WALTHAM, MASS.
AUGUST 1975

lishment by the Corps of a satellite data relay network serving all parts of the country. The division is also making a study of the imagery regularly collected by LANDSAT to determine its usefulness in planning, designing, and managing water resource systems. Initiated under contract by the University of Connecticut, this investigation is being continued by the Cold Regions Research and Engineering Laboratory at Hanover, New Hampshire. Through photo interpretation and computer analysis, imagery studies and measurements are being made of fluctuations in river, lake, and reservoir stages, tidal changes, icing of water surfaces, the location and depth of snow cover, the moisture content of soil, and water quality parameters.

During the spring snowmelt, several weeks of reservoir regulation within watersheds is a nearly annual occurrence. But since there is no flood-free time of year in New England, the operation of the flood control system is far from seasonal. Fiscal Year 1974 was an exceptionally busy one. Heavy rainfall late in June 1973 threatened severe floods in Vermont and New Hampshire, and several of the reservoirs in the Connecticut and Merrimack watersheds rose to near-record levels. In December, two heavy storms four days apart and a rapid melting of most of the northern snow cover by unseasonably warm temperatures caused rising riverflows in the Naugatuck, Connecticut, Merrimack, and Thames river basins that quickly approached flood stage. For the first time all thirty-five reservoirs stored floodwater simultaneously, with storages ranging up to 43 percent of capacity. The damages prevented by the reservoirs and by local protection projects during these floods of July and December totaled $54.5 million.[26]

While the primary function of the reservoirs is to control floods, these land and water areas, set aside in a near-natural state from the ordinary encroachments of society, are uniquely fitted for filling other environmental and social needs. Two reservoirs constructed in the 1960s were specifically authorized by Congress as multiple-purpose projects. Littleville Lake on the Middle Branch of the Westfield River, Massachusetts, was designed as a future water supply for the city of Springfield, and Colebrook River Lake on West Branch Farmington River, Connecticut, stores water for the Hartford Metropolitan Water District and for downstream fishery improvement by low flow augmentation. Another project, the East Brimfield Reservoir on the Quinebaug River in Sturbridge, Massachusetts, provides storage for industrial water supply. Reservoirs are also used to meet emergency situations. During a severe drought lasting through most of 1966, emergency water was stored in four reservoirs in the Connecticut and Thames basins at the request of the Commonwealth of Massachusetts in case the drought should continue for another year.[27]

Much more obvious to New Englanders seeking relaxation at woods and lakes are the recreational opportunities offered at the reservoirs. The New England Division has maintained recreational facilities at a number of its projects since the Corps was first authorized to construct them by a provision of the Flood Control Act of 1944. But what was hardly more than an incidental amenity became a major program after the passage of the Federal Water Project Recreation Act of 1965. This measure went beyond recognizing recreation as an appropriate function of reservoirs to requiring that consideration be given whenever possible to providing outdoor

LANDSAT satellite.

LANDSAT tracking antenna, NED, Waltham, Massachusetts.

Data Collection Platform.

Telocommunications control equipment, NED, Waltham, Massachusetts.

recreational opportunities at federal projects. It also encouraged local participation in their development by provisions for sharing management and costs. Implementing this act, the New England Division maintains recreational pools or lakes at twenty-one reservoirs and offers recreational opportunities at all thirty-one operated by the Corps. Many of the recreational areas are managed by state agencies, and state authorities stock a number of them with fish and game. Outdoor enthusiasts flock to the reservoirs to picnic, camp, swim, boat, or fish, and to hike, hunt, study nature, and snowmobile. Visitor-day attendance at the reservoirs in 1974 totaled over three million.

The 1965 Federal Water Project Recreation Act also encouraged conservational programs at federal water resource projects. In New England, the Corps of Engineers administers approximately 54,000 acres of federal land at the flood-control reservoirs and the Cape Cod Canal, and over 34,500 of these acres have been leased to the states of Vermont, New Hampshire, Massachusetts, and Connecticut for state development of recreational, forestry, and fish and wildlife management programs.

As the Corps and the states enlarged their recreational and conservational activities at the reservoirs, demands for even more facilities and services by a public eager to enjoy them multiplied rather than slackened. Recognizing the need for a full-time professional staff to keep on top of the situation, the division created in 1973 a Recreation-Resources Management Section with responsibility for developing and administering a comprehensive program. The next year it began implementing the program in the field by staffing its principal river basin offices with uniformed Park Rangers with professional degrees in forestry and wildlife management. Within a decade a minor function of the division had grown into one of its most visible interests.

Bathing beach at Clough State Park, Everett Dam, New Hampshire.

Trout fishing below Blackwater Dam, New Hampshire.

Duck hunting in the Stumpfield Marsh Waterfowl Management Area administered by the New Hampshire Fish and Game Department at the Hopkinton-Everett Flood Control Project.

Camping area at Birch Hill Dam, Massachusetts.

Snowmobiling at North Springfield Dam reservoir area, Vermont.

The dams, dikes, and barriers constructed by the Corps have done their jobs well. But they also adversely affect to some degree various economic, environmental, aesthetic, or other interests, and plans for them have not always met with unrestrained public enthusiasm. In March 1974 the New England Division was authorized to carry out a different type of project—the first of its kind in the country—to control flooding. This is by the protection of flood plains, or more correctly, the remaining wetland "natural valley storage" areas of the plains. Carved out by the rivers themselves over aeons of meandering, flood plains are natural safety valves that absorb and diminish high flows. But three centuries of settlement and development in New England have seen the building on flood plains of communities dependent upon water for transportation, power, and industrial processes, and the stringing along river banks of railroads and highways to service expanding towns and cities. In recent years the unchecked momentum of urban growth has encroached on even those wetland areas of flood plains once considered unsuitable for building but now too often regarded merely as mistakes of nature in need of correction. Some river basins may still be naturally protected from serious flooding by the existence of substantial wetlands, but if floods of increasing severity even by minor storms are to be prevented in these watersheds in the future, their natural valley storage capabilities must not be further depleted.

In 1965 Congress directed the Corps to make a comprehensive study of the 307-square-mile Charles River Watershed in eastern Massachusetts with a view to multiple-purpose improvement. Beginning the study in 1967, the New England Division worked closely with a Coordinating Committee representing the major federal, state, and regional agencies with responsibilities in the watershed and with a Citizens' Advisory Committee speaking for the people of the valley. The study concentrated first on the lower Charles River, a densely urbanized area most exposed to the threat of serious flood damages. The division engineers noted that the congested cities of Boston and Cambridge and their immediate upstream neighbors experienced intensive flooding in severe storms. From subbasins extending back into the communities of Watertown, Waltham, Brookline, and Newton, storm flows raced unchecked across paved surfaces and through culverted tributaries and drains into the Charles River Basin, that stretch of the river impounded between the Charles River Dam near its mouth and the Watertown Dam about eight and a half miles upstream. Submitting an Interim Report in 1968, the division recommended as the only feasible solution the construction of a pumping station capable of rapidly discharging the floodwater into Boston Harbor, which for nearly ten hours daily has tide levels equal to or greater than the water level in the basin. The station would be incorporated into a new Charles River Dam that would also contain navigation locks adequate to handle the ever-increasing boat traffic into the Basin.[28]

Turning to the middle and upper reaches of the Charles, the engineers found that the communities above Newton had a history of only minimal flooding. Extensive marshes, swamps, and wet meadows scattered around the upper watershed were apparently taking care of things very well by holding floodwaters and then only slowly letting them go. As if to prove its efficiency, nature provided an intense storm in March 1968 to give the engineers

Medfield-Millis wet meadow in the Charles River Watershed. Normal spring high water.

the opportunity to observe the workings of its system under flood-of-record conditions. The wetlands, the investigators noted, restrained flood crests until four days after the storm, while in the basin below, high flows occurred within a few hours. These natural reservoirs released water so gradually that lower basin flows could pass out to sea before upstream flows arrived.

From the approximately 20,000 acres of wetlands scattered through the upper watershed, the engineers identified some 8,500 acres in seventeen parcels as most critically in need of preservation. These areas, all of 100 acres or more, were large enough to be the most effective hydrologically, were in the right places to perform in a synchronized fashion, were of practical size for efficient management, and were still undeveloped. But they obviously would not long remain undeveloped unless protected. They were already threatened by urban expansion, and the completion in 1970 of Interstate Route 495 promised another industrial alley arcing around Boston with the same instant construction of businesses and homes as sparked by inner belt Route 128 a decade or so before. If in the scramble for building sites the wetlands were filled in, the Charles River communities were headed for trouble.

Sending its final report to Washington in 1972, the division recommended the protection of the crucial 8,500 acres of wetland through federal purchase or through easements restricting building and filling, at an estimated cost of some $7 million. While preserved primarily for flood control under the supervision of the division, the lands would be managed by governmental and private agencies as wildlife refuges and compatible recreational areas.

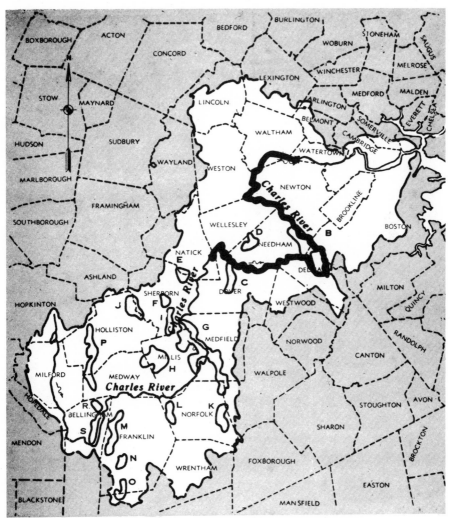

CHARLES RIVER WATERSHED

NEW ENGLAND DIVISION, CORPS OF ENGINEERS

0   SCALE IN MILES   5

NATURAL VALLEY STORAGE AREAS
AREA OF HIGH LOSS POTENTIAL

The report also recommended that state and local authorities adopt measures for protecting the remaining 11,500 acres of smaller wetlands to reinforce the federal flood control program. Further proposals dealing more broadly with the environment of the watershed appended by the Coordinating Committee called for state and local action relating to sewage and waste disposal, insurance of future water supply, and schemes for recreational and conservational facilities, including the carving out of a green parkland corridor along both banks of the Charles from end to end.[29]

An Environmental Protection Award was presented by Bruce L. Lund, President of the Charles River Watershed Association, to New England Division Deputy Engineer Col. Charles J. Osterndorf, in October 1973. John W. McCormack, former Speaker of the U.S. House of Representatives, was present at the ceremony. The Association's award, the first of its kind, cited the New England Division for "a national pioneering use of natural valley flood water storage in the Charles River Watershed."

Thus the Charles River Study resulted in recommendations for structural measures where flooding was already a problem and no other solution was possible and for a nonstructural approach where flood damages do not yet occur and can be forestalled. Not every watershed lends itself to the concept of natural valley storage. The natural reservoirs must be there, and in the right places and of the right dimensions to function in an effective, synchronized way. Even on the Charles this concept is applicable only to the upper portion of the river. Yet the popular reaction to this imaginative approach of the Corps, overlooking the fact that the largest structural project in the history of the division's civil works mission is necessary to protect the communities of the Lower Charles, tended to be simply that the Corps, rather than building dams, should recognize that "nature's way is best."[30]

A new Charles River Dam was authorized by Congress in 1968 and construction began in February 1973. The original dam was completed by the Commonwealth of Massachusetts in 1910 to prevent tidal flooding along the lower reach of the river and to create a recreational pool covering unsightly and maloderous tidal flats. The pool, or Charles River Basin, modeled on the Alster River Basin of Hamburg, Germany, soon became a major recreational

Artist's rendering of the new Charles River Dam.

and aesthetic feature of Boston. But with the growth of the city and its environs over the course of a half century, the dam became unsuited to the needs of the community. Its sluice gates are no longer adequate to handle floodwater coursing into the basin, and its single navigation lock cannot accommodate recreational river traffic growing in volume every year. The new dam, located a short way downstream, will expel floodwater with six huge pumps having a discharge capacity of 8,400 cubic feet per second, and will contain two navigation locks designed for small craft and one for larger recreational boats and commercial vessels. It will also include a fishway to allow shad and other anadromous fish to migrate up the river. The cost of the project is estimated at $55.9 million, to which local interests will contribute $16.8 million. The dam's average annual benefits, largely the prevention of flood damage, will run to $4,163,500. The natural valley storage project for the

The pumping station and fishway structures of the Charles River Dam
under construction.

Upper Charles was authorized by the Water Resources Development Act of
March 1974. It has been funded by Congress, hydraulic design studies have
been completed, and real estate studies necessary for federal acquisition of
land are under way.

Despite several decades of effort and a huge investment of money in flood
control works, property damage and human suffering from flooding throughout the country has steadily increased. The reason is simply that the construction of homes, apartments, industries, and commercial facilities on the
flood plains of rivers and coasts has outraced the building of flood control
works. Without the works, damages would be astronomical. Nevertheless,
they continue to grow. The losing battle cannot be turned around without the
exercise of greater wisdom in the use of flood plains, which requires both
adequate knowledge of flood hazards and cooperative action by governmental and private interests. Recognizing this, Congress in 1960 authorized the
Corps of Engineers to compile and disseminate information relating to floods
and flood damage for guidance in flood plain management. Later legislation
and Presidential executive order broadened the responsibilities of the Corps
in this field of activity.

Through a Flood Plain Management Services program, the Corps assists
federal agencies in evaluating flood hazards when planning new facilities,
disposing of properties, or issuing grants, loans, or mortgage insurance for
non-federal construction projects. It also provides technical assistance and

One of the six giant pumps of the Charles River Dam that together will discharge 3,700,000 gallons per minute of flood runoff from the Charles River Basin into Boston Harbor against a high tide.

guidance to state and local governments and to private citizens involved in flood plain management planning and regulation. The FPMS specialists of the New England Division respond to about three hundred requests for such aid every year.

Upon request by local agencies with relevant jurisdiction under state law, the Corps carries out flood plain information studies for the guidance of planning groups, zoning boards, real estate developers, and anyone else to whom they may be of use. The study reports identify and map areas subject to flooding, document the flood history of the region, define the scope of possible future floods, and offer suggestions to prevent or minimize future flood damage. By 1975 the New England Division had made forty-four such studies involving some one hundred communities, and had twelve more studies in progress.

Flooding of the Black River at Ludlow, Vermont, showing the need for flood plain management.

The Corps' FPMS specialists also conduct flood insurance studies in eligible communities for delineating risk zones for the determination of insurance rates under the National Flood Insurance Program. These studies are made pursuant to the National Flood Insurance Act of 1969 (as amended by the Flood Disaster Act of 1973), which authorized federal subsidization of flood insurance on homes and small business properties in communities that agree to meet certain requirements relating to zoning and to building in potential flood areas. By 1975 the New England Division had completed seventy-three flood insurance studies, and had three additional studies underway.[31]

IX DESIGNS FOR HYDROELECTRIC POWER

At the request of the Federal Power Commission to provide for possible future generation of hydroelectric power, several of the first flood control dams constructed in New England—Knightville, Blackwater, and Tully Lake—were designed so that they might later be raised and penstocks installed. But linking power generation with flood control in New England was a scheme nature and economic development had already largely ruled out long before it became the casualty of conflicting federal and state political interests. Army Engineers did initiate two major hydroelectric power projects in New England, but neither developed out of river basin plans for flood control. The first, the Passamaquoddy Tidal Power Project, was conceived as a federal work relief measure during the Great Depression of the 1930s, and the second, the Upper Saint John River Hydroelectric Power Development, grew out of continued interest in the aborted Passamaquoddy project.

Passamaquoddy and Cobscook bays, arms of the Bay of Fundy, are located at the mouth of the St. Croix River, the boundary stream between Maine and New Brunswick. The international boundary runs through Passamaquoddy Bay, while Cobscook Bay lies wholly within the United States. Nearly landlocked by headlands and islands, the bays form large natural and adjacent basins. The mean range of tides in the area is approximately eighteen feet, with a maximum of twenty-six feet and a minimum of eleven feet. About four billion tons of water flow in and out of the bays twice a day—a volume equal to the average flow of nearly two weeks of the Mississippi River below all its tributaries. The plan for harnessing this wide range of tides for the generation of electric power was conceived by an American engineer, Dexter P. Cooper, while residing on Campobello Island in 1919. Cooper would close Passamaquoddy and Cobscook bays by a series of dams, equipped with regulating gates and navigation locks, to form two huge pools. Passamaquoddy Bay would be filled at high tide and used as a high-level pool, and Cobscook Bay would be emptied at low tide and maintained as a low-level pool. Power would be generated by drawing water through turbines in a powerplant located between the two pools. Compared to most river hydroelectric projects the average hydraulic head of the tidal project would be quite small and the energy output per turbine limited; but the very large quantities of water available for power production were perpetual, dependable, and fully predictable, unaffected by rainfall, drought, or silting.[1]

In 1925 and 1926 Cooper formed companies in Maine and New Brunswick to develop his scheme. In 1929, however, Canada, fearing that closing Passamaquoddy Bay would injure herring fisheries, denied Cooper a development permit. This forced a major revision of the project, confining it to Cobscook Bay and reducing its power potential. Cooper suffered another serious setback when private investment capital mostly shied away from the enterprise. Turning to the government for financial backing, he applied in 1933 for a loan from the Public Works Administration, which was denied

High and low tides at Eastport, Maine, site of the Passamaquoddy Tidal Power Project. The Corps' inspection boat *Sea King* is at the dock.

when the Federal Power Commission determined that the project would not be self-liquidating. Cooper then proposed that his enterprise be taken over by the government as a federal work-relief project. President Franklin D. Roosevelt, long a summer resident on Campobello Island and himself intrigued since 1921 with harnessing tidal power at Passamaquoddy Bay, favored the idea, as did the state of Maine. Secretary of the Interior Harold Ickes, who headed the Public Works Administration, appointed a four-member, wholly civilian, Passamaquoddy Bay Tidal Power Commission, chaired by Cooper, to consider the project further. Reporting in January 1935, the commission recommended the allotment of $30 million for the construction of "Quoddy," as the project came to be known, under the direction of the Chief of Engineers.

Lt. Col. Philip B. Fleming, Eastport District Engineer.

Events then moved quickly. Further studies were initiated, and application was made for funds under the Emergency Relief Appropriation Act of April 1935. On May 17 the Chief of Engineers established the Eastport District and three days later designated Lieutenant Colonel (then Major) Philip B. Fleming, formerly assigned to the Engineering Division of the Public Works Administration, as district engineer. On May 28 the President approved an initial allotment to Quoddy of $10 million of relief funds, which was later reduced to $7 million. Meantime negotiations were under way with Cooper to take over the assets of his companies. A preliminary agreement was signed on June 26 (a final agreement was reached on October 18), according to which all rights and assets were conveyed to the United States for $60,000 and Cooper was appointed Advisor to the National Power Policy Committee to find a market for Quoddy power. The next day, June 27, the active prosecution of Quoddy began.

Fleming started the organization of the Eastport District with five military and ten senior civilian assistants; six months later the administrative, technical, and supervisory force of the district had grown to 754 people. The development they were to construct would be unique in the world. Although studies relating to tidal hydroelectric power had been made in several countries, the idea was yet to be applied. The design of Quoddy, as revised by Cooper and modified by the Eastport Office, was a single-pool scheme employing Cobscook Bay as a high-level pool. The pool would be filled through sluice gates at high tide. When the tide ebbed and the difference in head between the pool and the Bay of Fundy reached five and a half feet, the turbines of a main power station would be started and power generated until with the incoming tide the difference in head again became five and a half feet. Since under a one-pool plan the main power plant would be shut down for about five hours twice each day, surplus peak power would be used to pump water to an elevated basin. While the main station was not operating, this water would be drawn through the turbines of an auxiliary plant to provide a continuous supply of energy. The major structures of Quoddy were to include five rock-filled dams between the headlands and islands across the entrance to Cobscook Bay; a filling-gate structure with multiple gates; a two-way navigation lock; a main power station with ten turbines and structural provisions for the later installation of ten more turbines; and a pumped-storage plant consisting of nine pumps, two turbines and an 8,000-acre storage reservoir located near Haycock Harbor, some twenty miles south of Eastport. The annual energy output of the development would be 262 million kilowatt-hours, a somewhat greater output than the large Moore Station of the New England Power Company on the upper Connecticut River. Leaving a door open to the future, the whole project was so designed that it could be incorporated into a larger international two-pool plan at any time.

The Passamaquoddy Bay Tidal Power Commission had relied on Cooper's estimates to figure the cost of Quoddy at about $30 million. The Office of the Chief of Engineers, making its own study of Cooper's estimates, had raised the sum to over $36 million and cautioned that Cooper's estimates had been made in the absence of complete surveys and foundation explorations. The Eastport Office, undertaking comprehensive investigations and detailed engineering studies, now found that even after modifying Cooper's plan in several respects to reduce costs, his estimates had been quite inadequate, and in December 1935 it submitted a new estimate of $61.5 million. Upon President Roosevelt's request, the United States Reclamation Service appointed a Board of Review to study the findings and estimates of the Eastport Office. Reporting the next April, the board increased the cost of Quoddy to $68.5 million.

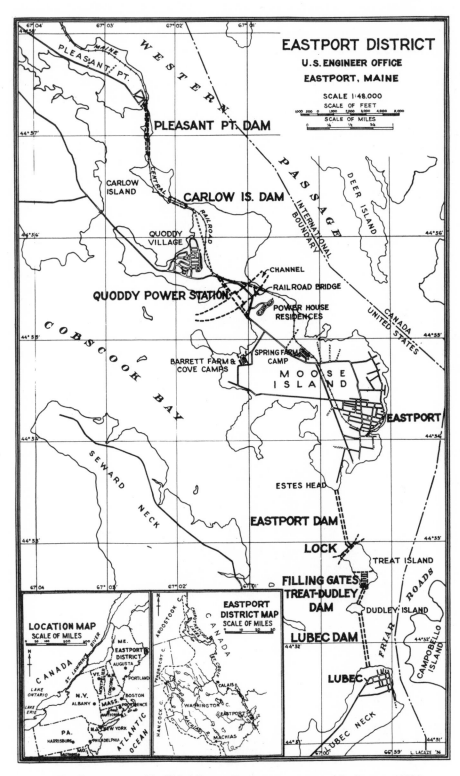

The Passamaquoddy Tidal Power Project as proposed in January 1936.

226

Meantime the Eastport Office had proposed and the Chief of Engineers had approved, in January and February 1936, a revised plan of development. Topographical surveys of the Haycock Harbor site for the pumped-storage reservoir had indicated excessive construction costs, and investigations of other possible sites had produced the same findings. The revised plan therefore eliminated the pumped-storage feature of the project in favor of a thermal-electric auxiliary plant or interconnection with existing utilities. It also reduced the number of generating units in the tidal power plant to five while providing for the same annual energy output. The estimated cost of the new plant was $37,985,250.

Many features of Quoddy were of a pioneering nature, necessitating extensive investigations to determine designs, suitable materials, and methods of construction. Studies were made to ascertain the proper type of concrete to withstand the severe climatic conditions of the area. Extensive soil tests, including the use of model structures, were made to determine such things as the settlement of dams built on marine clay and seepage and percolation through dams. Much had to be learned about the corrosive effects of salt water on various kinds of metals, an area in which, surprisingly, few comprehensive investigations had been made. Experiments were made to determine the effects of salt water upon metals individually, the effects of electrolytic action between different types of metals in close contact in sea water, and the resistance of metals to erosion under cavitation conditions in sea water. The latter studies, which were wholly novel, were conducted at

Deep water core drilling in Quoddy foundation explorations.

the Massachusetts Institute of Technology with newly developed apparatus. Still other studies dealt with the chemistry of sea water and the likely degree of fouling of turbines and other structures by marine growth of the area.

Seepage studies for Quoddy using a model structure.

Hydraulic model tests to establish designs and construction methods for the dams, filling gates, and navigation lock were carried out under contract with the Alden Hydraulic Laboratory of the Worcester Polytechnic Institute. Comprehensive studies were made relating to generating and other electrical equipment. Since almost no data was available with which to predict the performance of the required low-head turbines under all conditions of operation, experiments were necessary to determine the proper spacing of units, the design of water passages, and the depth of excavation required for the power station. These investigations, conducted with models, were carried out under contract by four turbine manufacturers under the supervision of engineers from the Eastport District.

Quoddy presented a full share of administrative as well as engineering challenges. Cooper's companies had not purchased any land, and in acquiring sites for the project's structures the Eastport District encountered unusual difficulties. Some owners demanded exorbitant prices for their properties, and uncertainty over whether condemnation proceedings could be invoked hampered and delayed negotiations. Land titles were uncertain. Ownership for generations had almost without exception been transferred by inheritance, usually without record. It was often difficult to ascertain the real owners, and then to find them. The division and subdivision of property rights among heirs of owners dying intestate had become so involved that individual equities had become in one case as small as 1/504 of the value of

Personnel of the Eastport District Soils Laboratory. Left to right: (top row) W. J. Byrne; W. I. Kenerson; C. E. Browne, Jr.; J. H. Parsons; B. S. Longfellow; J. C. Mahle, Jr.; C. B. Stoddard; J. M. Stoddard; F. V. Libby; Chief Gen. Eng'r M. B. Pike; (bottom row) E. J. Lavin; S. J. Templeton; P. J. Roche; Assist. Eng'r R. M. Haines; B. F. Witham; Chief, Soils Laboratory, B. K. Hough, Jr.; D. M. Mills; Hydro. Eng'r G. H. Rich; E. C. Camick; B. J. Shaw; W. A. Balkam, Jr.

the property. Reliable definitions of properties in deeds were almost nonexistent. Descriptions in most cases had been copied from original grants based on an inaccurate survey and map made about 1794. The purchase by the district of 288.45 acres for $52,250.58 and the completion of surveys and negotiations for several thousand more acres amounted to a minor miracle.

Eastport was a small community of about 3,200 people, remotely located in a sparsely settled section of Maine. Dependent mostly on the packing of seafood, the city's business and commerce had been declining, along with an ailing fishing industry, for thirty years. To cope with an influx of people that would nearly triple its population was beyond the city's resources. Its finances were bankrupt, fire and police protection and municipal utilities were inadequate, hospital facilities and health supervision of any kind were nonexistent, and available housing was limited and primitive. As the first district employees began to arrive in July 1935, rents for rooms and houses in Eastport doubled and board increased nearly as much. By August shelter of any kind was difficult to find, and employees were compelled to take accommodations in distant villages, farmhouses, and summer cottages, all generally lacking modern heating or plumbing facilities. Office accommodations were equally limited, and at one time the district's administrative and engineering personnel were scattered around the city in over twenty different churches, halls, and warehouses.

Housing for the district's employees was an obvious and immediate necessity. Facilities for the engineering, administrative, and supervisory personnel were grouped in "Quoddy Village," built from scratch on Moose Island about two and a half miles north of Eastport. Construction of the village, however, did not start until late August because of difficulties in securing land and failure to receive satisfactory bids on much of the work. Contrac-

Two of the more than twenty halls, churches, and warehouses that housed the Eastport District's first offices.

tors were apprehensive about the use of relief labor, the inadequacy of rail and highway transportation, and prevalent rumors that the project might be abandoned at any time. Hopes for completing construction before winter set in were further frustrated by difficulties in procuring materials and labor, adverse weather, and problems attending a new and largely untrained organization. By late December a few families could move into the village, and by mid-April 1936 it was completed. Single-family houses, duplex houses, four-family apartments, two large apartment buildings, and a dormitory provided 450 housing units. The village also included an administration building, a laboratory, various utility buildings, and a thirty-bed hospital. Later an exhibition hall containing a working model of the project and other displays was added. About one-third of the construction was accomplished by contract and two-thirds by hired labor and government plant.

To lodge hundreds of workers coming from all parts of the state of Maine, two camps, located near the principal construction and warehousing sites, were completed by hired labor by mid-November 1935. Consisting of twelve bunkhouses and three mess halls of standard CCC type, recreation halls, and other facilities, the camps accommodated at peak quartering a total of 1350 men. Other necessary early construction included maintenance shops, warehouses, railroad yards and wharves, roads and walks, and sewer, electric, and water systems. Water was obtained from the local servicing corporation, whose equipment was so antiquated that the district had to repair, improve, and maintain portions of the utility. Since the local electric company could furnish only a limited supply of additional power, an auxiliary generating unit was installed in Quoddy Village and more were planned for other locations.

The work-relief nature of Quoddy created problems. The district was

Aerial view of Quoddy Village.

Administration Building of the Eastport District in Quoddy Village.

Working model of the Passamaquoddy Tidal Power Project in the exhibition hall of Quoddy Village.

required to recruit all personnel through the newly organized National Reemployment Service, which was at first unprepared to handle the district's demands for labor effectively. Moreover, NRS referrals had to be made from relief rolls prepared by the Federal Emergency Relief Administration for the state of Maine, and the rolls were often faulty. They failed to include many people in the vicinity of Eastport who urgently needed work while including numerous others who had apparent means of support. This created considerable local resentment, which was unfairly directed against the Eastport District. Many workers referred under skilled categories proved not to have the necessary qualifications. Since Works Progress Administration regulations required that at least 90 percent of all employees be procured from relief rolls, exemptions had to be obtained from Washington to hire skilled non-relief personnel such as carpenters and diesel shovel operators. When common laborers were required beginning in September 1935, less than 30 percent of the number requisitioned reported for work. Not enough relief workers resided in northeastern Maine, and many workers elsewhere in the state were unwilling to leave their families for the security wages prescribed by WPA regulations. Therefore during the period of urgent housing construction in the fall of 1935, approximately 45 percent of the district's field employees were from non-relief sources. The extensive red tape involved in obtaining exemptions from WPA rules caused considerable loss of time and efficiency.

By late October workers were arriving at Quoddy at the rate of over one hundred a day. Most were destitute of funds, some were without adequate outer clothing, some even without shoes. Many were too aged or otherwise physically unable to work. To cope with the situation the district established a Welfare Department of five people. Through Herculean efforts the department provided the needy with shelter, food, clothing, and medical treatment.

It arranged with state and other welfare agencies for the return to their homes of people unable to work. It also provided non-sectarian religious services, attended to the distribution of mail, collected reading material, and organized recreational and athletic activities.

The district also had to establish its own Medical Department. Not only were local doctors too few and a hospital nonexistent, but relief labor on unfamiliar construction work spelled accidents, and there was not a surgeon in the area. Unable to attract established doctors from their practices, or secure physicians from the Army Medical Corps or the Civil Service, the district assembled a team of highly competent though relatively inexperienced young men through recommendations from leading surgeons of prominent Boston and New York hospitals. First aid stations were established, a house in Eastport was converted into an infirmary, and, finally, on May 1, 1936, the Quoddy Hospital, a modern, complete, and compact unit of thirty-bed capacity, was opened.

The distance to Eastport and the volunteer nature of the city's Fire Department ruled out reliance upon it by the district, which consequently organized its own seven-man department, complete with combination pumper engine and company of volunteer assistants. Nor could Eastport's two-man Police Department be expected to maintain order. The huge influx of people inevitably brought in some undesirables. Petty thievery became extensive, and disorders common. Gangs of smugglers, accustomed to operating on this stretch of the international border, also concentrated at Quoddy, and watchmen were intimidated and even shot at. The district therefore assembled a police force of nineteen trained men who did watchman duty, arrested thieves and bootleggers, maintained order in the labor camps, and controlled the traffic that sometimes choked the area. The Police Department also had to handle an estimated 180,000 visitors to Quoddy during the summer of 1936, an inpouring that culminated with thousands of people congesting Quoddy Village on the occasion of President Roosevelt's visit to the project late in July.

Quoddy boasted all the other institutions and attributes of a typical American small town. It had its own news journal, *The Quoddy Courier,* its Boy Scout and Girl Scout troops, its gun club, its Quoddy Engineer ball team, Quoddy Village Garden Club, and Quoddy Junior Theater Guild. Its citizens met, fell in love, and married. They organized soft ball teams, danced on week-end evenings, and went on fishing trips, outings, and scavenger hunts. They produced plays and minstrel shows.[2] Quoddyites lived in their brand-new town just as they always had lived elsewhere.

Despite the huge investment of effort by the Corps of Engineers in Quoddy, the future of the project was uncertain from the beginning. Because of unsettled questions of cost and design, and the failure of the state of Maine to enact legislation providing for the leasing and operation of the development, work on Quoddy was limited for several months by directive of the Chief of Engineers to temporary housing and to studies and design. Employment on the project peaked at the end of November 1935, when the district was racing to construct housing before winter. Over 5,400 people were employed, about four-fifths working directly for the district and the remainder for contractors. On December 18 the Chief of Engineers, acting at

President Roosevelt inspects the working model of the Passamaquoddy Tidal Power Project upon his visit to the project in July 1936. Capt. Donald J. Leehey, Administrative Officer of the Eastport District, demonstrates with a pointer while District Engineer Lt. Col. Philip Fleming, on Roosevelt's left, looks on.

the request of the administration, directed that a force of about 4,000 should be continuously employed on the project if possible. Minor permanent features of the development were to be undertaken with hired labor as units of the housing project were completed, thus holding a labor pool available for contractors pending the letting of contracts for major features of the work. With the approval of the revised and less costly plan for Quoddy in February 1936, active construction was begun on the three smaller dams of the project with hired labor, and preparations were made to call for contractors' bids on other structures of the development.

Before any contracts were made, Quoddy was suspended by Congress. When the annual War Department Appropriation Bill came before Congress in March 1936, it included a recommendation from the Bureau of the Budget for $9 million for Quoddy and $20 million more for four other work-relief projects currently underway, including the construction of a ship canal across Florida. But the House of Representatives, stating that the projects had never been approved by Congress, refused to make the appropriations.

The possibility of continuing Quoddy with relief funds was also blocked by Congress. The Emergency Relief Appropriation Act of June 1936 gave the President discretion within certain limits, as had the relief act of the year before, to allocate funds for work-relief projects. But funds for Quoddy and the Florida canal, both of which had come under severe political attack, were deftly debarred. No project could be undertaken or prosecuted under the appropriation, the act stipulated, "unless and until an amount sufficient for its completion has been allocated and irrevocably set aside for its completion," and both projects were too large for this requirement to be met. When the bill was before the Senate, Democratic majority leader Joseph Robinson of Arkansas had offered an amendment authorizing the President to appoint independent boards of engineers to study all questions relating to the controversial projects. If the reports were favorable, the President could allot $9 million to carry on Quoddy and $15 million to continue work on the Florida canal. The Senate rejected the amendment as it applied to Quoddy, while approving it in relation to the Florida canal. Ultimately, the canal provision was also stricken from the bill.[3]

Republicans had discovered in Quoddy a vulnerable point of attack on the administration's public works program, and Democrats were conceding that it had become a political liability. Since few people had any notion of how power could be generated by tides, the whole concept was easy to ridicule, and the escalating cost of Quoddy fitted nicely into the image of a pipedream of irresponsible advocates. Charges of boon-doggling became common, and stories spread of how the Army Engineers had bought a $17,000 yacht and built expensive houses. In some quarters Quoddy was condemned as an experiment in socialism. More justifiable complaints were that it would be cheaper to build a steam generating plant, that Quoddy power would cost more than steam-generated power, that there was no present or prospective market for Quoddy power, and that hydroelectric power, when needed, could be more cheaply produced on Maine's undeveloped rivers. Republican Senator Arthur Vandenberg of Michigan, Quoddy's foremost critic in the upper house, used these arguments with telling effect.

Quoddy might still have survived had the administration chosen to support it. Both Roosevelt and Public Works Administrator Ickes had been quick to display their interest in the project in 1934, when it was expected to have beneficial results in Maine in the September elections. A year and a half later, however, when it appeared that the project would cost about $65 million rather than $35 million, and Quoddy had become a prime target of opposition criticism, Roosevelt's interest began to cool. Both he and Ickes were inclined to blame the Army Engineers for accepting Dexter Cooper's figures on cost without checking them until after the government was committed and work actually started. It was not in fact the Engineers who had hastily committed the government, nor had they accepted Cooper's figures. Yet Ickes, after appointing Cooper to head the Passamaquoddy Bay Tidal Power Commission, the civilian panel which *had* relied on Cooper's figures, criticized the Engineers for "accepting a promoter's estimate of costs."

By March 1936 Roosevelt was expressing a wish to get out of the project as quickly and as gracefully as possible, but apparently was not wholly decided. He brought up the question of the comparative costs of producing power with Chief of Engineers Major General Edward M. Markham. When Markham said that Quoddy power would be more costly than steam-generated power unless the whole original project was developed, which would require an international agreement with Canada, the President began figuring. He suggested that if a generous amount of work-relief money was applied to the project, the cost on the basis of non-relief money would be lower than for current produced by steam. This, of course, was no new idea. That Quoddy could be economically justified only if developed as a relief project had been evident from the beginning. Yet Ickes, never enthusiastic about the project or about Army Engineers, now advised that the country "would consider the total cost, regardless of how it was divided or what it was called, and... the best possible position to take was that the project would not be justified unless it went forward as a whole in cooperation with Canada." Roosevelt agreed. Although a few months later, upon his visit to Quoddy in July, the President revived the project as a possibility, an act Ickes thought "very unwise indeed," nothing came of this momentarily renewed interest.[4]

On July 6, 1936 the order was issued to demobilize Quoddy. In addition to the temporary housing, the three smaller dams of the project were by this time essentially completed, nine permanent residences for the operating personnel of the project had been built, the site of the navigation lock had been

First and last train-loads of fill in the construction of Pleasant Point Dam. The dam was built from and encased a railway trestle of the Maine Central Railroad line to Eastport.

cleared, and excavation for the filling gates and minor work in connection with the power house had been started. Thereafter construction was limited to the fulfillment of minor contractual obligations until all active operations ceased on August 16. On that date Lieutenant Colonel Fleming was transferred to duty with the Resettlement Administration in Washington and Captain Samuel D. Sturgis, Jr., was appointed Acting District Engineer. All facilities at Quoddy were turned over to the National Youth Administration, and plant, stock, and per annum employees were transferred to other governmental activities. On October 31 the Eastport District was discontinued and operations relating to the final demobilization of the project were placed under the direction of the Boston District. About $5.9 million had been expended on the project.

Quoddy, however, continued to have its advocates. And, ironically, it was Senator Vandenberg who introduced a resolution in February 1939 requesting the Federal Power Commission to review its reports on Quoddy and bring them up to date. In April 1941 the commission filed an adverse report on the economic feasibility of an all-American project. Yet it predicted that as fuel prices increased and markets for power expanded in the Northeast, the power potentially available in Passamaquoddy tides would one day be developed. "The event seems certain," it commented, "the only uncertainty is in point of time."

There the matter rested until 1947, when Maine was struck by disastrous forest fires and drought. Its rivers ran low and power was in such short supply that naval vessels had to be sent to pump power from their plants into the Maine towns. The state's congressional delegation, led by Senator Margaret Chase Smith, now opened a campaign for the revival of Quoddy on an international basis. Consequently in November 1948 the governments of the United States and Canada requested the International Joint Commission, a body established in 1909 for the regulation of boundary waters, to determine the practicability and cost of a complete survey for an international development. The Corps of Engineers, which carried out the investigation, reported in March 1950 that the project was physically feasible and the survey would cost $3.9 million. Two years later the Engineers scaled down their estimate to $3 million. During the summer of 1951 the New England Division and the United States Geological Survey had tested at Eastport depth-finding sonic equipment recently developed by the Magnolia Oil Corporation of Dallas, Texas. By comparing sonic data with boring data obtained by the Eastport District in 1935-36, they had established the reliability of the new fathometer, called a Sonoprobe, for determining the depth of overburden, or sediment layers, above bedrock. The new equipment would cut sharply the cost of bottom and foundation explorations.[5]

In January 1951 and again in January 1953, the Maine congressional delegation introduced joint resolutions in the House and Senate for authorization of the survey. In 1955 these efforts were given a boost by the report of the New England-New York Interagency Committee. The report included all information on the Passamaquoddy Bay region available at the time and recommended that the survey be undertaken. Canada, at first skeptical of the project, later agreed to bear ten percent of the cost of a survey. In January 1956 Congress authorized the study, and in August the United States and

Canada requested the International Joint Commission to make the necessary arrangements.

To supervise the study the commission established the International Passamaquoddy Engineering Board, composed of two representatives each from the United States and Canada. The American section of the board was headed by recently retired Chief of Engineers Lieutenant General Samuel D. Sturgis, Jr., who had seen service at Quoddy twenty years before. The New England Division carried out the engineering phases of the investigation; the Federal Power Commission and the New Brunswick Electric Power Commission conducted power-market surveys; and an International Passamaquoddy Fisheries Board studied the effects the project might have upon the fisheries of the area.

To supplement the mass of information collected by the Eastport Office in 1935-36, New England Division engineers established a field office and a soils laboratory at Eastport to gather and analyze new data obtained by aerial topographical surveys, tidal observations, hydrographic surveys, and subsurface explorations. The most difficult and most costly phase of the field investigations was core drilling to determine the location and design of dams and regulation gates. The drilling, carried out in waters up to 300 feet deep swept by reversing tidal currents reaching velocities of 10 feet per second, was done under contract by a Texas firm using special oil-drilling equipment brought from the Gulf of Mexico. The test borings of overburden and bedrock were carefully selected so they could be supplemented with less expensively obtained sonic data.

Some sixty different engineering arrangements of dams and turbines were considered. The annual energy output of each was determined by an electronic computer, and the arrangement with the best relationship of installed capacity and energy output to construction cost was selected for design. Under this layout, Passamaquoddy Bay would form the high pool of the project and Cobscook Bay the low pool. The bays would be closed by nearly seven miles of rock-filled dams, and between the pools, at the same place on Moose Island selected for the earlier Quoddy project, would be an outdoor type powerhouse with thirty large-diameter turbines. There would be 90 vertical-lift filling and 60 emptying gates, each thirty feet square, and four navigation locks, two for fishing vessels and two for larger ships. On the

Artist's rendering of the outdoor type powerhouse proposed in 1959 by the International Passamaquoddy Engineering Board.

recommendation of the International Passamaquoddy Fisheries Board, the project would also include fishways into the bays and the relocation, if necessary, of two lobster pounds in the upper pool.

The average annual energy generation of the tidal power plant would be 1,843 million kilowatt-hours, seven times the planned output of the earlier Quoddy project. Unlike the earlier one-pool scheme, the two-pool project would generate power continuously, but because of a constantly changing available head, production would still be uneven. Although the installed capacity of the project would be 300,000 kilowatts, power output, varying with the ebb and flood of tides and with differences from spring to neap tides, would range from a dependable capacity of 95,000 kilowatts to a maximum of 345,000 kilowatts.

This variable output, together with the fifty-minute difference between lunar and solar days, meant that energy supplied could be out of step with the normal pattern of power demands. Peak demand for power might at times coincide with mimimum output. Therefore to supplement the varying output of the tidal power project, the Engineering Board considered several different types of auxiliary power sources, including river hydroelectric, pumped-storage, and steam-electric plants, to determine the type best suited for making the combined power output of the tidal project and its auxiliary match the characteristic load pattern. The auxiliary selected was a hydro-electric plant at Rankin Rapids on the upper Saint John River in Maine, about three and a half miles upstream from the town of St. Francis and 175 air miles from Quoddy.

Power development at the Rankin Rapids site had already been suggested by other agencies. Studies of its power potential had recently been made by the International Saint John River Engineering Board and by the New England-New York Interagency Committee. The Rankin Rapids auxiliary project, whose embankment would be 7,400 feet long and 333 feet high, would impound 8.23 million acre-feet of water, of which 2.8 million acre-feet would be usuable storage. A powerhouse of eight units would have a dependable capacity of 460,000 kilowatts and would generate 1,220 million kilowatt-hours annually. The tidal project and the Rankin Rapids auxiliary together would have a dependable capacity of 555,000 kilowatts and would generate 3,063 million kilowatt-hours annually.

The estimated cost of the tidal project was $484 million, and with the Rankin Rapids auxiliary, $630 million. Power market studies showed that the output of the project could be readily absorbed by the growing utility markets of Maine and New Brunswick. Because of differences in interests rates and in values of alternative power prevailing in the United States and Canada, it was necessary to compute separate benefit-cost ratios for the two areas. The International Passamaquoddy Engineering Board concluded that, assuming an equal division of power and first costs between the United States and Canada, the project was not economically justifiable for Canada. If built entirely by the United States, however, Quoddy and its Rankin Rapids auxiliary was economically feasible.

The International Joint Commission, reviewing the conclusions of the Engineering Board presented in October 1959, agreed with the engineering findings of the report, but not with its economic analysis. The tidal project, when considered alone, was clearly not economically justifiable. The Rankin Rapids project, on the other hand, was economically feasible. The board, adding the costs and benefits of the two projects together, had determined a favorable benefit-cost ratio for the combined project. In the opinion of the commission, a benefit-cost ratio determined on this basis was not a valid representation of the economic worth of the tidal project—the favorable ratio for the joint project could not be construed as indicating economic feasibility for the tidal power project.

Concluding that the tidal power project was not economically feasible under present conditions, the commission recommended that its development be viewed as a long-range possibility having better prospects of realization when other less costly energy resources available in the area were exhausted. It noted that the economic feasibility of the project might be affected by future changes in the costs and benefits considered in the evaluation of the project. It also observed that the two governments might wish to consider crediting the tidal project with certain public benefits that were not included in the economic feasibility determinations presented in the report.

The International Joint Commission issued its report in April 1961. The following month President John F. Kennedy requested the Department of the Interior to review the report with a view to changes in fuel, engineering, and financial costs that might make the project economically feasible. In July 1963 Secretary of the Interior Stewart L. Udall reported that, with modifications that would present no major problems, the development of Passamaquoddy and the upper Saint John River was both desirable and economically justified. He recommended authorization for their development by the Corps of Engineers and the marketing of the power by the Department of the Interior. The President thereupon directed the Departments of the Interior and Army to proceed with additional studies. At the suggestion of the Chief of Engineers, an Army-Interior Advisory Board was created to assist the field agencies making the studies. Originally consisting of members from the Corps of Engineers and the Department of the Interior, the board was later expanded to include representatives of other governmental agencies.[6]

Studies relating to the economic aspects of the project were the responsibility of the Department of the Interior, those dealing with its physical components the concern of the Corps of Engineers. The requisite field work, detailed engineering studies, and cost estimates of the structures were performed by the New England Division. The findings of these more detailed economic and engineering studies were submitted to the Secretary of the Interior in August 1964.

Quoddy emerged from the 1961-64 studies with a new purpose. Under previous concepts Quoddy was to produce continuous base load power for a local area. Now it was to be operated to supply a substantial proportion of the peaking power requirements of an extensive marketing area embracing all New England and New Brunswick. The two pools of the project would be regulated to provide the maximum amount of head on the powerplant turbines at the start of each peaking period of two hours duration. During the preceding high and low tides the high pool would be filled and the low pool emptied to the greatest extents possible, and these pool elevations would be maintained until the start of the peaking period. By using reversible pump-turbines the generating units of the powerplant could pump water from the low pool to the high pool during periods of neap tides, thereby increasing the available head beyond what nature at these times provided. Thus the powerplant could be operated at full installed capacity during all peaking periods. Following the peaking period, off-peak energy could be produced until it was time for the pools to be filled and emptied in preparation for the next peaking period.

The layout and design of Quoddy were to be the same as proposed in the previous plan with the exception of the powerplant. Instead of a 300,000-kilowatt plant equipped with thirty conventional vertical shaft turbines, the station would contain fifty inclined axis turbines with an installed capacity of 500,000 kilowatts. Additionally, layouts were completed for the construction of a second 500,000-kilowatt plant when warranted by growing power demands.

On the upper Saint John River the power development was relocated. Although the Rankin Rapids site was the best in the region from the standpoint of power production, a development there would flood a series of rapids in the lower reaches of the Allagash River, esteemed by environmentalists and sportsmen for its wild river characteristics, trout fishing, and white water canoeing. Therefore a damsite was selected at Dickey, just above the confluence of the Allagash with the Saint John. The main dam across the river, 9,200 feet long and 340 feet high, and perimeter dikes at five scattered locations would be of the earthfill type. They would impound 8.08 million acre-feet of water, of which 2.9 million acre-feet would be actively utilized for power purposes. The powerplant, with eight turbines operating under an average head of 293 feet, would have an installed capacity of 760,000 kilowatts and would generate 750 million kilowatt-hours of energy annually.

Water releases from the Dickey Dam would be irregular. Therefore a re-regulating reservoir would be located about eleven miles downstream at Lincoln School. The earthfill dam here, having a crest length of 1,290 feet and a maximum height of 87 feet, would impound the Dickey discharges and regulate them for more effective use by existing and proposed hydroelectric plants downstream in New Brunswick. Impounding 52,500 acre-feet of water, of which 16,000 acre-feet would be active storage, the dam would also include a two-turbine, 34,000-kilowatt powerplant capable of generating 260 million kilowatt-hours of energy each year.

Both powerplants on the Saint John would be operated primarily to generate peaking power in conjunction with the plant at Passamaquoddy, but substantial quantities of load factor power could also be produced.

The total cost of the Passamaquoddy-Upper Saint John power development was estimated at $845.1 million, which included $541.9 million for Passamaquoddy, $218.7 million for Dickey-Lincoln School, and $84.5 million for a transmission system interconnecting the powerplants and linking them with load centers in Maine and in the vicinity of Boston. Both the Passamaquoddy and the Saint John projects were determined to be economically feasible independently of each other, although Passamaquoddy was only marginally so. While the development would provide significant additional benefits in the form of recreational opportunities, area redevelopment in economically distressed counties, and flood control, its predominant benefit would be the generation of approximately 3 billion kilowatt-hours of electrical energy annually in a region where power rates were 28 percent above the national average.

Secretary Udall transmitted the report of the study to President Lyndon B. Johnson in July 1965. But by then fast-changing circumstances had al-

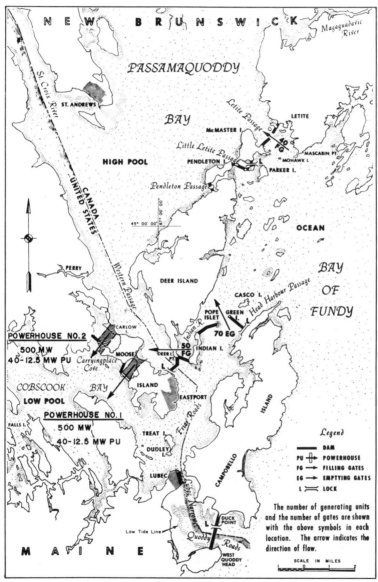

TIDAL POWER PROJECT PLAN 6/15/76

Plan of the International Passamaquoddy Tidal Power Project resulting from new studies authorized in March 1975. Except for the installation of 40 rather than 50 power units in each powerhouse, which will provide the same energy output, the plan is the same as that proposed in 1964.

tered the economics of power production. The power benefits analyzed in the report were derived from power value estimates furnished by the Federal Power Commission in December 1963 and from the interest rate in use at that time for federal water resource projects. The power value estimates were based on the generating costs of the steam-electric plants in use in Maine and in the vicinity of Boston. But meantime the utility companies had developed larger-capacity plants, which were being installed or were scheduled for installation, that would reduce power values. And a week before Udall made his report, the interest rate prescribed for federal water resource projects was raised. The result was that while the combined Passamaquoddy-Dickey-Lincoln School development still had a favorable benefit-cost ratio, Passamaquoddy by itself again was not economically justified.

The Dickey-Lincoln School project, however, could still produce low-cost load factor power for Maine and low-cost peaking power for the remainder of New England, which Udall thought should tend to reduce rates in the area. He therefore recommended the immediate authorization and construction of these works on the Saint John and a transmission system to serve them. He also recommended continued study on the Passamaquoddy project.

Three days after receiving Udall's report, President Johnson approved the Dickey-Lincoln School project. In October 1965 Congress voted authorization. After thirty years punctuated by studies, delays, and modified recommendations, Army Engineers were again directed to construct a federal power project in New England. With funds appropriated for preconstruction planning, the New England Division began advanced engineering and design work, including photogrammetric mapping of the project areas, subsurface explorations, topographic surveys, real estate planning, and preliminary design activity. In the course of this planning minor alterations were made on the dimensions of the dams and reservoirs, and the installed capacity of the Lincoln School powerplant, still to be equipped with two generating units, was increased from 34,000 to 70,000 kilowatts. By November 1967 preconstruction planning was about 50 percent completed. Then it came to a halt.[7]

Private power companies were opposing the project, and were disputing government claims about its power benefits and costs. The House Committee on Public Works, hoping to unravel the snarl with which it was faced, conducted its own staff investigation of the project. In the course of this study, investigators visited the Dickey site, consulted the files of the New England Division, and conferred with New England power companies. Convinced that the project was economically feasible and would provide efficient hydroelectric power at reasonable rates, the committee supported a budget request for $1,676,000 for FY 1968 to continue preconstruction planning. The full House, however, deleted the item from the committee report. Since the Senate approved the budget request, the conference committee split the difference and proposed $875,000. But not inclined to appropriate anything for the project, the House sliced the sum from the conference report.[8] For the next six years the Senate included funds for the Dickey-Lincoln School project in appropriation bills, even though for the last three

Artist's rendering of interim general plan of the Dickey dam and reservoir.

years no budget requests were made for them. Each time, however, the House blocked the appropriation.

But the future is perhaps with Dickey-Lincoln School, and perhaps even with Quoddy. The Arab oil embargo in 1973 and doubling costs of fuel and electric power heightened public awareness of the necessity for exploring and utilizing alternatives to fossil fuels for energy. When public works appropriations were voted for FY 1975, though no budget request for Dickey-Lincoln School was made, Congress voted $800,000 to resume preconstruction planning. Attention was inevitably directed also to the wasted energy in the unharnessed tides at Quoddy. And on March 21, 1975 the Senate Committee on Public Works requested the Board of Engineers for Rivers and Harbors to review the report submitted to President Johnson in July 1965, and other pertinent reports, with a view to determining the current feasibility of the Passamaquoddy Tidal Power Project in the interests of providing tidal power, recreation, economic development, and related land and water resource projects.[9]

The New England Division thus turned its attention once again to Passamaquoddy and the upper Saint John River.

X NEW CHALLENGES AND TASKS

Roads and canals, navigable rivers and safe harbors—the vital transportation needs of an economically bustling new nation—these were in the eye of Congress in 1824 when it first entrusted the Corps of Engineers with a civil mission. And for more than a decade Army Engineers assigned to New England were as occupied with planning canals and laying out railroads as with developing harbors and deepening rivers. Canal and railroad construction in the United States, however, was soon left wholly to private enterprise, and public demands on the technical expertise of the Corps focused largely on the improvement of navigable waterways. For over half a century this constituted the main function of the engineer districts and then divisions created after the Civil War to carry out unprecedented amounts of work legislated in Washington. With aid to commerce the end in view, the civil mission of the Corps thus came to be oriented to the water resources of the nation.

Narrowly defined by the aspirations of the nineteenth century, the dimensions of the Corps' mission were to expand tremendously in the twentieth. Pressures of urban growth, economic development, technological change, and rising standards of living upon water resources gave rise to new public concerns about water management and in turn to new tasks for the Corps of Engineers. In New England the "308" surveys starting in the late 1920s, flood control work beginning in the 1930s, and the Passamaquoddy Tidal Power Project of the latter decade launched the region's engineer districts into new areas of study and construction.

The 1930s also saw the beginnings of a systematic approach toward the control of beach and shore erosion along the nation's coasts. Federal interest in shore erosion had formerly been limited to improvements for navigation and for protection of federal property. In 1930, however, Congress established under the Chief of Engineers a Beach Erosion Board (replaced in 1963 by a Coastal Engineering Research Center), staffed by officers of the Corps and engineers from state agencies, whose function was to make studies of beach erosion in cooperation with state authorities. In 1936 Congress defined more precisely the functions of the board and, more importantly in terms of federal objectives, declared it to be the policy of the United States to assist state and local agencies in the improvement and protection of beaches, where federal interests were involved, not only to prevent damage to property but to promote and encourage "the healthful recreation of the people."[1] Recreation for the first time became a stated purpose of federal water resources projects.

For a decade federal assistance was limited to conducting studies and providing technical advice. In 1946 federal contributions to construction costs of projects protecting publicly owned shores were authorized; and in 1950 the first shore protection projects in New England were initiated. Since then the New England Division has participated in the restoration and protection of over thirty beaches and shores. In consultation with state or local sponsoring agencies, the division determines whether federal investments are justified and develops plans and specifications for projects. The federal financial contribution to projects usually may not exceed 50 percent of costs, though in certain publicly owned park and conservation areas it may be up to 70 percent. In most cases the states have supervised the work on projects, but in recent years the division itself has awarded the contracts. Measures taken have included the replenishment of beaches and sand dunes, the construction of groins extending into the water to intercept sand movements along the shore and widen beaches, and, where necessary, the building of seawalls, sand fences, and jetties.[2]

Wallis Sands State Beach, Rye, New Hampshire. This project, authorized in 1962 and completed the next year, included widening about 800 feet of the beach to a general width of 150 feet by direct placement of sandfill, and constructing an impermeable groin at the southern limit of the sandfill. The public facilities were constructed by the state.

Most shore protection projects planned by the New England Division have been on publicly owned beaches, but under present law federal aid may also be extended to privately owned shores if they are open to public use or essential to the protection of nearby public property. A project within this criteria was the restoration in 1971-72 of a large portion of the popular and historic Cliff Walk that skirts the ocean bluffs in front of some of the country's most palatial turn-of-the-century summer homes at Newport, Rhode Island. The walk, which was partially destroyed by the 1938 hurricane and further damaged by later storms, traverses privately owned land but is open to the public. Restoration of the famous Newport feature included placing riprap, backfill, and stone slope revetment where necessary to protect the shore, repair of seawalls, and grading and surfacing the walk. Spectators came in such numbers to sidewalk superintend the project that the division engineer arranged for the construction of an observation platform for their convenience and safety. The Cliff Walk Shore Restoration was selected in

Aerial view of the Cliff Walk Shore Restoration, Newport, Rhode Island.

New England Division Engineer Colonel John H. Mason displays the Chief of Engineers' Award of Merit for Landscape Architectural Design, presented to the division for the Cliff Walk Shore Restoration. John Wm. Leslie, Chief, Engineering Division, holds an aerial photograph of the project while George Sarandis, Project Engineer, looks on.

1973 for the Chief of Engineers' Award of Merit for Landscape Architectural Design.[3]

The promotion of outdoor recreation, declared by Congress in 1936 an essential purpose of shore protection work, became in subsequent years an increasingly important function of other Corps projects as well. Many of New England's small harbors were improved wholly or in part in the interests of recreational boating, and at flood control reservoirs opportunities were sometimes provided for picnicking, boating, and other activities. But it was in the 1960s that the recreational aspects of the Corps' civil mission came into their own. Recreational demands on water resources virtually skyrocketed, and Congress mandated that whenever possible provision should be made for recreational opportunities at federal projects. Under this authorization the New England Division intensified its efforts and expanded the construction and management of recreational facilities at flood control reservoirs and the Cape Cod Canal into major programs. Public enjoyment of reservoir areas is furthered too by ways that are small in themselves but indicative of the increasing emphasis placed on the recreational features of Corps projects. At Ball Mountain Lake in Vermont and at Knightville Dam in Massachusetts, for example, water releases are regularly made for white water canoe and kayak races that draw hundreds of contestants and thousands of spectators. At West Thompson Lake in Connecticut the conservation pool is raised every year after Labor Day weekend to provide satisfactory water levels for annual three-day retriever trials held by the Shoreline Retriever Club of Connecticut.[4]

Recreation is the most prominent ancillary purpose of Corps projects in New England. But the Corps may also incorporate other purposes beneficial to the public into projects designed primarily for navigation improvement, flood control, or other conventional objectives. Several New England flood control reservoirs were authorized as multiple-purpose projects so as to provide municipal or industrial water supply and to augment low river flows to improve downstream fisheries; and at all projects the conservation of fish and wildlife resources in cooperation with other agencies has become a routine part of Corps planning, construction, and management.

The evolution of multiple-purpose projects has been accompanied by the even more far-reaching development of comprehensive, long-range planning for water use and water control. The "308" surveys, the pioneer efforts in this direction, were valuable compendiums of information on major river basins. But their scope was limited, and in time they became outdated. Far more exhaustive was a comprehensive survey of the New England-New York region authorized by the Flood Control Act of 1950. Broadened by executive order from a Corps survey into a cooperative undertaking, the study was directed by a New England-New York Interagency Committee, chaired by the Corps of Engineers, which represented seven federal agencies and agencies of the seven states involved. Completed in 1957, after four years of research and field investigation by a team of about one thousand engineers and other professionals, the study inventoried the water and related land resources of twenty-eight river basins and drainage areas and formulated general plans for their use and conservation. The study report, filling forty-six volumes, went beyond the conventional subjects of navigation, flood control, and power development to deal with water supply and pollution control, beach erosion, fish and wildlife preservation, recreation, land management, mineral resources, and insect control. It did not propose specific projects and programs for authorization, but was intended to serve as a guide for future planning by federal, state, and local agencies.[5]

"The New England-New York report is an excellent example of what is needed to achieve comprehensive river basin planning," commented Bureau of the Budget Director Percival Brundage. "The report provides the type of information which should be available for the major river basins of the Nation." Action to this end had been urged as early as 1951 by a Water Resources Planning Commission appointed by President Truman and more recently by a Presidential Advisory Committee on Water Resources Policy appointed by President Eisenhower. A bill for appropriate legislation was introduced in the House in 1959, and in 1961 a Senate Select Committee on National Water Resources again recommended, and President Kennedy requested Congress to authorize, comprehensive, coordinated federal-state planning for the nation's water resources.[6] The sense of urgency for such planning was heightening, and in the next several years guidelines for planning were laid down, machinery for implementing the guidelines was established, and studies were got under way.

Policies to govern water resources planning were set forth in 1962 in Senate Document No. 97. Prepared under the direction of the Water Resources Council, a group of appropriate cabinet secretaries acting at President Kennedy's request, the document provided uniform standards and procedures for the formulation and evaluation of both comprehensive river basin and individual project plans. To achieve optimum use and development of water and related land resources, emphasis was placed upon coordinating the efforts and objectives of all planning agencies—federal, state, regional, and local.[7]

Delineation of policy was followed by the Water Resources Planning Act of 1965, authorizing new key planning instrumentalities. Officially establishing the Water Resources Council and charging it with general oversight and coordination of all federal water resources programs and policies, the act also authorized the President to create river basin planning commissions to coordinate joint-agency planning within major watersheds. It further provided for financial assistance to states in order to increase state participation in planning. At the request of the governors of the New England states and New York, the President established a New England River Basins Commission under the provisions of the act in September 1967. A partnership of the water resources agencies of the seven member states, six interstate commissions, and nine federal departments or agencies, the commission exercises jurisdiction over the whole of New England and over portions of New York State draining into Long Island Sound.[8]

Public concern over the quality of the total environment, rising to full force late in the 1960s, further shaped the objectives and methods of water resources planning. The National Environmental Policy Act of 1969 dedicated the federal government to preserving and improving the natural environment and established in the executive office a Council on Environmental

Quality whose duties include analyzing important environment conditions and trends, appraising federal programs having an impact on the environment, and recommending policies for carrying out the intentions of the act. The next year the President set up the Environmental Protection Agency, placing for the first time executive responsibility for enforcing environmental protection laws and for recommending additional legislation in a regulatory body devoted solely to that purpose.[9] As an aspect of their broadly conceived objectives, both agencies became major participants in water resources planning.

Even before the passage of the National Environmental Policy Act, the Corps of Engineers had begun reorganizing its own planning structure to place greater emphasis on environmental considerations. In 1966 the Chief of Engineers, Lt. Gen. Frederick W. Cassidy, established a recreation and environmental branch within his office's planning division and defined environmental quality as a "primary goal" of the Corps. Cassidy's successor, Lt. Gen. Frederick J. Clarke, making new environmental initiatives a major theme of his tenure as Chief of Engineers, created an Environmental Advisory Board of outside experts to help define the Corps' responsibility to the environment and restructured the Corps to emphasize planning, conservation, and resources management.[10]

The first of the new comprehensive studies in New England—one of a series of similar planning efforts initiated throughout the nation—was authorized in 1962 when the Senate Committee on Public Works requested the Corps of Engineers to review reports on the Connecticut River with a view to formulating a multiple-objective plan of improvement for the 11,250-square-mile basin. In accordance with the developing emphasis upon joint-agency planning, the study was directed by a Connecticut River Basin Coordinating Committee. Chaired by the New England Division Engineer, the committee represented six federal agencies, the states of Vermont, New Hampshire, Massachusetts and Connecticut, and, after September 1967, the New England River Basins Commission.

In wide-ranging investigations, teams from the various agencies examined the basin's needs relating to flood control, navigation, power development, and water supply. They investigated its requirements for water quality, fish and wildlife conservation, anadromous fisheries restoration, and outdoor recreation. They took under consideration upstream water and related land resource potential, and identified some 850 archeological, historical, and natural resources sites that should be preserved from disturbance by future development within the basin. Since the study was more broadly conceived in terms of multiple-purpose programs and projects than any earlier survey, fresh investigative tools had to be devised. New evaluation techniques, new methods of cost and benefit allocations, and better ways to project future conditions and needs were all required. Planning work also included contracting the research firm of Arthur D. Little Company of Cambridge to prepare a projective economic study of New England through the year 2020.

The Connecticut River Basin Study Report, completed in 1970, analyzes in nine volumes the basin's multiple water resources needs, recommends numerous structural projects and water management programs for initiation during the next ten to fifteen years, and identifies further studies and measures necessary to meet the basin's requirements through the year 2020. Like the earlier New England-New York Interagency Committee report, its purpose is not to provide a basis of authorization for its various recommendations, but to constitute a guide for federal, state, local, and private development of the watershed.[11]

The impulses motivating comprehensive river basin studies inevitably inspired even broader regional planning efforts. In 1965 the President's Water Resources Council designated the North Atlantic Region one of twenty in the United States for comprehensive study, and later in the year Congress in the Flood Control Act of 1965 directed the Corps of Engineers to prepare "a framework plan for developing the water resources of the region." The North Atlantic Regional Water Resources Study, begun in 1966 and completed in 1972, embraced all river basins draining into the Atlantic Ocean from the St. John River in northern Maine to the James River in southern Virginia—a 1,000-mile seaboard stretch that includes the Eastern chain of metropolitan areas from Boston to Richmond and contains approximately one-quarter of the nation's population. A Coordinating Committee representing some twenty-five federal, regional, and state agencies, chaired by the division engineer of the North Atlantic Division, guided all phases of investigation and planning. The North Atlantic Division acted as the executive agent of the committee, and the New England Division assisted in planning relating to the New England states.

For planning purposes the North Atlantic Region was divided into twenty-one hydrologically defined areas ranging from large river basins to small coastal drainages. And through a multiple-objective planning approach that considered alternative objectives, needs, devices, benefits, and costs, a fifty-year management program for the region's water and related land resources was developed. Municipal and industrial water supply, water quality maintenance, irrigation, rural water supply, navigation, hydroelectric power, power plant cooling water, recreation, fish and wildlife conservation, health, visual and cultural environment resources, flood control, drainage control, and erosion control all came under the study's purview. The study report, consisting of a main report, two annexes, and twenty-two appendices, provides an extensive set of recommendations for guiding appropriate agencies in establishing water development programs involving both structural measures and managerial action. It establishes priorities for additional detailed river basin and project studies that need to be made, and it identifies subjects and fields in which further research and study are necessary for better water resources management.[12]

The congressional legislation authorizing the NAR Study also directed the Corps of Engineers to cooperate with other governmental agencies in preparing plans to meet long-range water needs in the northeastern United States. A severe drought then in its fifth year, which caused unprecedented water supply emergencies and restrictions in many localities along the northeastern seaboard, had brought to national attention the growing problem of assuring adequate supplies of water to the nation's constantly expanding metropolitan centers. The resulting Northeastern United States Water Supply Study, covering approximately the same area as the NAR Study, includes all river basins draining into the Atlantic Ocean from Maine to Virginia, into Lake Ontario, and into the St. Lawrence River. Overall responsibility for planning was assigned to the North Atlantic Division.

The New England Division is participating in the effort, conducting specific studies within its area of jurisdiction. The first, completed in 1969, was an engineering feasibility study exploring various alternatives for meeting water demands through the year 2020 in heavily populated eastern Massachusetts and Rhode Island. This was followed by studies on two projects to meet future water supply needs in eastern Massachusetts—the Northfield Mountain and the Millers River projects—which were recommended for authorization and construction by the Board of Engineers for Rivers and Harbors in March 1975. Both projects propose to employ skimming techniques to divert water during high flows from the Connecticut River Basin through acqueducts to the huge Quabbin Reservoir in the center of the state operated by the Metropolitan District Commission of the Commonwealth of Massachusetts. Adding about 148 million gallons per day to the region's water supply, they will help sixty-five communities to meet their water demands in the near future and will assist possibly sixty-six more cities and towns that may wish to join the MDC system after 1990.[13]

Although the Northfield Mountain and the Millers River projects will contribute significantly to future water needs in eastern Massachusetts, additional projects will be necessary. The Corps is therefore examining the potential of the Merrimack River as a supply source. Since the Merrimack is presently a grossly polluted stream, the first step was an examination of the feasibility of establishing wastewater systems covering the entire 5010 square miles of the river basin. Authorized by Congress in April 1971 and completed by the following September, the study was directed by the North Atlantic Division in cooperation with other governmental agencies. The results showed that river restoration was possible and would produce beneficial impacts.

The next year the Senate and House committees on public works authorized a Merrimack Wastewater Management Study of the Massachusetts portion of the basin. Carried out by the New England Division in cooperation with the Environmental Protection Agency and the Commonwealth of Massachusetts, the study was undertaken by the Corps as part of a pilot program addressed to the water pollution problems of six metropolitan areas across the nation. After considering a number of alternative wastewater treatment schemes, the study team recommended in November 1974 a plan employing both water- and land-oriented treatment facilities capable of processing about 120 million gallons per day, the projected average daily flow of wastewater in 1990. Consisting of three secondary and six advanced treatment facilities,* the system will meet the goal laid down by Congress in the Federal Water Pollution Control Act Amendments of 1972 for the zero discharge of pollutants by 1985. A complementary wastewater management plan for the New Hampshire portion of the Merrimack Basin was completed in November 1973 by the New Hampshire Water Supply and Pollution Control Commission.[14]

---

*Primary treatment of wastewater removes solids; secondary treatment removes about ninety percent of organic matter; advanced treatment removes nutrients.

The Committee resolutions authorizing the Merrimack Wastewater Management Study also directed the Corps to undertake a joint study with the Commonwealth of Massachusetts to recommend improvements and alternatives for wastewater management in the Boston metropolitan area. In November 1972 the Corps and the Commonwealth reached an agreement under which a Boston Harbor-Eastern Massachusetts Metropolitan Area Wastewater Management Study would be conducted by a multi-agency Technical Subcommittee on Boston Harbor. Chaired by the Metropolitan District Commission, the subcommittee included the New England Division and several other federal and state agencies involved in water pollution control. Its task was to provide guidelines for wastewater management by the commission for the next eighty years. In pursuit of this objective the Corps contributed approximately 50 percent of the study effort, which initially included 109 cities and towns within a thirty-mile radius of Boston. By the close of 1975 the study was completed. The key recommendations emerging from the final study report, dated March 1976, were to expand the service of the Metropolitan Sewerage District from its present forty-three communities to fifty-one; upgrade the present primary treatment plants at Deer and Nut islands to provide secondary treatment and handle greater flows; construct two advanced treatment facilities; and construct or replace various pumping stations and interceptors that collect wastewater from the sewers of the MSD member communities.[15]

In 1971 the New England Division joined multi-agency teams in two regional studies conducted under the general direction of the New England River Basins Commission. Both studies, in the jargon by now in use, were "level B" studies: broad and comprehensive surveys of an array of water and related land resources needs, problems and solutions, designed to serve as planning tools and guides for the future development of their respective regions.

One study focused on Long Island Sound and the crowded lands enclosing it. From this effort evolved a *Plan for Long Island Sound*, completed in July 1975, which proposed numerous interim and long-range policies and programs for institution by federal, state, and local governments. Under the plan appropriate agencies will guide future growth and development around the sound, clean up its waters, open its shores to greatly increased recreational use, improve fishing, protect natural areas, and reduce flood damage. They will increase ferry services, redevelop rundown urban waterfronts, relocate tank farms and non-water-dependent industries inland, and consolidate the existing eighteen petroleum receiving and distribution facilities into five centers so as to reduce the likelihood of oil spills and free waterfronts for other uses. Totally the programs aim to improve the environmental quality and enhance the usefulness of the sound yet at the same time encourage the continuation of a healthy economy for the millions of people who live around it. In the implementation of the plan the Corps of Engineers will be especially involved in programs relating to marine transportation, flood management, and shoreline preservation and improvement.[16]

The second study took a hard look at the southeastern corner of New England, where water and related land resources are under equally intense pressure. The study area, which includes most of eastern Massachusetts, all of Rhode Island, and a small bit of southeastern Connecticut, has a growing population that already numbers about five million people. Here nearly 50 percent of New England's population live on barely 7 percent of its lands. In the course of the Southeastern New England Study, completed in December 1975, the New England Division investigated the region's needs for flood protection, preservation of natural valley storage, shore erosion control, and navigation. It cooperated with other agencies in studies relating to water supply, water quality control, land use management, and coastal resources. It also compiled hydrologic and geologic basic data for the entire study. The study's findings, presented in a regional report, ten planning area reports, and over a dozen special reports, bulge with recommendations for both structural and non-structural measures to insure the balanced development and protection of the region's resources. Like the plan for Long Island Sound, the reports include policies and programs for dealing with water supply, land use, water quality, outdoor recreation, marine resources, flood and erosion protection, and siting of key economic facilities. "Southeastern New England is, to put it simply, a good place to live and work," stated the chairman of the New England River Basins Commission in submitting the study's recommendations. "The resources management strategy offered in this report is designed to help keep it that way."[17]

The Southeastern New England Study fashioned a broad framework for assisting subsequent specific planning of greater depth and detail. The New England Division is now undertaking this type of planning for the drainage basins of the Pawcatuck River and Narragansett Bay, a cluster of watersheds covering nearly half of the SENE Study area, under guidelines laid down by the Corps for a recently established Urban Studies Program. Designed to cope in a coordinated way with one of the most compelling questions facing the nation, the Urban Studies Program seeks to develop plans that not only provide solutions for specific urban water resources problems, but also offer the potential to assist in the solution of other related urban problems.[18]

The Pawcatuck River and Narragansett Bay Drainage Basins Study began with more limited goals. Following heavy flood damage in southern New England during a storm of March 1968, the Senate and House committees on public works adopted a series of resolutions requesting the Corps to review the advisability of improvements in the basins in the interests of flood control, navigation, water supply, water quality control, recreation, low flow augmentation, and other allied water uses. In keeping with the intent of these directives, the division initiated the study with primary emphasis upon solving the immediate flood problems of the area. The authorizing resolutions, however, allowed for wider multiple-objective planning and thus could embrace the broad concepts and approaches to urban water resources planning that were later developed by Congress in the Federal Water Pollution Control Act Amendments of 1972. A more comprehensive approach was also in accordance with the Corps' current philosophy on water resources planning. Therefore in February 1973 the Office of the Chief of Engineers directed the New England Division to reorient the PNB Study to an Urban Study.

Implementing this directive, the division has drafted a plan of study outlining the procedures, activities, and costs, the interagency coordination, and the public involvement that will govern the effort. Under the overall direction of the New England Division, the Commonwealth of Massachusetts, the State of Rhode Island, and the various regional planning agencies within the study area will all contribute to the development of a resources management plan. This will be directed to problems of inland flood control and flood plain management, water supply management, coastal area restoration and protection, and navigation. Conjunctive with the study, wastewater management programs will be developed under the overall responsibility of the governments of Massachusetts and Rhode Island.[19]

The extensive search of recent years for solutions to water-related problems has involved the New England Division in still other regional studies. Because of increasing public concern over the costly financial and environmental damages of shoreline erosion, Congress in 1968 directed the Corps to appraise shore erosion and shore protection needs of the nation's coasts with a view to assisting all levels of government in developing shoreline erosion programs. Completed in 1971, the study developed general guidelines for shore protection by engineering techniques and for shore management by regulative procedures. It also compiled regional inventories for each of nine major drainage areas into which the nation was divided that assessed the nature and extent of erosion within the area, presented conceptual plans for remedial action, and made general estimates of the costs of these protective measures. The inventory for the North Atlantic region, covering the ten coastal states from Maine to Virginia, was prepared by the North Atlantic Division. The New England Division cooperated in the effort by developing the data for the New England shoreline.[20]

Another problem of growing magnitude in recent years is how to accommodate ships of rapidly increasing size in American ports and waters. Few U.S. ports have naturally deep water. Major harbors have been deepened to 36 to 45+ feet by dredging, but supercarriers now more and more in use in world trade, especially in shipping crude oil, require 70 feet or more of water. In 1971 the Senate Committee on Public Works requested the Corps to review reports on commercial navigation between Eastport, Maine, and Hampton Roads, Virginia, to determine the best way of providing facilities for very large bulk carriers. Major responsibility for the study was assigned to the Philadelphia District Engineer, acting under the direction of the North Atlantic Division Engineer. The New England Division carried out those aspects of the study relating to the New England coastline, examining ten potential deepwater sites. The findings of the study, reported by the Board of Engineers for Rivers and Harbors in 1973, were that offshore deepwater facilities are needed and are economically justifiable. They are also environmentally preferable to present methods of bringing in crude petroleum, where oil is either shipped in numerous small tankers or is transferred from large tankers into lighters without the use of fixed mooring structures. The study concluded, however, that there is presently no foreseeable need, nor precedent, for the federal government to undertake the major capital investments that would be required to bring deepwater crude oil transshipment facilities into operation. Private or non-federal public ownership of the facilities would be compatible with the public interest if accomplished under effective federal and state or local regulation.[21]

The construction of navigation, flood control, and other civil works by the New England Division is a well-known activity. Its recent military construction program touched New England in about every corner. Its regulative and planning functions also bring it into contact with many interested groups. Another activity of the division, however, seldom comes to public attention—except in time of crisis. Whenever natural disaster strikes or threatens, the Corps responds to requests from state and local officials, and cooperates with the Federal Disaster Assistance Administration, to ward off destruction, keep essential facilities in operation, and repair damage.

Operation Noah—the largest disaster relief program in Corps history—is the most notable but by no means the only instance of the New England Division swinging into action. Since the passage of the Federal Disaster Act of 1950, the Corps has provided the principal engineering support to agencies administering federal assistance under that and subsequent legislation. In 1955 Congress assigned various responsibilities for meeting flood emergencies directly to the Corps. To keep in readiness, the Corps prepares Flood Emergency Manuals and from time to time conducts emergency practice exercises in cooperation with other governmental and private organizations. The New England Division has not been required to hold such exercises: it has sharpened its capabilities through actual experience. Between 1970 and 1976, for example, the division responded to 407 requests for aid on ten occasions of flood destruction caused by ice jams, coastal storms, rampaging rivers, or hurricane. Division personnel temporarily loaned to the division's Emergency Operations Center completed 2,032 damage survey reports, provided state and local authorities with technical advice and assistance, and handled contracts for repairing or rebuilding hundreds of damaged structures and waterways. The total cost to the Federal Disaster Assistance Administration was about $29 million.

Since prevention is better than cure, averting flood destruction by breaking up ice jams and other measures has become a routine part of the division's work. Occasionally, these activities have been quite extensive. In the winter of 1968-69 record snowfalls across the northern half of the nation posed the threat of major flooding when the spring thaw began. To cope with the danger, President Nixon called for a coordinated preventive effort by federal agencies, code-named "Operation Foresight." In emergency operations beginning the first of March and lasting into May, the New England Division supplied local and state authorities with technical assistance, sandbags, and pumps. It cleared streams and culverts of obstructive debris, replaced undersized drains, and strengthened dams, dikes, and floodwalls. It constructed channel diversions, built temporary dikes, protected bridges, and broke up ice jams. All told it awarded sixty-one contracts and expended nearly $863,000. The damages prevented were estimated at about $5 million. Two years later, in a second "Operation Foresight" lasting from February to June 1971, the division carried out similar though less extensive flood emergency measures.[22]

"Operation Foresight," March-May 1969. Bulldozers working in the Saco River at Bartlett, New Hampshire, to clear the channel.

Restoration of seawall at Roughan's Point, Revere, Massachusetts, for the Federal Disaster Assistance Administration.

Getting explosives ready to break up an ice jam on the Connecticut River at White River Junction, Vermont.

Expertise acquired in flood disaster work will do in other catastrophes as well, and in 1973 the New England Division played a major part in the first federally assisted operation to help a city recover from fire damages. In Chelsea, Massachusetts, a crowded suburb of Boston, a fire raging through the night of October 14 wiped out eighteen city blocks containing five hundred houses and businesses. President Nixon immediately declared Chelsea a disaster area, and federal aid was extended through the Federal Disaster Assistance Administration. The administration turned to the New England Division, assigning it the task of clearing streets of debris and demolishing safety hazards. During the next two months, from October 15 to December 19, an emergency operations team of twenty-eight administrative and engineering specialists under the direction of Assistant Division Engineer Major John G. Benca awarded and supervised contracts amounting to $550,000 for razing unsafe structures, clearing away debris, repairing water and sewer lines, and protecting health through decontamination measures. It was an "outstanding job," congratulated the regional director of the Federal Disaster Assistance Administration. "Hardly a day goes by that I do not hear laudatory comments on the speed with which the Corps of Engineers brought together the contractors' organizations into an effective working unit; I also continue to hear comments on the efficiency with which the Corps directed the clean-up work so essential to the health, safety and well-being of the citizens of Chelsea."[23]

Fire rubble in eighteen-city-block area in Chelsea, Massachusetts, is shown in this aerial photograph taken by a New England Division cameraman on October 15, 1973, the morning after the disaster.

The same area two months later, after the New England Division razed fire-gutted buildings, removed debris, eliminated health hazards, and made the area ready for redevelopment.

An "outstanding job" would serve as a fitting citation for the entire history of military and civil work in New England by the Corps of Engineers. Many challenges have been met and numerous tasks well done since Colonel Gridley first marked out field fortifications for New England militiamen confronting the British at Boston in 1775.

Weapons of war and the conduct of war underwent great transformations in two hundred years, and so did the character of Corps military construction in New England. From the American Revolution to World War II, seacoast fortifications were erected under a half-dozen successive harbor defense programs. From simple earthen redoubts shielding primitive muzzle-loaders, defense structures evolved through the granite-walled fortresses that still stand at New England harbors, to the thickly parapeted batteries of the Endicott period, to the even more massive casemates of the Second World War. Even greater demands were placed on the competence of Army Engineers in New England when the Corps took over the gigantic military building program of World War II and continued on to meet the much larger construction requirements of the Cold War. People who had been planning and supervising the dredging of harbors, the building of breakwaters, or the erection of flood control dams now unrolled blueprints for airfields, cantonments, missile facilities, research laboratories, and other military projects new to their experience.

While military construction took precedence during World War II and the early years of the Cold War, the civil work of the Corps has for more than a century been its larger mission. As the focus of civil work broadened from river and harbor improvement to include flood control, shore preservation, power development, water supply, and every aspect of water resources management, the New England districts and later the New England Division responded with increasing technical know-how and engineering versatility. The New England Division today, a highly professional organization of military and civilian specialists in many fields of engineering and management, is a far cry from the small district offices established a century ago.

Much has been accomplished, and much more remains to be done. Ongoing planning for navigation improvement, flood control, and shoreline stabilization, for example, will continue to be necessary. Problems to which public and congressional concern have more recently directed the talents of the Corps, including flood plain management, water supply provision, and water quality control, still largely remain to be solved. But as the challenges of the past have been taken in their stride by Army Engineers in New England, they will no doubt be met with the same ability in the future.

APPENDIX

1. Boston District Engineers

2. Providence District Engineers

3. Portland District Engineers

4. Newport District Engineers

5. New London District Engineers

6. Portsmouth District Engineers

7. Eastport District Engineers

8. New England Division Engineers

9. Flood Control Projects

1. BOSTON DISTRICT ENGINEERS

Name of Officer	From	To
Lt. Col. John G. Foster	10 May 1867	25 May 1871
	11 June 1874	24 Aug. 1874
Maj. Charles W. Raymond	18 Jan. 1883	4 Feb. 1886
Lt. Col. George L. Gillespie	5 Feb. 1886	20 Dec. 1888
Lt. Col. Samuel M. Mansfield	21 Dec. 1888	31 Oct. 1898
Col. Charles R. Suter	1 Nov. 1898	31 May 1901
Col. William S. Stanton	1 June 1901	16 June 1906
Lt. Col. Edward Burr	17 June 1906	24 May 1910
Col. Frederic V. Abbot	25 May 1910	13 June 1913
Col. John Millis	14 June 1913	14 Feb. 1914
Lt. Col. William E. Craighill	15 Feb. 1914	27 Oct. 1916
Maj. Frederick B. Downing	28 Oct. 1916	22 Nov. 1916
Col. Charles L. Potter	23 Nov. 1916	31 Oct. 1917
Col. Francis R. Shunk	1 Nov. 1917	19 Dec. 1919
Maj. Gilbert Van B. Wilkes	20 Dec. 1919	9 June 1920
Lt. Col. Wildurr Willing	10 June 1920	20 Aug. 1923
Maj. Stuart C. Godfrey	21 Aug. 1923	26 Aug. 1925
Maj. Roger G. Powell	27 Aug. 1925	12 Jan. 1926
Maj. Francis K. Newcomer	13 Jan. 1926	5 May 1927
Col. Sherwood A. Cheney	6 May 1927	26 Aug. 1932
Lt. Col. Richard Park	27 Aug. 1932	15 Jan. 1934
Lt. Col. John J. Kingman	16 Jan. 1934	31 July 1936
Lt. Col. Albert K. B. Lyman	1 Aug. 1936	1 May 1940
Maj. Leonard B. Gallagher	2 May 1940	5 June 1942
Maj. William G. Van Allen	6 June 1942	15 Oct. 1942
Col. George W. Gillette	16 Oct. 1942	29 Apr. 1943
Lt. Col. Bruce D. Rindlaub	30 Apr. 1943	26 Nov. 1943
Lt. Col. Henry P. Dunbar	27 Nov. 1943	20 Sept. 1944
Col. Homer B. Pettit	21 Sept. 1944	13 Aug. 1945
Col. Clifton T. Hunt	14 Aug. 1945	30 Sept. 1946

2. PROVIDENCE DISTRICT ENGINEERS

Name of Officer	From	To
Maj. Thomas M. Robins	1 Jan. 1920	3 Jan. 1921
Maj. Virgil L. Peterson	4 Jan. 1921	22 July 1924
Maj. Roger G. Powell	23 July 1924	16 June 1926
Maj. Francis K. Newcomer	17 June 1926	26 Aug. 1926
Maj. Raymond F. Fowler	27 Aug. 1926	7 Nov. 1927
Col. Sherwood A. Cheney	8 Nov. 1927	12 July 1928
Maj. Frederick S. Skinner	13 July 1928	21 July 1930
Maj. Charles J. Taylor	22 July 1930	11 Sept. 1933
Lt. Col. John J. Kingman	12 Sept. 1933	30 June 1934
Maj. Mason J. Young	1 July 1934	5 July 1937
Lt. Col. John S. Bragdon	6 July 1937	10 May 1941
Lt. Col. Harley Latson	11 May 1941	29 Sept. 1941
Lt. Col. Leonard B. Gallagher (acting)	30 Sept. 1941	31 Oct. 1941
Col. Hoel S. Bishop, Jr.	1 Nov. 1941	28 May 1943
Lt. Col. Edgar W. Garbisch	29 May 1943	13 Jan. 1944
Lt. Col. Samuel G. Neff	14 Jan. 1944	22 May 1944
Lt. Col. George L. Cook (acting)	23 May 1944	5 June 1944
Col. Walter J. Truss	6 June 1944	6 May 1945
Col. Thomas F. Kern	7 May 1945	30 Sept. 1946

3. PORTLAND DISTRICT ENGINEERS

Name of Officer	From	To
Lt. Col. George Thom	8 Nov. 1866	16 Jan. 1883
Col. Charles E. Blunt	17 Jan. 1883	28 Feb. 1886
Lt. Col. Jared A. Smith	1 Mar. 1886	3 Dec. 1891
Lt. Col. Peter C. Hains	4 Dec. 1891	5 Nov. 1894
Lt. Col. David P. Heap	6 Nov. 1894	19 Oct. 1895
Lt. Col. Andrew N. Damrell	20 Oct. 1895	27 Apr. 1897
Maj. Richard L. Hoxie	28 Apr. 1897	15 Oct. 1898
Maj. Solomon W. Roessler	16 Oct. 1898	2 Aug. 1904
Lt. Col. William M. Black	3 Aug. 1904	12 Oct. 1906
Capt. Curtis W. Otwell	13 Oct. 1906	24 Nov. 1906
Lt. Henry C. Jewett (acting)	25 Nov. 1906	15 Jan. 1907
Maj. Edward Burr (acting)	16 Jan. 1907	18 May 1907
Lt. Col. George A. Zinn	19 May 1907	15 Oct. 1910
Lt. Col. William E. Craighill	16 Oct. 1910	6 Nov. 1914
Maj. Francis A. Pope	7 Nov. 1941	22 Aug. 1917
Col. Charles L. Potter	23 Aug. 1917	14 Sept. 1917
Mr. H. W. Hobbs	15 Sept. 1917	
Mr. C. F. Porter		30 Aug. 1919
Maj. Charles L. Hall	31 Aug. 1919	1 Nov. 1919
Mr. H. W. Hobbs	2 Nov. 1919	8 June 1920

4. NEWPORT DISTRICT ENGINEERS

Name of Officer	From	To
Maj. David C. Houston	21 July 1866	1 May 1870
Lt. Col. Gouverneur K. Warren	2 May 1870	8 Aug. 1882
Maj. John W. Barlow	9 Aug. 1882	1 Nov. 1882
Lt. Col. George H. Elliot	2 Nov. 1882	1 Apr. 1887
Maj. William R. Livermore	2 Apr. 1887	7 Dec. 1891
Capt. William H. Bixby	8 Dec. 1891	8 June 1895
Lt. William W. Harts (acting)	9 June 1895	12 Sept. 1895
Maj. Daniel W. Lockwood	13 Sept. 1895	25 July 1900
Lt. Robert P. Johnston (acting)	26 July 1900	31 Aug. 1900
Maj. George W. Goethals	1 Sept. 1900	22 May 1903
Capt. Cassius E. Gillette	23 May 1903	10 Dec. 1903
Lt. Col. Joseph H. Willard	11 Dec. 1903	28 Feb. 1908
Maj. Harry Taylor (acting)	1 Mar. 1908	6 Oct. 1908
Lt. Col. James C. Sanford	7 Oct. 1908	22 Apr. 1911
Col. Frederic V. Abbot	23 Apr. 1911	8 Aug. 1912
Col. John Millis	9 Aug. 1912	22 July 1916
Col. William E. Craighill	23 July 1916	27 Oct. 1916
Capt. Frederick B. Downing	28 Oct. 1916	24 Nov. 1916
Col. Charles L. Potter	25 Nov. 1916	25 Apr. 1917
Col. Joseph H. Willard (retired)	26 Apr. 1917	18 Aug. 1919
Col. Raymond A. Wheeler	19 Aug. 1919	12 Sept. 1919
Col. William P. Wooten	13 Sept. 1919	6 Oct. 1919
Maj. Thomas M. Robins	7 Oct. 1919	31 Dec. 1919

5. NEW LONDON DISTRICT ENGINEERS

Name of Officer	From	To
Maj. John W. Barlow	1 July 1874	23 May 1883
Maj. Smith S. Leach	5 Aug. 1896	7 Jan. 1902
Lt. Col. Charles F. Powell	8 Jan. 1902	8 Mar. 1906
Capt. Gustave R. Lukesh (acting)	9 Mar. 1906	19 Apr. 1906
Lt. Col. Harry Taylor	20 Apr. 1906	13 May 1911
Capt. Albert E. Waldron	14 May 1911	1 Oct. 1912
Maj. George B. Pillsbury	2 Oct. 1912	22 Jan. 1916
Lt. Col. Charles H. McKinstry	23 Jan. 1916	21 Mar. 1917
Maj. Harley B. Ferguson	29 Mar. 1917	15 June 1917
Col. Solomon W. Roessler (retired)	16 June 1917	20 Aug. 1919
Col. Charles P. Gross	21 Aug. 1919	15 Sept. 1919
Maj. Thomas M. Robins	16 Sept. 1919	31 Dec. 1919

6. PORTSMOUTH DISTRICT ENGINEERS

Name of Officer	From	To
Maj. Walter L. Fisk	30 Sept. 1899	15 Dec. 1900
Capt. Harry Taylor	16 Dec. 1900	31 Aug. 1903

7. EASTPORT DISTRICT ENGINEERS

Name of Officer	From	To
Lt. Col. Philip B. Fleming	20 May 1935	15 Aug. 1936
Capt. Samuel D. Sturgis, Jr. (acting)	17 Aug. 1936	31 Oct. 1936

8. NEW ENGLAND DIVISION ENGINEERS

Name of Officer	From	To
Col. Leonard B. Gallagher	1 May 1942	6 Aug. 1942
Col. Douglas L. Weart	7 Aug. 1942	9 Dec. 1942
Col. George W. Gillette	10 Dec. 1942	4 Feb. 1945
Brig. Gen. James A. O'Connor	8 Feb. 1945	6 Dec. 1945
Maj. Gen. William M. Hoge	13 Dec. 1945	10 Jan. 1946
Brig. Gen. Douglas L. Weart	2 Feb. 1946	31 Oct. 1946
Brig. Gen. Raymond G. Moses	12 Nov. 1946	17 Nov. 1948
Col. James H. Stratton	18 Nov. 1948	31 July 1949
Col. Bartley M. Harloe	24 Oct. 1949	31 Dec. 1949
Col. Henry J. Woodbury	24 July 1950	11 May 1952
Col. Leland H. Hewitt	24 July 1952	31 Mar. 1954
Col. Richard W. Pearson	22 May 1954	14 Jan. 1955
Brig. Gen. Robert K. Fleming, Jr.	15 Jan. 1955	7 Apr. 1957
Brig. Gen. Alden K. Sibley	8 Apr. 1957	9 Sept. 1960
Brig. Gen. Seymour A. Potter, Jr.	17 Oct. 1960	30 Sept. 1962
Brig. Gen. Peter Hyzer	1 Oct. 1962	25 Jan. 1965
Brig. Gen. Robert R. Ploger	30 Apr. 1965	31 Aug. 1965
Col. Remi O. Renier	12 Jan. 1966	29 Aug. 1968
Col. Frank P. Bane	25 Sept. 1968	31 July 1972
Col. John H. Mason	1 Aug. 1972	30 Aug. 1976
Col. John P. Chandler	31 Aug. 1976	

9. FLOOD CONTROL PROJECTS

CONNECTICUT RIVER BASIN
DAMS AND LAKES

NAME	RIVER AND STATE	DRAINAGE AREA (sq. mi.)	FLOOD CONTROL STORAGE (ac. ft.)	CONSTRUCTED
Union Village	Ompompanoosuc, Vt.	126	38,000	1947-50
No. Hartland	Ottauquechee, Vt.	220	71,400	1958-61
No. Springfield	Black, Vt.	158	50,600	1957-60
Ball Mountain	West, Vt.	172	54,600	1957-61
Townshend	West, Vt.	278	33,200	1958-61
Surry Mountain	Ashuelot, N.H.	100	32,500	1939-42
Otter Brook	Ashuelot (Otter Brook), N.H.	47	17,600	1956-58
Birch Hill	Millers, Mass.	175	49,900	1940-42
Tully	Millers (Tully), Mass.	50	22,000	1947-49
Barre Falls	Chicopee (Ware), Mass.	55	24,000	1956-58
Knightville	Westfield, Mass.	164	49,000	1939-41
Littleville	Westfield (Middle Br.), Mass.	52.3	23,000	1962-65
Conant Brook	Chicopee (Conant Brook), Mass	8	3,740	1964-66
Colebrook River	Farmington (West Br.), Conn.	119	50,800	1965-69
Mad River	Farmington (Mad), Conn.	18.2	9,510	1961-63
Sucker Brook	Farmington (Still), Conn.	3.4	1,480	1966-70

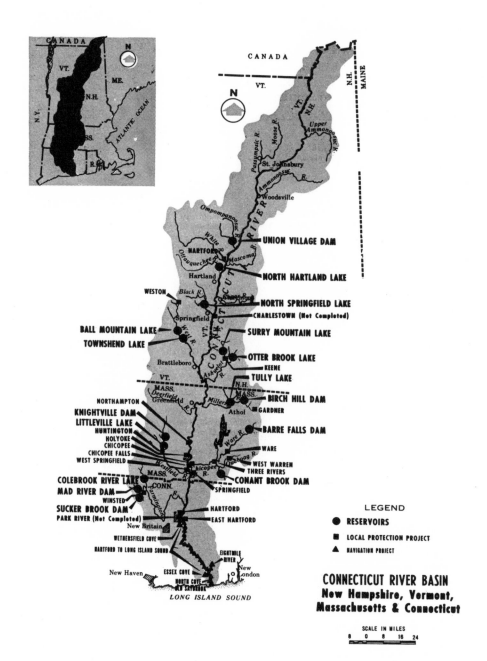

CONNECTICUT RIVER BASIN
New Hampshire, Vermont,
Massachusetts & Connecticut

CONNECTICUT RIVER BASIN
LOCAL PROTECTION WORKS

LOCATION	RIVER	CONSTRUCTED
Hartford, Vt.	White	1970
Weston, Vt.	West	1957
Keene, N.H.	Ashuelot	1954
Gardner, Mass.	Millers (Mahoney and Greenwood Brooks)	1964-65
Northampton, Mass.	Connecticut and Mill	1939-41
Ware, Mass.	Chicopee (Ware)	1958-59
West Warren, Mass.	Chicopee (Quaboag)	1962-63
Holyoke and Springdale, Mass.	Connecticut	1938-40 1947-50
Three Rivers, Mass.	Chicopee, Ware and Quaboag	1964-66
Chicopee Falls, Mass.	Chicopee	1963-65
Chicopee, Mass.	Connecticut and Chicopee	1936-41
Huntington, Mass.	Westfield	1959
West Springfield and Riverdale, Mass.	Connecticut and Westfield	1936-53
Springfield, Mass.	Connecticut and Mill	1937-48
Winsted, Conn.	Farmington (Mad)	1951
Hartford, Conn.	Connecticut and Park Rivers, Gully and Folly Brooks	1938-57
East Hartford, Conn.	Connecticut and Hockanum	1938-43

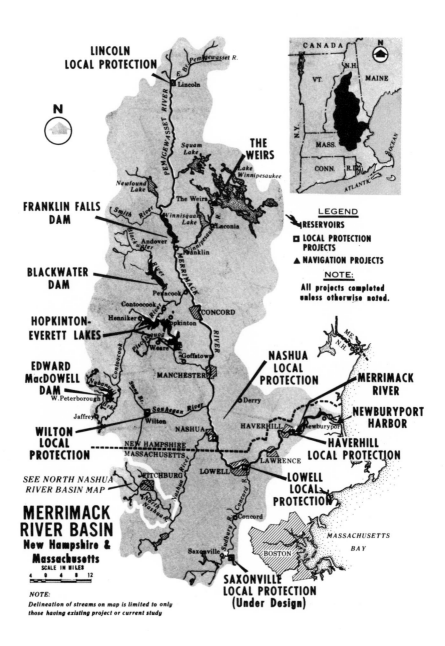

LINCOLN
LOCAL PROTECTION

THE
WEIRS

FRANKLIN FALLS
DAM

BLACKWATER
DAM

HOPKINTON-
EVERETT LAKES

EDWARD
MacDOWELL
DAM

WILTON
LOCAL
PROTECTION

NASHUA
LOCAL
PROTECTION

MERRIMACK
RIVER

NEWBURYPORT
HARBOR

HAVERHILL
LOCAL PROTECTION

LOWELL
LOCAL
PROTECTION

SAXONVILLE
LOCAL PROTECTION
(Under Design)

LEGEND
RESERVOIRS
LOCAL PROTECTION
PROJECTS
NAVIGATION PROJECTS
NOTE:
All projects completed
unless otherwise noted.

CANADA

N.H.
VT.   MAINE
N.Y.
MASS.
CONN.   R.I.
ATLANTIC

SEE NORTH NASHUA
RIVER BASIN MAP

MERRIMACK
RIVER BASIN
New Hampshire &
Massachusetts
SCALE IN MILES
4 0 4 8 12

NOTE:
Delineation of streams on map is limited to only
those having existing project or current study

MASSACHUSETTS
BAY

E. Br. Pemigewasset R.
Lincoln
PEMIGEWASSET RIVER
Squam
Lake
Lake
Winnipesaukee
Newfound
Lake
The Weirs
Smith River
Winnisquam
Lake
Laconia
Blackwater River
Andover
Franklin
MERRIMACK
Penacook
Contoocook
River
Henniker
Hopkinton
CONCORD
Weare
Piscataquog
Goffstown
RIVER
Contoocook River
MANCHESTER
Nubanusit Br.
W.Peterborough
Souhegan River
Jaffrey
Wilton
NASHUA
Derry
HAVERHILL
Newburyport
NEW HAMPSHIRE
MASSACHUSETTS
LAWRENCE
LOWELL
FITCHBURG
Nashua River
North Nashua R.
Concord River
Concord
Sudbury R.
Saxonville
BOSTON
ME.
N.H.

MERRIMACK RIVER BASIN
DAMS AND LAKES

NAME	RIVER AND STATE	DRAINAGE AREA (sq.mi.)	FLOOD CONTROL STORAGE (ac.ft.)	CONSTRUCTED
Franklin Falls	Pemigewasset, N.H.	1,000	154,000	1939-43
Edward MacDowell	Contoocook (Nubanusit Brook), N.H.	44	12,800	1948-50
Blackwater	Contoocook (Blackwater), N.H.	128	46,000	1940-41
Hopkinton-Everett	Contoocook and Piscataquog, N.H.	490	157,300	1959-62

MERRIMACK RIVER BASIN
LOCAL PROTECTION WORKS

LOCATION	RIVER	CONSTRUCTED
Lincoln, N.H.	E. Br. Pemigewasset	1960
Nashua, N.H.	Merrimack and Nashua	1948
Wilton, N.H.	Stony Brook	1971
Lowell, Mass.	Merrimack	1936-44
Haverhill, Mass.	Merrimack and Little	1936-38
Fitchburg, Mass.	North Nashua	1936-38

276

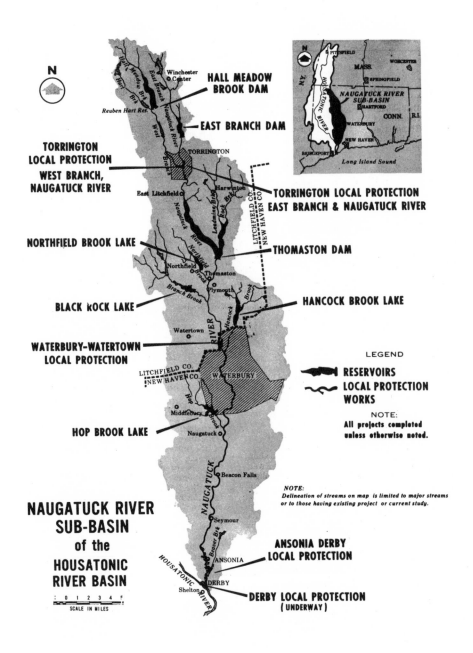

HALL MEADOW
BROOK DAM

EAST BRANCH DAM

TORRINGTON
LOCAL PROTECTION
WEST BRANCH,
NAUGATUCK RIVER

TORRINGTON LOCAL PROTECTION
EAST BRANCH & NAUGATUCK RIVER

NORTHFIELD BROOK LAKE

THOMASTON DAM

BLACK ROCK LAKE

HANCOCK BROOK LAKE

WATERBURY-WATERTOWN
LOCAL PROTECTION

LEGEND

RESERVOIRS
LOCAL PROTECTION
WORKS

NOTE:
All projects completed
unless otherwise noted.

HOP BROOK LAKE

NOTE:
Delineation of streams on map is limited to major streams
or to those having existing project or current study.

NAUGATUCK RIVER
SUB-BASIN
of the
HOUSATONIC
RIVER BASIN

: 0 1 2 3 4 F
SCALE IN MILES

ANSONIA DERBY
LOCAL PROTECTION

DERBY LOCAL PROTECTION
(UNDERWAY)

N

HOUSATONIC RIVER BASIN
DAMS AND LAKES

NAME	RIVER (All in Naugatuck River sub-basin, Connecticut)	DRAINAGE AREA (sq. mi.)	FLOOD CONTROL STORAGE (ac. ft.)	CONSTRUCTED
Hall Meadow Brook	Hall Meadow Brook	17.2	8,620	1961-62
East Branch	East Branch, Naugatuck	9.3	4,350	1963-64
Thomaston	Naugatuck	97.0	42,000	1957-60
Northfield Brook	Northfield Brook	5.7	2,430	1963-66
Black Rock	Branch Brook	20.4	8,700	1966-70
Hancock Brook	Hancock Brook	12.0	4,030	1963-66
Hop Brook	Hop Brook	16.4	6,970	1965-68

HOUSATONIC RIVER BASIN
LOCAL PROTECTION WORKS

LOCATION	RIVER	CONSTRUCTED
Torrington	East Branch, Naugatuck	1957-58
Torrington	West Branch, Naugatuck	1959-60
Waterbury-Watertown	Naugatuck	1960-61
Ansonia-Derby	Naugatuck	1968-73
Derby	Housatonic & Naugatuck	1970-73

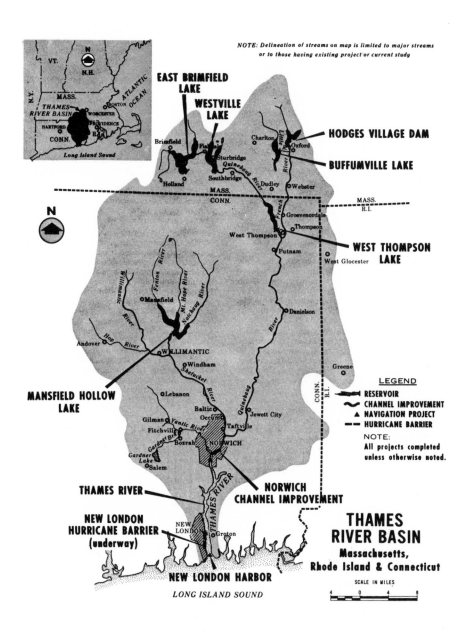

NOTE: Delineation of streams on map is limited to major streams or to those having existing project or current study

EAST BRIMFIELD LAKE

WESTVILLE LAKE

HODGES VILLAGE DAM

BUFFUMVILLE LAKE

WEST THOMPSON LAKE

MANSFIELD HOLLOW LAKE

THAMES RIVER

NORWICH CHANNEL IMPROVEMENT

NEW LONDON HURRICANE BARRIER (underway)

NEW LONDON HARBOR

LONG ISLAND SOUND

LEGEND

RESERVOIR
CHANNEL IMPROVEMENT
NAVIGATION PROJECT
HURRICANE BARRIER

NOTE:
All projects completed unless otherwise noted.

THAMES RIVER BASIN
Massachusetts,
Rhode Island & Connecticut

SCALE IN MILES
4   0   4   8

THAMES RIVER BASIN
DAMS AND LAKES

NAME	RIVER AND STATE	DRAINAGE AREA (sq. mi.)	FLOOD CONTROL STORAGE (ac. ft.)	CONSTRUCTED
East Brimfield	Quinebaug, Mass.	67.5	28,800	1958-60
Westville	Quinebaug, Mass.	99.5	11,100	1960-62
Hodges Village	French, Mass.	31.1	12,800	1958-59
Buffumville	Little, Mass.	26.5	11,300	1956-58
Mansfield Hollow	Natchaug, Conn.	159.0	52,000	1949-52
West Thompson	Quinebaug, Conn.	173.5	25,600	1963-65

THAMES RIVER BASIN
LOCAL PROTECTION WORKS

LOCATION	RIVER	CONSTRUCTED
Norwich, Conn.	Shetucket	1947-49 1957-58

BLACKSTONE RIVER BASIN
DAMS AND LAKES

NAME	RIVER AND STATE	DRAINAGE AREA (sq. mi.)	FLOOD CONTROL STORAGE (ac. ft.)	CONSTRUCTED
West Hill	West, Mass.	28	12,400	1959-61

BLACKSTONE RIVER BASIN
LOCAL PROTECTION WORKS

LOCATION	RIVER	CONSTRUCTED
Worcester (Diversion) Mass.	Leesville Pond, Middle, & Blackstone	1957-60
Woonsocket, R.I.	Blackstone	1959
Woonsocket, Lower	Blackstone, Mill, & Peters	1960-66

CONNECTICUT WESTERN COASTAL AREA
LOCAL PROTECTION WORKS

LOCATION	RIVER	CONSTRUCTED
Pemberwick	Byram	1959-60
Norwalk	Norwalk	1951

MASSACHUSETTS COASTAL AREA
LOCAL PROTECTION WORKS

LOCATION	RIVER	CONSTRUCTED
Canton	Neponset, East Branch	1962-63

PISCATAQUA RIVER BASIN
LOCAL PROTECTION WORKS

LOCATION	RIVER	CONSTRUCTED
Farmington, N.H.	Cocheco	1956, 1961

MAINE EASTERN COASTAL AREA
LOCAL PROTECTION WORKS

LOCATION	RIVER	CONSTRUCTED
Cherryfield (Ice Dam)	Narraguagus	1960-61

NOTES

CHAPTER I

1. *The Journals of each Provincial Congress of Massachusetts in 1774 and 1775*, p. 157.
2. Daniel T. V. Huntoon, *History of the Town of Canton, Norfolk County, Massachusetts*, pp. 361-63; William Johnson, *The Papers of William Johnson*, 1:292.
3. Huntoon, *Canton*, p. 363; Francis Parkman, *A Half-Century of Conflict*, 2:173-74.
4. Huntoon, *Canton*, pp. 364-65; Francis Parkman, *Montcalm and Wolfe*, 1:169; Johnson, *Papers*, 2:104, 223-24, 236.
5. Huntoon, *Canton*, pp. 365-67; William Pitt, *Correspondence of William Pitt*, 1:436; Parkman, *Montcalm and Wolfe*, 2:295.
6. *Journals of each Provincial Congress of Massachusetts*, pp. 153, 212, 373, 378; Allen French, *The First Year of the American Revolution*, pp. 73-74; Huntoon, *Canton*, p. 370.
7. Richard Frothingham, Jr., *History of the Siege of Boston and of the Battles of Lexington, Concord, and Bunker Hill*, pp. 113-35, 184, 198-99; French, *Revolution*, pp. 211-28; Huntoon, *Canton*, pp. 371-72.
8. *Journals of the Continental Congress, 1774-1789*, 2:89-90, 94.
9. Frothingham, *Siege of Boston*, pp. 210-12, 217; Rufus Putnam, *The Memoirs of Rufus Putnam*, pp. 54-55.
10. Frothingham, *Siege of Boston*, p. 274.
11. Ibid., pp. 233-34, 268-72, 295-96; French, *Revolution*, pp. 481, 490, 654-56.
12. Putnam, *Memoirs*, pp. 55-58; French, *Revolution*, pp. 656-63; Frothingham, *Siege of Boston*, pp. 297-309.
13. French, *Revolution*, p. 521; Huntoon, *Canton*, pp. 367, 371-73, 375, 376.
14. *American Archives*, ed. Peter Force, 4th ser. 5:872-73; Ibid., 6:423-24; *Journals of the Continental Congress*, 4:361.
15. Putnam, *Memoirs*, pp. 58-75; W. F. Heavey, "The Corps in the Days of the Revolution," *Military Engineer* 31 (1939): 410-13; Raleigh B. Buzziard, "Washington's Favorite Engineer," *Military Engineer* 40 (1948): 115-17.
16. Raphael P. Thian, comp., *Legislative History of the General Staff of the Army of the United States*, pp. 487-90.
17. *Statutes at Large*, 1:345-46, 366-67; *American State Papers: Military Affairs*, 1:71-72 (hereafter cited as *ASP:MA*); Raleigh B. Buzzaird, "Washington's Last Chief Engineer: Etienne Becket, Sieur de Rochefontaine," *Military Engineer* 45 (1953): 118-22.
18. *ASP:MA*, 1:71, 72-75.
19. Ibid., 1:74-77, 110-11, 115-16.
20. *Dictionary of American Biography*, s.v. "Tousard, Anne Louis de."
21. *ASP:MA*, 1:193, 245; George W. Cullum, *Historical Sketch of the Fortification Defenses of Narragansett Bay*, pp. 19-21; Joseph Gardner Swift, *The Memoirs of Gen. Joseph Gardner Swift*, pp. 74-75.
22. *ASP:MA*, 1:75, 77, 192, 245; Historical Information Relating to Military Posts and Other Installations, ca. 1700-1900, Microfilm Publication M661, rolls 1, 3, Records of the Adjutant General's Office, Record Group 94, National Archives; Justin Winsor, ed., *Memorial History of Boston, 1630-1880*, 3:305; Emanuel Raymond Lewis, *Seacoast Fortifications of the United States*, p. 40.
23. *Statutes at Large*, 2:132; *ASP:MA*, 1:228.
24. Swift, *Memoirs*, p. 39.

25. Ibid., pp. 20-78.

26. Ibid., pp. 76, 87; *ASP:MA*, 1:238, 245-46.

27. Swift, *Memoirs*, 75-76; *ASP:MA*, 1:238, 245.

28. *Statutes at Large*, 3:330, 342; Swift, *Memoirs*, pp. 144-88, *passim*; George W. Cullum, *Biographical Sketch of Brigadier-General Joseph G. Swift*, pp. 15-19; Swift to Secretary of War William Crawford, June 21, 1816, Miscellaneous Letters Sent, 1812-69, 1:11-12, Textual Records of the Office of the Chief of Engineers, Record Group 77, National Archives (hereafter cited as RG 77, NA).

29. "Report of the Board of Engineers on the defense of the seaboard, February 7, 1821,"*ASP:MA*, 2:305-12; ibid., 3:143; H. Ex. Doc. 5, 32 Cong., 1 sess., *Letter from the Secretary of War, Reference to Fortifications, December 11, 1851*, pp. 18-30, 90-93.

30. S. Doc. 85, 28 Cong., 2 sess., *Report on the Means of National Defense*, pp. 10-11; *Annual Reports of the Secretary of War, 1835, 1836, 1838; Annual Reports of the Chief Engineer, 1835, 1836, 1839-43* (hereafter cited as *ARCE*).

31. William M. Black, director, *Pamphlet on the Evolution of the Art of Fortification*, pp. 98-99; E. E. Winslow, *Lectures on Seacoast Defense*, pp. 7-8.

32. Cullum, *Defenses of Narragansett Bay*, pp. 29-30.

33. J. G. Barnard, "Biography of . . . Joseph G. Totten" in *Historical Papers Relating to the Corps of Engineers and to Engineer Troops of the United States Army*, pp. 144-52; Lewis, *Seacoast Fortifications*, pp. 43-45.

34. *ARCE, 1824-58*; Barnard, "Totten," pp. 132-36; George W. Cullum, *Biographical Register of the Officers and Graduates of the U. S. Military Academy at West Point, N. Y.*, 1:65-66; Cullum, *Defenses of Narragansett Bay*, p. 30.

35. *ARCE, 1825-29, 1833*; H. Doc. 243, 24 Cong., 1 sess., *Military and Naval Defenses*, p. 58.

36. Cullum, *Biographical Register*, 1:81-87; George W. Cullum, *Biographical Sketch of Brigadier-General Sylvanus Thayer*; Forest G. Hill, *Roads, Rails & Waterways*, pp. 14-17; *Dictionary of American Biography*, s.v. "Thayer, Sylvanus."

37. *ARCE, 1834-1861*.

38. *ASP:MA*, 5:296-99, 474, 500-501; H. Doc. 86, 23 Cong., 2 sess., *Fortifications in Boston Harbor*.

39. *ARCE, 1838-50; ARCE, 1883*, p. 15; Cullum, *Biographical Register*, 1:535.

40. *ASP:MA*, 7:895-97; *Statutes at Large*, 5:209, 284.

41. *Statutes at Large*, 5:351, 355, 360; *Annual Report of the Secretary of War, 1840*, p. 23; *ARCE, 1842*, p. 239.

42. *ARCE, 1842*, pp. 239-40; *ARCE, 1843-61*; H. Doc. 243, 24 Cong., 1 sess., *Military and Naval Defenses*, p. 58; *ASP:MA*, 4:269, 935; ibid., 5:127; Henry E. Dunnack, *Maine Forts*, p. 54; Monthly Returns of the Engineer Department, August 1843-December 1843, RG 77, NA.

43. *ARCE, 1839-61*.

44. *ARCE, 1842*, p. 243; *ARCE, 1855*, p. 190.

45. *ARCE, 1857-61*; Plan of a work projected for Clark's Point, dated July 1846, Cartographic Division, Drawer 25, Sheet 1, RG 77, NA.

46. *ARCE, 1857-61*; C. F. Porter, *A Brief History of Works Erected for the Defense of Portland, Maine*, U. S. Army Engineer School, Occasional Paper no. 18, p. 8; Memoir Descriptive of the Fort projected for Hog Island Ledge, Portland Harbor, Me., by J. D. Kurtz, Cartographic Division, Drawer 13, Sketch A, RG 77, NA; Fort Gorges, Portland Harbor, ibid., Drawer 13, Sketch B.

47. These so-called "Laird Rams," which were eventually purchased by the British government, proved to be unseaworthy craft, probably more dangerous to their

crews than to anyone else. See Wilbur D. Jones, *The Confederate Rams at Birkenhead*, pp. 118-20.

48. *ARCE, 1866*, pp. 417-21.

49. *ARCE, 1850-61, 1865*.

CHAPTER II

1. Forest G. Hill, *Roads, Rails & Waterways*, pp. 23-34; "Report of Secretary of War Calhoun to the President, November 29, 1823," *ASP:MA*, 2:554. For the reports of Gallatin and Calhoun see *American State Papers: Miscellaneous*, 1:724-45; ibid., 2:533-37.

2. Raphael P. Thian, comp., *Legislative History of the General Staff of The Army of the United States from 1775 to 1901*, pp. 483, 488, 492, 493, 499, 509; Henry P. Beers, "A History of the U.S. Topographical Engineers, 1813-1863," *Military Engineer* 34 (June 1942): 287-91, (July 1942): 348-52.

3. Carter Goodrich, "National Planning of Internal Improvements," *Political Science Quarterly* 63 (1948): 28-44.

4. A. Macomb to Bernard, Totten, and Sullivan, October 2, 5, 1824, Letters Sent Relating to Internal Improvements under an Act of April 30, 1824, RG 77, NA; H. Doc. 83, 18 Cong., 2 sess., *Report of the examination which has been made by the Board of Engineers with a view to internal improvements, February 14, 1825*, pp. 11-12; Massachusetts, *Public Documents, 1860*, No. 34: "Report of the Committee of Construction of Ship Canal between Buzzard's Bay and Barnstable Bay," pp. 26-57; Massachusetts, *Public Documents, 1863*, No. 41: "Report of the Joint Committee of 1860 upon The Proposed Canal to Unite Barnstable and Buzzard's Bays," pp. 8-23; *ARCE, 1870*, pp. 477-81, 492-95; William James Reid, *The Building of the Cape Cod Canal, 1627-1914*, pp. 1-18; William Barclay Parsons, "Cape Cod Canal," *Annals of the American Academy of Political and Social Science* 31 (January 1908): 81-84.

5. *ARCE, 1825-30; Annual Reports of the Topographical Bureau, 1831-35* (hereafter cited as *ARTB*); H. Rpt. 102, 19 Cong., 2 sess., *Surveys, with a View to Making Roads & Canals*, pp. 9-11; H. Doc. 83, 19 Cong., 2 sess., *Surveys-Roads and Canals*, sig. 2-3; H. Doc. 154, 19 Cong., 1 sess., *Survey-Connecticut River, &c*; H. Doc. 173, 20 Cong., 1 sess., *Surveys-Kennebec River, &c*; H. Doc. 118, 20 Cong., 2 sess., *Canal-Connecticut River to Lake Memphremagog, &c*; "Corps of Engineers, &c.," *Niles Weekly Register* 29 (October 22, 1825): 121-22.

6. Engineer Department to P. H. Perrault, June 13, 27, 1828, Letters Sent to Engineer Officers, 1812-69, 3:213, 223, RG 77, NA; Engineer Department to Hudson Railroad Committee, June 27, 1828, Miscellaneous Letters Sent, 1812-69, 5:129, RG 77, NA; *ASP:MA*, 4:16; H. Doc. 89, 20 Cong., 2 sess., *Hudson and Berkshire Rail Road*, p. 10.

7. *Dictionary of American Biography*, s.v. "McNeill, William Gibbs," "Whistler, George Washington," "Long, Stephen Harriman," "Swift, William Henry"; Carlisle Allan, "George W. Whistler, Military Engineer," *Military Engineer* 29 (1937): 178-79; Richard G. Wood, *Stephen Harriman Long, 1784-1864*, pp. 30-254, *passim*; Joseph Garner Swift, *The Memoirs of Gen. Joseph Gardner Swift*, p. 177; George W. Cullum, *Biographical Register of the Officers and Graduates of the U.S. Military Academy at West Point, N.Y.*, 1:237-39.

8. Cullum, *Biographical Register*, 1:162, 164, 216, 237; Wood, *Long*, pp. 178-86; Abert to McNeill, July 9, 1832, Abert to B. F. Butler, February 4, 1837, Letters Sent by the Topographical Bureau, Microfilm Publication M66, rolls 1, 2, RG 77, NA.

9. *ARTB, 1838*, pp. 370-72; Cullum, *Biographical Register*, 1:162, 164, 239; Abert to L. Cass, July 6, 1836, Letters Sent by the Topographical Bureau, Microfilm Publication M66, roll 2, RG 77, NA; *Statutes at Large*, 5:256.

10. Emory R. Johnson, "River and Harbor Bills," *Annals of the American Academy of Political and Social Science* 2 (1891-1892): 786; *Laws of the United States Relating to the Improvement of Rivers and Harbors*, 1:27-28.

11. *Laws Relating to Rivers and Harbors*, 1:33-37. The following account of river and harbor work is based on *ARCE, 1825-38* and *ARTB, 1835-39*.

12. *Laws Relating to Rivers and Harbors*, 1:29.

13. Goodrich, "Internal Improvements," pp 36-44.

14. *ARTB, 1842-46, 1848-50*. The maps are deposited in the Cartographic Archives Division of the National Archives.

15. Beers, "Topographic Engineers," pp. 288, 289; *ASP:MA*, 4:766; Cullum, *Biographical Register*, 1:238-39; Sidney Forman, "The First School of Engineering," *Military Engineer* 44 (1952): 110.

16. *ASP:MA*, 4:745; ibid., 5:390; L. D. Ingersoll, *A History of the War Department of the United States*, p. 282; *ARTB, 1843*, pp. 126, 170-80; *ARTB, 1850*, pp. 395-96.

17. *ARTB, 1847*, pp. 658-66; *ARTB, 1850*, pp. 396-7, 432-47; Cullum, *Biographical Register*, 1:240-41.

18. Isaac Lippincott, "A History of River Improvement," *Journal of Political Economy* 22 (1914): 641; *Laws Relating to Rivers and Harbors*, 1:119-24; *ARCE, 1852*, p. 158.

19. *ARCE, 1852-57*.

20. *ARCE, 1840-45, 1848-50; Laws Relating to Rivers and Harbors,* 1:91-92, 96, 98, 113, 120.

21. Cullum, *Biographical Register*, 2:117-19; J. G. Barnard, "Lighthouse Engineering as Displayed at the Centennial Exhibition," *Transactions of the American Society of Civil Engineers* 8 (1879): 59-61; Barton S. Alexander, "Minot's Ledge Lighthouse," *Transactions of the American Society of Civil Engineers* 8 (1879): 84-93; Barnard, "Biography of Totten," pp. 155-58.

CHAPTER III

1. Isaac Lippincott, "A History of River Improvement," *Journal of Political Economy* 22 (1914): 632, 649-50.

2. *Laws of the United States Relating to the Improvement of Rivers and Harbors*, 1:144, 147. This chapter draws heavily on *ARCE, 1865-1972*.

3. *Laws Relating to Rivers and Harbors*, 1:151-56; W. Stull Holt, *The Office of the Chief of Engineers of the Army*, p. 136.

4. Prior to 1882 the Secretary of War could at his discretion require an examination or survey or both. In 1882 the policy of making preliminary examinations was established by law. In 1880 the Board of Engineers for Fortifications was reorganized so as to include in its duties whatever review and revision of plans for river and harbor improvement was necessary. In 1902 the Board of Engineers for Rivers and Harbors was established, and all reports of examination and surveys were referred to it.

5. Thomas M. Robins, "The River and Harbor Functions of the Corps of Engineers," *Military Engineer* 32 (September-October 1940): 327; Holt. *Chief of Engineers*, pp. 63-68; *Laws Relating to Rivers and Harbors*, 1:175, 389; ibid., 2:1006, 1336, 1609-10, ibid., 3:1809; *Statutes at Large*, 27:300.

6. *ARCE, 1884*, p. 67; Emory R. Johnson, "Inland Waterways, Their Relation to Transportation," Supplement to *Annals of the American Academy of Political*

and Social Science, September 1893, pp. 113, 117; Robins, "Corps of Engineers," pp. 327-28.

7. Johnson, "Inland Waterways," pp. 113, 119-20; Robins, "Corps of Engineers," p. 327.

8. J. Newton to R. T. Lincoln, May 20, 1884, copy in NED historical file.

9. Engineer Department to G. Thom, October 2, 3, November 17, 23, 1866, Letters Sent to Engineer Officers, 1812-69, 40:238, RG 77, NA.

10. Engineer Department to D. Houston, September 17, October 20, 1886, ibid., 40:172-73; Monthly Returns of the Engineer Department, October 1867, RG 77, NA.

11. Corps of Engineers, General Order No. 12, December 3, 1888, copy in NED historical file; Henry L. Abbot, "The Corps of Engineers," *Journal of the Military Service Institution* 15 (1894): 424.

12. During this period the Wilmington District was absorbed by the Philadelphia District, the two New York districts were consolidated, and a new district office was opened at Binghamton, New York, to supervise flood control work.

13. Press copies of Letters Sent, Jan. 1907-Dec. 1919, Newport, R. I., Engineer Office, 7:111, 85:250, RG 77, Federal Records Center, Waltham, Mass.

14. G. P. Pillsbury to Commanding General, Department of the East, November 12, 1912, Press Copies of Letters Sent Relating to Personnel, 1909-12, New London, Conn., Engineer Office, 2:14, RG 77, Federal Records Center, Waltham, Mass.

15. "Boston District Position Charts, 1 July 1946"; Personnel Directories of New England Division Office 1 June 1945 and 16 December 1946, with Supplement 22 January 1947; Robert F. Lafrenz, Robert B. Taylor, and Warren R. Davidson, "History of the New England Division for Period June 25, 1950 through September 8, 1951," pp. 1, 2, 42-43; A. K. Sibley to E. C. Itschner, July 1, 1960, Newsletters from the New England Division Engineer to the Chief of Engineers; Records of Personnel Office, NED.

16. Lillian D. Parks, "History of the U. S. Engineer Office, Boston, Mass.," pp. 3-4; Lafrenz, "New England Division," p. 49. Letterheads in correspondence.

CHAPTER IV

1. This figure includes waterways presently within the New England Division. New England engineer offices also improved waterways on the south shore of Long Island Sound and on Lake Champlain during the years their jurisdictions extended over these areas. The account of river and harbor work draws heavily from *ARCE, 1866-1973*, and from the *Water Resources Development by the U. S. Army Corps of Engineers* booklets for the New England states published by NED.

2. Colonel William E. Craighill, a Boston District Engineer, later wrote that the Secretary of War, on consultation with the Chief of Engineers, concluded that Congress had determined that the harbor should be built if the board of engineers were of the opinion that it was the best location. The board having so decided, the Secretary considered it his duty to direct beginning of work. (William E. Craighill, "Breakwater at Sandy Bay, Cape Ann, Massachusetts," *Professional Memoirs* 8 [September-October 1916]: 590).

3. H. Doc. 411, 64 Cong., 1 sess., *Harbor of Refuge at Sandy Bay, Cape Ann, Mass.*

4. S. Doc. 124, 87 Cong., 2 sess., *Plymouth Harbor, Massachusetts*; H. Doc. 600, 80 Cong., 2 sess., *Provincetown Harbor, Mass.*

5. *ARCE, 1885*, p. 495.

6. In 1881 the construction of a timber dike to close Plum Island Basin, which opens

into the river, was added to the project to prevent the river, upon being restricted, from opening a new channel by breaking through the outer shore of the island. Completed in 1883, it was later found to be unnecessary and fell into disrepair.

7. William E. Leuchtenburg, *Flood Control Politics*, p. 17; H. Doc. 136, 55 Cong., 2 sess., *Survey of Conn. River between Hartford, Conn., and Holyoke, Mass.*; H. Doc. 231, 58 Cong., 3 sess., *Report of a Survey of the Connecticut River between Hartford and Holyoke*; H. Doc. 323, 59 Cong., 2 sess., *Connecticut River Between Hartford, Conn., and Holyoke, Mass.*; H. Doc. 1311, 60 Cong., 2 sess., *Connecticut River between Hartford and Holyoke*.

8. H. Doc. 818, 61 Cong., 1 sess., *Connecticut River, Connecticut and Massachusetts*; S. Doc. 1067, 62 Cong., 3 sess., *Proposed Agreement with the Connecticut River Company*; H. Doc. 417, 64 Cong., 1 sess., *Connecticut River, Between Hartford, Conn., and Holyoke, Mass.*; Leuchtenburg, *Flood Control Politics*, p. 18.

9. H. Doc. 35, 71 Cong., 2 sess., *Connecticut River above Hartford, Conn.*; H. Doc. 36, 71 Cong., 2 sess., *Connecticut River above Hartford, Conn.*

10. Leuchtenburg, *Flood Control Politics*, p. 19.

11. H. Doc. 27, 73 Cong., 1 sess., *Connecticut River between Hartford, Conn., and Springfield and Holyoke, Mass.*

12. H. Doc. 165, 76 Cong., 1 sess., *Connecticut River Above Hartford, Conn.*

13. Leuchtenburg, *Flood Control Politics*, pp. 147-57.

14. NED, *Connecticut River, Connecticut-Massachusetts, Navigation Study, Survey Report, Long Island Sound to Holyoke, Mass., June 3, 1949.*

15. Leuchtenburg, *Flood Control Politics*, pp. 236-39.

16. NED, *Connecticut River, Hartford, Connecticut, to Holyoke, Massachusetts (Review of Reports), September 1973.*

17. Albert E. Cowdrey, "The Corps as Pioneer: The Case of the Refuse Act" (MS, which in revised form was published as "Pioneering Environmental Law: The Army Corps of Engineers and the Refuse Act," *Pacific Historical Review* 44 [August 1975]: 331-49), p. 2.

18. Waste was being thrown into the river from both sides. Canada had a statute prohibiting this practice, but made no effort to enforce it as long as the United States took no measures to apply a similar law.

19. *ARCE, 1887*, p. 480.

20. Cowdrey, "Pioneering Environmental Law," p. 334; *ARCE, 1877*, pp. 828-30. Humphreys's authority for drafting a bill was an order by Congress directing the Secretary of War to report what legislation might be necessary to prevent private injury to public works. Humphreys broadly interpreted "works" to include every navigable waterway on which federal money had been expended.

21. Sometimes Congress in authorizing the construction of a bridge spanning state lines would require the builder to submit information concerning it to the Secretary of War for approval, but there were no general laws covering the construction of bridges. Moreover, many bridges were authorized by state legislatures. If a bridge would seriously impair navigation, the Secretary's only recourse was to try, not always successfully, to prevent its erection through the Department of Justice (W. Stull Holt, *The Office of the Chief of Engineers of the Army*, p. 42).

22. Cowdrey, "Pioneering Environmental Law," p. 335.

23. *Laws of the United States Relating to the Improvement of Rivers and Harbors*, 1:329-30, 383, 517, 583; *Index to the Reports of The Chief of Engineers, U. S. Army*, 2:2139-2247, *passim*, 2264-78; ibid., 3:347-48, 377; *ARCE, 1889*, pp. 374-76.

24. *Laws Relating to Rivers and Harbors*, 1:518; *ARCE, 1889*, pp. 368, 601; *ARCE,*

1890, pp. 331-32, 682; *ARCE, 1891*, pp. 424, 621-24; *Index to Reports of The Chief of Engineers*, 2:2253-61; Holt, *Office of the Chief of Engineers*, p. 73.

25. Cowdrey, "Pioneering Environmental Law," pp. 337-38; *Laws Relating to Rivers and Harbors*, 1:580-84.
26. *Index to the Reports of the Chief of Engineers*, 2:2139-2247, *passim*.
27. Crowdrey, "Pioneering Environmental Law," pp. 338-40.
28. *Laws Relating to Rivers and Harbors*, 2:886-92.
29. Cowdrey, "Corps as Pioneer," p. 12.
30. Files of the Permits Branch, NED.
31. *Statutes at Large*, 80:940-41.
32. Cowdrey, "Pioneering Environmental Law," pp. 341-48; *ARCE, 1971*, 1:14-15.
33. *ARCE, 1972*, 1:23-24; *Statutes at Large*, 86:816.
34. Files of the Permits Branch, NED.
35. Cowdrey, "Corps as Pioneer," pp. 15-16.

CHAPTER V

1. The account of the Cape Cod Canal draws heavily from the thorough study by William James Reid, *The Building of the Cape Cod Canal, 1627-1914*, The quotation is from p. 99.
2. Massachusetts, *Public Documents, 1863*, no. 41, "Report of the Joint Committee of 1860 upon The Proposed Canal to Unite Barnstable and Buzzard's Bays," pp. 24-57.
3. *ARCE, 1870*, pp. 481-90.
4. S. Ex. Doc. 104, 47 Cong., 1 sess., *Buzzard's and Barnstable Bays, Massachusetts*.
5. Reid, *Cape Cod Canal*, pp. 13-33.
6. Ibid., pp. 48-49.
7. Ibid., pp. 43-45, 60-62; H. Committee on Rivers and Harbors Doc. 3, 69 Cong., 1 sess., *Report of Colonel Edw. Burr upon the Cape Cod Canal*, pp. 19-23.
8. Reid, *Cape Cod Canal*, pp. 64-65; *Laws Relating to Rivers and Harbors*, 3:1733-34.
9. H. Doc. 1768, 65 Cong., 3 sess., *Report of Proceedings to Date in Determining Value and Advisability of Purchase of the Cape Cod Canal Connecting Buzzards Bay and Cape Cod Bay, Mass.*
10. Reid, *Cape Cod Canal*, pp. 63, 70-83.
11. S. Rept. 924, 68 Cong., 2 sess., *Purchase of the Cape Cod Canal Property*, pp. 6-7.
12. H. Committee on Rivers and Harbors Doc. 3, 69 Cong., 1 sess., *Report of Colonel Edw. Burr upon the Cape Cod Canal*.
13. H. Doc. 139, 67 Cong., 2 sess., *Correspondence Concerning the Purchase of the Cape Cod Canal*.
14. Reid, *Cape Cod Canal*, pp. 91-92, 96-98.
15. Ibid., 104; *ARCE, 1929*, pp. 79-80; *ARCE, 1930*, pp. 86-87; *ARCE, 1931*, pp. 82-83.
16. H. Doc 795, 71 Cong., 3 sess., *Cape Cod Canal, Mass.*
17. Reid, *Cape Cod Canal*, pp. 107-8; *Laws Relating to Rivers and Harbors*, 3:2202, 2251.
18. *ARCE, 1934*, p. 50; Harry B. Ivers, ed., *The Official Old Home Week and Canal Bridge Dedication Book, Cape Cod*, pp. 18, 20, 38.
19. H. Committee on Rivers and Harbors Doc. 15, 74 Cong., 1 sess., *Cape Cod Canal, Mass.*; *Laws Relating to Rivers and Harbors*, 3:2331.
20. Reid, *Cape Cod Canal*, pp. 110-11; J. E. Allen, "A Case History of the Cape

Cod Canal," paper presented at the Third Conference on Coastal Engineering at the Massachusetts Institute of Technology, October 22, 1952, pp. 7-11.

21. Reid, *Cape Cod Canal*, pp. 111-16.
22. H. Doc. 431, 77 Cong., 1 sess., *Cape Cod Canal (Onset Bay), Mass.*; H. Doc. 168, 85 Cong., 1 sess., *East Boat Basin, Cape Cod Canal, Mass.*

CHAPTER VI

1. Harold & Margaret Sprout, *The Rise of American Naval Power, 1776-1918*, pp. 110-15, 124-26, 141-50, 156-62; Carroll Storrs Alden and Allan Wescott, *The United States Navy*, pp. 155-56; William M. Black, director, *Pamphlet on the Evolution of the Art of Fortification*, pp. 99-100.
2. This chapter draws extensively on reports on fortifications which were included in *ARCE* until 1922. District reports were included until 1902, thereafter only summary reports were given.
3. H. Ex. Doc. 271, 41 Cong., 2 sess., *Sea-Coast Defenses*.
4. E. E. Winslow, *Lectures on Seacoast Defense*, p. 18; Emanuel Raymond Lewis, *Seacoast Fortifications of the United States*, p. 69; *ARCE, 1876*, p. 5; *ARCE, 1880*, p. 16.
5. H. Ex. Doc. 32, 43 Cong., 1 sess., *Amount Expended on Permanent Forts and Batteries*, pp. 2-4.
6. *ARCE, 1876*, p. 5; *ARCE, 1880*, p. 6. In 1880 Congress made an appropriation for the manufacture of four 12-inch rifled guns, but this effort was soon suspended.
7. *ARCE, 1878*, p. 4; *ARCE, 1884*, p. 5. The most detailed arguments for fortifications may be found in *ARCE* for the years 1876, 1880, 1881, and 1884.
8. *Statutes at Large*, 22:474, 477-78; ibid., 23:434.
9. H. Ex. Doc. 28, 49 Cong., 1 sess., *Report of the Board on Fortifications or Other Defenses*. Also published in *ARCE, 1886*, pp. 499-525.
10. Winslow, *Seacoast Defense*, p. 165.
11. George W. Goethals, "Fortifications," *Transactions of the American Society of Civil Engineers* 14 (October 1904): 65-69; Lewis, *Seacoast Fortifications*, p. 79. The 12-inch rifled mortars fired 700-pound projectiles for a maximum range of about 8.5 miles. The range of the 8- to 12-inch guns, which until about the time of World War I were fired in flat trajectory, was about 8 to 9 miles.
12. Lewis, *Seacoast Fortifications*, p. 78.
13. See ibid., map, p. 11, and table, pp. 140-41.
14. Battery ledgers and journals in box 1, fld. "Boston," box 2, flds. "Kennebec River, Portland, Me., and Portsmouth, N.H.," "Long Island Sound," box 3, fld. "New Bedford and Narragansett Bay," Coast Defense Fortification File, 1898-1920, RG 77, NA; *ARCE, 1897-1901*; Henry E. Dunnack, *Maine Forts*, pp. 138-41.
15. S. Doc. 248, 59 Cong., 2 sess., *Coast Defenses of the United States and the Insular Possessions*.
16. Lewis, *Seacoast Fortifications*, p. 93; Goethals, "Fortifications," p. 75.
17. Letters in box 29, flds. 96, 98 (2) (fire control, mine and tide observing stations), boxes 21-24, flds. 78 (27) (searchlights), box 2, fld. 4, box 32, fld. 125 (hoists), box 31, fld. 107 (wireless stations), box 29, fld. 95, box 33, fld, 146, box 40, fld. 171, box 55, fld. 305 (materials for Philippine batteries), Correspondence Relating to Fortifications, 1906-35, Boston District Office, RG 77, Federal Records Center, Waltham, Mass.
18. Letters in box 37, fld. 159, ibid.; *Boston Sunday Post*, August 29, 1909.
19. Letters in box 54, flds. 282 (8), box 55, fld. 309, Correspondence Relating to

Fortifications, 1906-35, Boston District Office, RG 77, Federal Records Center, Waltham, Mass.

20. David P. Kirchner, "American Harbor Defense Forts," *United States Naval Institute Proceedings* 84, no. 8 (August 1958): 95; Lewis, *Seacoast Fortifications,* pp. 100-101; *ARCE, 1915*, p. 7.

21. F. V. Abbot to Secretary of War, August 30, 1906, E. Burr to Chief of Engineers, December 23, 1909, box 33, fld, 140, Report of operations for the year ending June 30, 1919, Boston District, box 29, fld. 95, letters relating to construction of battery at Nahant, box 72, flds. 511(3), Correspondence Relating to Fortifications, 1906-35, RG 77, Federal Records Center, Waltham, Mass.

22. Reports of operations for the years ending June 30, 1919 and June 30, 1920, Boston District, box 29, fld, 95, S. A. Cheney to Chief of Engineers, December 26, 1928, box 57, fld. 337, letters relating to the construction of the battery on Hog Island, boxes 67-68, flds. 497 (8), letters relating to the purchase of Calf Island, box 68, fld. 498, ibid.

23. Battery journals in box 2, flds. "Portland," "Long Island Sound," box 3, fld. "New Bedford and Narragansett Bay," Coast Defense Fortification File, 1898-1920, RG 77, NA.

24. G. Van Deurs, "And the Navy got its Wings," *American Heritage* 7 (October 1956): 78-79; Alden and Wescott, *United States Navy*, pp. 357-58.

25. Report of operations for the year ending June 30, 1919, Boston District, box 29, fld. 95, letters in box 64, flds. 463 (4), Correspondence Relating to Fortifications, 1906-35, RG 77, Federal Records Center, Waltham, Mass.

26. Reports on operations for the years ending June 30, 1919 and June 30, 1920, box 29, fld. 95, letters in box 64, fld. 460 (dismounting guns), ibid.

27. Stetson Conn, Rose C. Engelman, and Byron Fairchild, *Guarding the United States and Its Outposts*, pp. 46-48; D. P. Kirchner and E. R. Lewis, "American Harbor Defenses: The Final Era," *United States Naval Institute Proceedings* 94, no. 1 (January 1968): 95.

28. Conn. Engelman, and Fairchild, *Guarding the United States*, pp. 49, 53-54.

29. Lewis, *Seacoast Fortifications,* pp. 117-18; Kirchner and Lewis, "American Harbor Defenses," p. 95.

30. For information on World War II battery construction I am especially indebted to Mr. Gerald Butler of Swampscott, Mass.

31. Lewis, *Seacoast Fortifications*, p. 120.

32. Memo from Wilbar M. Hoxie to author, January 23, 1975.

33. Lewis, *Seacoast Fortifications*, p. 124.

CHAPTER VII

1. Lenore Fine and Jesse A. Remington, *The Corps of Engineers: Construction in the United States*, pp. 3-40, 84-93, 107-8, 239-41, 246-55, 270, 460-76.

2. Wesley Frank Craven and James Lea Cate, *The Army Air Forces in World War II*, Vol. 1: *Plans and Early Operations, January 1939 to August 1942*, p. 344, Vol. 6: *Men and Planes*, pp. 128, 135, 136; "New England Salutes the Corps of Engineers," *Boston Sunday Post*, December 25, 1955, p. 18A.

3. Fine and Remington, *Corps of Engineers*, pp. 440-41, 443-44, 446-47, 614-44.

4. Ibid., p. 455.

5. Ibid., pp. 447-50.

6. Ibid., p. 252; Craven and Cate, *Men and Planes*, pp. 133-34, 148.

7. "History of the Boston District Engineer Office," p. 10; "History of the Providence District Engineer Office," pp. 4-5.

8. Craven and Cate, *Men and Planes*, pp. 97-98, 146.

9. The author is indebted to many past and present NED employees for information on World War II construction.

10. Clarence McKittrick Smith, *The Medical Department: Hospitalization and Evacuation, Zone of Interior*, pp. 73-76, 305; "History of the Boston District Engineer Office," pp. 9-10.

11. William C. Hall, "Veterans Hospital Program," *Military Engineer* 39 (December 1947): 519; [Col. Richard W. Pearson], Address delivered at Norwich University Post, Society of American Military Engineers, December 2, 1954, p. 11.

12. Robert F. Lafrenz, Robert B. Taylor and Warren R. Davidson, "History of the New England Division for Period June 25, 1950 through September 8, 1951," p. 1.

13. Ibid., pp. 2, 10-13, 60-61; Fine and Remington, *Corps of Engineers*, p. 562.

14. Lafrenz, "New England Division," pp. 16-17.

15. Ibid., pp. 41, 43, 59.

16. John E. Allen, Elliot F. Childs, and John Wm. Leslie, "The Limestone Air Force Base," *Journal of the Boston Society of Engineers* 36 (October 1949): 458-81; John E. Allen, "Construction of Long-Span Concrete Arch Hangar at Limestone Air Force Base," *Journal of the American Concrete Institute* 21 (February 1950): 405-8; "New England Salutes the Corps of Engineers," pp. 6A-8A.

17. Jack Scanlon, "Bangor's Big Stick," *New England Construction* 21 (January 21, 1957): 26-31, 78-79; "New England Salutes the Corps of Engineers," pp. 13A, 17A; Lafrenz, "New England Division," pp. 5, 6, 7.

18. John W. Leslie and Anthony Minichiello, "The Portsmouth Air Force Base," *Journal of the Boston Society of Civil Engineers* 43 (April 1956): 89-105.

19. Lafrenz, "New England Division," pp. 6, 8; "New England Salutes the Corps of Engineers," p. 14A; [Pearson], Address at Norwich University, p. 9; S. A. Potter, to W. K. Wilson, June 9, 1961, Newsletters from the New England Division Engineer to the Chief of Engineers.

20. Lafrenz, "New England Division," pp. 63-64; Files on microwave control studies, 1960-61, NED; Potter to Wilson, June 9, 1961, Newsletters. Gap fillers were located at Stoddard and Rye, N.H.; Westboro, New Salem, and Chilmark (Martha's Vineyard), Mass.; and Middletown, Conn.

21. Files on microwave control studies; K. F. Eklund to E. C. Itschner, October 10, 1960, Newsletters; Emerson C. Itschner, "Missile Construction for Security," *Military Engineer* 15 (July-August): 257-62. For brief descriptions of missiles see M. K. Lutz, "Military Missiles and Rockets," *Military Engineer* 51 (September-October 1959): 349-55.

22. A. K. Sibley to Itschner, May 9, 1960, Potter to Wilson, May 1, 1962, Newsletters.

23. Fine and Remington, *Corps of Engineers*, pp. 647-48; Lynn C. Barnes, "Permafrost: A Challenge to Engineers," *Military Engineer* 38 (January 1946): 9-11.

24. "General Fact Sheet, U. S. Army Corps of Engineers," Research and Development, p. 5.

25. For the building of Thule see "Birth of a Base," *Life* 33 (September 22, 1952): 130-51.

26. "Organization and Construction Projects," New England Division [1963]; P. Hyzer to Wilson, August 2, 1963, Newsletters.

27. Lafrenz, "New England Division," p. 10; "Organization and Construction Projects"; Hyzer to Wilson, January 17, 1963, July 15, 1964, January 14, 1965, R. O. Renier to F. W. Cassidy, February 5, 1968, F. P. Bane to F. J. Clarke, December 1, 1969, Newsletters.

28 "Organization and Construction Projects"; Potter to Wilson, June 9, 1961, Renier to Cassidy, May 4, 1966, Newsletters.

29. Lafrenz, "New England Division," pp. 6, 8; "New England Salutes the Corps of Engineers," p. 9A.

30. Lafrenz, "New England Division," pp. 7-8; "Organization and Construction Projects"; *Connecticut Aircraft Nuclear Engine Laboratory, Current Facilities, Middletown, Connecticut, December 15, 1957.*

31. Lafrenz, "New England Division," pp. 6, 9.

32. *Statutes at Large*, 69:651; Potter to Wilson, July 11, 1961, May 1, 1962, Newsletters; Alden K. Sibley, "From Bunker Hill to the Bay of Fundy," address delivered November 16, 1959, p. 1.

33. Division Newsletters and other records contain references to work at Fort Devens, Reserve Training Centers, and National Guard installations, but the author is especially indebted for information to division personnel.

34. Frederic H. Fay and Charles R. Gow, "The Boston Army Supply Base," *Journal of the Boston Society of Civil Engineers* 6 (March 1919): 71-95.

35. Robert J. Basso, F. L. Lincoln, and Joseph Peraino, "Rehabillitation of the Wharves and Piers, Army Base, South Boston, Mass.," *Journal of the Boston Society of Civil Engineers* 44 (January 1957): 70-97.

36. "Organization and Construction Projects"; Potter to Itschner, February 7, March 9, 1961, Sibley to Itschner, April 15, 1960, Newsletters.

37. "Program Review and Analysis" (NEDOP 64), p. 1; Hyzer to Wilson, October 8, 1964, Ribbs to Cassidy, January 26, 1966, Renier to Cassidy, August 19, 1966, Newsletters.

38. Ribbs to Wilson, April 14, 1965, Renier to Cassidy, May 4, 1966, Newsletters.

39. Renier to Cassidy, November 10, 1966, February 5, 1968, Newsletters.

40. Hyzer to Wilson, August 2, 1963, January 17, 1964, Newsletters; *Washington Post*, January 22, 1964.

41. Hyzer to Wilson, April 10, November 8, 1964, January 14, 1965, Ribbs to Wilson, April 14, 1965, Renier to Cassidy, May 4, August 19, November 10, 1966, February 9, May 5, November 22, 1967, February 5, 1968, Newsletters.

42. Renier to Cassidy, November 10, 1966, February 5, 1968, F. P. Bane to F. J. Clarke, February 28, May 27, 1970, Newsletters.

43. Renier to Cassidy, February 9, May 26, November 22, 1967, February 5, November 19, 1968, Bane to Cassidy, February 27, May 28, 1969, Bane to Clarke, December 1, 1969, Newsletters.

44. Renier to Cassidy, February 5, August 16, November 19, 1968, Bane to Cassidy, February 27, 1969, F. R. Day to Cassidy, May 28, 1969, Newslettes; *Information Bulletin* (NED) 6, no. 1 (January 1969): 1; ibid, 6, no. 2 (February 1969): 1.

45. "Program Review and Analysis" (NEDOP 68): ibid. (NEDOP 69); ibid. (NEDOP 70); *Information Bulletin* (NED) 7, no. 3 (March 1970): 1; Bane to Clarke, August 20, 1970, Newsletters.

CHAPTER VIII

1. William E. Leuchtenburg, *Flood Control Politics*, pp. 46-48.

2. *Laws of the United States Relating to the Improvement of Rivers and Harbors*, 3:2404-39.

3. *Laws Relating to Rivers and Harbors*, 3:1903, 1972; H. Doc. 308, 69 Cong., 1 sess., *Estimate of the Cost of Examinations, Etc., of Streams where Power Development Appears Feasible; ARCE, 1951*, Appendix F, "Federal Flood Control

Program,'' pp. 331-33; Thomas M. Robins, "River and Harbor Function of The Corps of Engineers," *Military Engineer* 32 (September-October 1940): 329.

4. Leuchtenburg, *Flood Control Politics*, pp. 27-34.

5. The account of flood control work draws heavily from *ARCE, 1927-73* and from the *Water Resources Development by the U. S. Army Corps of Engineers* booklets for the New England states published by NED.

6. *Laws Relating to Rivers and Harbors*, 3:2405-7; H. Doc. 412, 74 Cong., 2 sess., *Connecticut River, Conn., Mass., N. H., and Vt.*, had proposed an initial system of ten reservoirs, ultimately to be expanded to thirty-three. H. Doc. 649, 71 Cong., 3 sess., *Merrimack River, N. H. and Mass.*, had not proposed a system of reservoirs, finding that "even if all possible reservoirs sites were utilized, their cost would largely exceed the value of the damages which they might prevent" (p.31), a judgment modified after the 1936 floods.

7. Leuchtenburg, *Flood Contol Politics*, pp. 52-81. Leuchtenburg's study deals specifically with the Connecticut River Valley. Parallel developments took place relating to the Merrimack River Valley.

8. *Laws Relating to Rivers and Harbors*, 3:2598-2601; H. Doc. 455, 75 Cong., 2 sess., *Connecticut River, Mass., N. H., Vt., and Conn.*; H. Doc. 689, 75 Cong., 3 sess., *Merrimack River, Mass. and N. H.*

9. Leuchtenburg, *Flood Control Politics*, pp. 110-20.

10. Ibid., pp. 121-46.

11. T. J. R., "Common Sense Flood Control in New England," New England Division, June 5, 1956, pp. 15-18.

12. For a discussion of how the topography of New England dictates the design of dams and planning of basin protection systems see John W. Leslie and Reuben M. Haines, "Design and Construction of Earth Dams in New England," paper presented at the Milwaukee Water Resources Engineering Conference of The American Society of Civil Engineers, Milwaukee, Wisconsin, May 17, 1963.

13. "History of the Boston Engineer District," pp. 7-8.

14. Leuchtenburg, *Flood Control Politics*, pp. 158-211, *passim*.

15. The account of Hurricane Diane and Operation Noah is drawn largely from *New England Division, Final Report, "Operation Noah," May 1958*, and *New England Floods of 1955*, a five-part report of the New England Division. See also *Western Connecticut's Great Flood Disaster of August 19, 1955*, published by the Waterbury (Conn.) *Republic-American; Boston Traveler*, August 23, 1955; and *New England Division, Preliminary Report, "Operation Noah."*

16. The President declared disaster areas under authority of Public Law 875, 81 Cong., September 30, 1950. By Executive Order No. 10427, January 16, 1953, the responsibility for carrying out the provisions of P. L. 875 was assigned to the Federal Civil Defense Administrator.

17. Robert J. Fleming, Jr., "Talk Before the Savings Bank Association of New Hampshire on 9 June 1956 by Brigadier General Robert J. Fleming, Jr.," pp. 4-7.

18. Edward P. Boland, " . . . both a blessing and a curse," in *New England Leads the Way: The story of the world's largest flood control and hurricane protection system*, p. 7; *Program, Ground Breaking Ceremonies, June 14, 1960, East Brimfield and Westville Dams and Reservoirs.*

19. Fleming, "Talk Before the Savings Bank Association of New Hampshire," pp. 18-19; Alden K. Sibley, "A Milestone in Flood Control," *The New Englander*, no. 427, (October 1959): 30.

20. Sibley, "A Milestone in Flood Control," p. 30; John William Leslie, "New Hampshire's Twin-Dam Reservoir," *Military Engineer* 56 (March-April 1964): 106-8.

21. A. K. Sibley to E. C. Itschner, April 14, May 9, 1960, Newsletters from the New England Division Engineer to the Chief of Engineers.

22. Barriers were contemplated for the passages into Narragansett Bay, and a large-scale model of the bay and the proposed East Passage barrier was constructed at the Waterways Experiment Station at Vicksburg, Mississippi. Tests of its operation were carried out with a radio-controlled model of the aircraft carrier, *Forrestal*, built by the Navy. The project was dropped, however, when it met with organized opposition from both yachting interests and home owners (A. K. Sibley to E. C. Itschner, September 9, 1960, P. Hyzer to W. K. Wilson, Jr., April 10, 1964, Newsletters).

23. S. A. Potter to W. K. Wilson, May 1, 1962, P. Hyzer to Wilson, January 17, August 2, 1963, January 17, November 8, 1964, Newsletters.

24. Hyzer to Wilson, August 2, 1963, January 17, 1964, Newsletters.

25. *Information Bulletin* (New England Division, Corps of Engineers) 5, no. 11 (November 1968): 1.

26. *The Reservoir Control Center, Guidance Memorandum*, pp. 23-26; *Reservoir Control Center, Annual Report, Fiscal Year 1974*, pp. 4-5, 13-17; *The Earth Resources Technology Satellite Experiment and Flood Control in New England; The LANDSAT Satellite and Flood Control in New England;* Timothy D. Buckelew, *Operation of LANDSAT Automatic Tracking System*, pp. A1-A5.

27. R. O. Renier to W. F. Cassidy, May 4, August 8, November 10, 1956, Newsletters.

28. *Interim Report on Charles River for Flood Control and Navigation, Lower Charles River, Massachusetts*.

29. *Charles River, Massachusetts, Main Report & Attachments; Information Sheet No. 2, May 1973, Natural Valley Storage*.

30. For a delightfully written acticle on the problems of the Charles by the Executive Director of the Charles River Watershed Association, which recognizes the limitations of the natural valley storage approach, see Rita Barron, "The Charles River: Engineering by Nature," *Appalachia* 40, no. 2 (December 15, 1974): 102-11. For a less preceptive view of nature's engineering see "Ecology 'spies' police the Charles," *Christian Science Monitor*, July 7, 1972.

31. Files of the Flood Plain Management Services Branch, NED.

CHAPTER IX

1. The account of the first Passamaquoddy project was drawn from *Passamaquoddy Tidal Power Development, Final Report*, and *Appendices to Final Report, October 23, 1936*, United States Engineer Office, Eastport, Maine; *Principles and Facts Underlying Quoddy Tidal Power Project*, Eastport District, U. S. Engineer Office; *ARCE, 1935*, pp. 32-33; *ARCE, 1936*, pp. 33-34; *ARCE, 1937*, pp. 29-30.

2. *Quoddy Currier*, June 15, 1936.

3. *Congressional Record*, 80:8304-16, 8382-403; *Laws of the United States Relating to the Improvement of Rivers and Harbors*, 3:2440-41.

4. Harold L. Ickes, *The Secret Diary of Harold L. Ickes: The First Thousand Days, 1933-1936*, pp. 189-91, 513-14, 542-43, 654, 676.

5. The account of the revival of Quoddy as an international project was drawn from Margaret Chase Smith, "Brief History of Passamaquoddy Tidal Power Project," *Congressional Record*, 99: Appendix, 4510-11; *Let's get All the facts about Quoddy*, Maine Development Commission, 1950; Alden K. Sibley, "'Passamaquoddy'; A New Source of Energy''; *The International*

Passamaquoddy Tidal Project, Reports of the International Joint Commission, the International Engineering Board, and the International Fisheries Board, 1961.

6. The account of the review of the report of the International Joint Commission was drawn from *The International Passamaquoddy Tidal Power Project And Upper Saint John River Hydroelectric Power Development*, Report to President Kennedy by Secretary of the Interior Udall, July 1963; *Supplement to July 1963 Report, The International Passamaquoddy Tidal Power Project and Upper Saint John River Hydroelectric Power Development*, Report to Secretary of the Interior Udall by the Passamaquoddy-Saint John River study Committee, August 1964; *Conservation of the Natural Resources of New England: The Passamaquoddy Tidal Power and Upper Saint John River Hydroelectric Development*, Report to President Johnson by Secretary of the Interior Udall, July 1965.

7. *Statutes at Large*, 79:1073; *ARCE, 1966*, pp. 115-16; *ARCE, 1967*, pp. 113-16; *ARCE, 1968*, pp. 50-51.

8. R. O. Renier to W. F. Cassidy, November 10, 1966, Newsletters; H. Rpt. 505, 90 Cong., 1 sess., *Public Works and Atomic Energy Commission Appropriation Bill, 1968*; S. Rpt. 574, 90 Cong., 1 sess., *Public Works and Atomic Energy Commission Appropriation Bill, 1968*; H. Rpt. 820, 90 Cong., 1 sess., *Public Works and Atomic Energy Commission Appropriation Bill, 1968, Conference Report*.

9. H. Rpt. 93-1077, 93 Cong., 2 sess., *Public Works for Water and Power Development and Atomic Energy Commission Appropriation Bill, 1975*; S. Rpt. 93-1032, 93 Cong., 2 sess., *Public Works for Water and Power Development and Atomic Energy Commission Appropriation Bill, 1975;* Senate Public Works Committee, Resolution for Passamaquoddy Tidal Power Study, adopted March 2, 1975.

CHAPTER X

1. *Laws of the United States Relating to the Improvement of Rivers and Harbors*, 3:2125, 2452-53.

2. See *Shore Protection Program*, Department of the Army, Office, Chief of Engineers, July 1970, and *Water Resources Development by the U. S. Army Corps of Engineers* booklets for the New England states published by NED.

3. *ARCE, 1971*, 2:1 - 22-23; *ARCE, 1973*, 2:1 - 21-22; *Water Resources Development by the U. S. Army Corps of Engineers in Rhode Island*, 1975, pp. 34-35; News Release, NED, 14 July 1971.

4. See *Reservoir Control Center Annual Reports*, NED.

5. S. Doc. 14, 85 Cong., 1 sess., *Land and Water Resources of the New England-New York Region*.

6. Ibid., pt. 1, p. v; H. Rpt. 169, 89 Cong., 1 sess., *Water Resources Planning Act*, pp. 4-5.

7. S. Doc. 97, 87 Cong., 2 sess., *Policies, Standards, and Procedures in the Formulation, Evaluation and Review of Plans for Use and Development of Water and Related Land Resources*.

8. *Statutes at Large*, 79:244-254; Executive Order No. 11376, September 6, 1967.

9. *Statutes at Large*, 83:852-56; ibid., 84:2086-89.

10. Albert E. Cowdrey, "Pioneering Environmental Law: The Army Corps of Engineers and the Refuse Act," *Pacific Historical Review* 44 (August 1975): 346.

11. *Comprehensive Water and Related Land Resources Investigation, Connecticut River Basin*, Vol. I, *Main Report*, June 1970; John Wm. Leslie, "Water and Natural Resource Development in New England," paper presented at the Regional Science Association Meeting, Boston, Massachusetts, October 24, 1964,

pp. 2-6; E. J. Ribbs to F. W. Cassidy, January 20, 1966, Newsletters from the New England Division Engineer to the Chief of Engineers.

12. *Statutes at Large*, 79:1085-86; *North Atlantic Regional Water Resources Study, Report*.

13. *Statutes at Large*, 79:1073; *Draft, Feasibility Report of Alternative Regional Water Supply Plans for Southeastern New England*, November 1969; *Northeastern United States Water Supply Study, Northfield Mountain Water Supply Project*, Vol. 1, *Main Report*, October 1974; *Northeastern United States Water Supply Study, Millers River Basin Water Supply Project*, Vol. I, *Main Report*, October 1974.

14. *The Merrimack: Designs for a Clean River*, September 1971; *Merrimack Wastewater Management: Key to a Clean River*, November 1974.

15. *Northeastern United States Water Supply Study, Wastewater Management, Merrimack River Basin - Boston Metropolitan Area*, December 1975; *Wastewater Engineering and Management Plan for Boston Harbor-Eastern Massachusetts Metropolitan Area EMMA Study, Main Report*, March 1976.

16. *A Plan for Long Island Sound*, Vol. 1, *Summary*, July 1975.

17. *How to Guide Growth in Southeastern New England, Report of the Southeastern New England Water and Related Land Resources Study, Review Draft/May 1975; Report of the Southeastern New England Study, Summary*, December 1975.

18. Department of Defense, Corps of Engineers, Department of the Army, "Urban Studies Program, Proposed Policies and Procedures," *Federal Register* 39, no. 130, Pt. III, July 5, 1974, 24756.

19. *A Water and Related Land Resources Study of the Pawcatuck River and Narragansett Bay Drainage Basins, Plan of Study*, May 1976.

20. *National Shoreline Study, Shore Management Guidelines*, August 1971; *National Shoreline Study, Shore Protection Guidelines*, August 1971; H. Doc. 93-121, 93 Cong., 1 sess., *National Shoreline Study*, Vol. II, *Regional Inventory Report, North Atlantic Region*, 1973.

21. *Interim Report, Atlantic Coast Deep Water Port Facilities Study, Eastport, Maine, to Hampton Roads, Virginia*, June 1973.

22. Files of NED Emergency Operations Center; "After-Action Report for Operation Foresight, 1 March-16 May 1969"; "After-Action Report for Operation Foresight, February 1971-June 1971."

23. *The Chelsea, Mass. Urban Fire Debris Removal Operations, 14 October 1973 - 5 April 1974*; J. F. Sullivan, Jr., to J. H. Mason, December 17, 1973, NED files.

BIBLIOGRAPHY

Manuscripts

Files of the New England Division. Corps of Engineers.

Newsletters from the New England Division Engineer to the Chief of Engineers. New England Division. Corps of Engineers.

Records of the Adjutant General's Office. Record Group 94. National Archives, Historical Information Relating to Military Posts and Other Installations, ca. 1700-1900. Microfilm Publication M661.

Records of the Office of the Chief of Engineers. Record Group 77. National Archives. Cartographic Division. Fort Gorges, Portland Harbor, Drawer 13, Sketch B.

_____ . Memoir Descriptive of the Fort projected for Hog Island Ledge, Portland Harbor, Me., by J. D. Kurtz, Drawer 13, Sketch A.

_____ . Plan of a work projected for Clark's Point, New Bedford, Mass., dated July 1846, Drawer 25, Sheet 1.

Textual Records of the Office of the Chief of Engineers. Record Group 77. National Archives. Coast Defense Fortification File, 1898-1920.

_____ . Letters Sent by the Topographical Bureau. Microfilm Publication M66.

_____ . Letters Sent Relating to Internal Improvements under an Act of April 30, 1824.

_____ . Letters Sent to Engineer Officers, 1812-69.

_____ . Miscellaneous Letters Sent, 1812-69.

_____ . Monthly Returns of the Engineer Department, Apr. 1832-Aug. 1918.

Textual Records of the Office of the Chief of Engineers. Record Group 77. Federal Records Center. Waltham, Massachusetts. Correspondence Relating to Fortifications, 1906-35, Boston District Office.

_____ . Press Copies of Letters Sent, Jan. 1907-Dec. 1919, Newport, R. I., Engineer Office.

_____ . Press Copies of Letters Sent Relating to Personnel, 1909-1912, New London, Conn., Engineer Office.

Public Documents

Publications of the United States Government

American Archives. Edited by Peter Force. 4th ser., 6 vols. Washington: Prepared and published by an act of Congress by M. St. Claire Clarke and Peter Force, 1837-1853.

American State Papers. Edited by Walter Lowrie _et al_. 38 vols. Washington: Gales and Seaton, 1832-1861.

Conservation of the Natural Resources of New England: The Passamaquoddy Tidal Power and Upper Saint John River Hydroelectric Development. Report to President Lyndon B. Johnson. Stewart L. Udall, Secretary, U. S. Department of the Interior, July 1965.

Index to the Reports of the Chief of Engineers, U. S. Army, 1866-1912. 2 vols. (H. Doc. 740, 63 Cong., 2 sess., 1914). Washington: Government Printing Office, 1916.

Index to the Reports of The Chief of Engineers, U. S. Army, 1913-1917. (H. Doc. 724, 66 Cong., 2 sess., 1920). Washington: Government Printing Office, 1921.

The International Passamaquoddy Tidal Power Project. Reports of the International Joint Commission, the International Engineering Board, and the International Fisheries Board. Washington and Ottawa, April 1961.

The International Passamaquoddy Tidal Power Project And Upper Saint John River Hydroelectric Power Development. Report to President John F. Kennedy. Stewart L. Udall, Secretary of the Interior, July 1963.

Journals of the Continental Congress, 1774-1789. Washington: Government Printing Office, 1905.

Laws of the United States Relating to the Improvement of Rivers and Harbors. 3 vols. and index. (H. Doc. 1491, 62 Cong., 3 sess.; H. Doc. 379, 76 Cong., 1 sess.). Washington: Government Printing Office, 1913, 1940.

Smith, Margaret Chase. "Brief History of the Passamaquoddy Tidal Power Project." *Congressional Record*, 80:4510-11.

Supplement to July 1963 Report, The International Passamaquoddy Tidal Power Project and Upper Saint John River Hydroelectric Power Development. Report to Stewart L. Udall, Secretary, U. S. Department of the Interior, by Passamaquoddy-Saint John River Study Committee, August 1964.

Thian, Raphael P., comp. *Legislative History of the General Staff of the Army of the United States from 1775 to 1901*. (S. Doc. 229, 56 Cong., 2 sess.). Washington: Government Printing Office, 1901.

U. S. Department of the Army. *Annual Reports of the Secretary of War*.

_____ . *Annual Reports of the Topographical Bureau, 1831-1851*.

_____ . *Annual Reports of the Chief of Engineers*.

_____ . Corps of Engineers. *National Shoreline Study. Shore Management Guidelines*. Washington, D.C., August 1971.

_____ . Corps of Engineers. *National Shoreline Study. Shore Protection Guidelines*. Washington, D. C., August 1971.

_____ . Office, Chief of Engineers. *Shore Protection Program*. Washington, D. C., July 1970.

U. S. Congress. *Congressional Record*, 80:8301-16, 8382-403.

U. S. Congress. House. *Amount Expended on Permanent Forts and Batteries*. H. Ex. Doc. 32, 43 Cong., 1 sess., 1874.

_____ . *Canal–Connecticut River to Lake Memphremagog, &c*. H. Doc. 118, 20 Cong., 2 sess., 1829.

_____ . *Cape Cod Canal, Mass*. H. Doc. 795, 71 Cong., 3 sess., 1931.

_____ . *Cape Cod Canal (Onset Bay), Mass*. H. Doc. 431, 77 Cong., 1 sess., 1941.

_____ . *Connecticut River above Hartford, Conn*. H. Doc. 35, 71 Cong., 2 sess., 1930.

_____ . *Connecticut River above Hartford, Conn*. H. Doc. 36, 71 Cong., 2 sess., 1930.

_____ . *Connecticut River above Hartford, Conn*. H. Doc. 165, 76 Cong., 1 sess., 1939.

_____ . *Connecticut River between Hartford and Holyoke*. H. Doc. 1311, 60 Cong., 2 sess., 1909.

_____ . *Connecticut River between Hartford, Conn., and Holyoke, Mass*. H. Doc. 323, 59 Cong., 2 sess., 1906.

_____ . *Connecticut River, Between Hartford, Conn., and Holyoke, Mass*. H. Doc. 417, 64 Cong., 1 sess., 1915.

_____ . *Connecticut River between Hartford, Conn., and Springfield and Holyoke, Mass*. H. Doc. 27, 73 Cong., 1 sess., 1933.

_____ . *Connecticut River, Connecticut and Massachusetts*. H. Doc. 818, 61 Cong., 1 sess., 1910.

_____ . *Connecticut River, Conn., Mass., N. H., and Vt*. H. Doc, 412, 74 Cong., 2 sess., 1936.

_____ . *Connecticut River, Mass., N. H., Vt., and Conn*. H. Doc. 455, 75 Cong., 2 sess., 1937.

_____ . *Correspondence Concerning the Purchase of the Cape Cod Canal*. H. Doc. 139, 67 Cong., 2 sess., 1921.

_____ . *East Boat Basin, Cape Cod Canal, Mass*. H. Doc. 168, 85 Cong., 1 sess., 1957.

_____ . *Estimate of Cost of Examinations, Etc., of Streams where Power Development Appears Feasible*. H. Doc. 308, 69 Cong., 1 sess., 1926.

_____ . *Fortifications in Boston Harbor*. H. Doc. 86, 23 Cong., 2 sess., 1835.

_____ . *Harbor of Refuge at Sandy Bay, Cape Ann, Mass*. H. Doc. 411, 64 Cong., 1 sess., 1915.

_____ . *Hudson and Berkshire Rail Road*. H. Doc. 89, 20 Cong., 2 sess., 1829.

_____ . *Letter from the Secretary of War, Reference to Fortifications, December 11, 1851*. H. Ex. Doc. 5, 32 Cong., 1 sess., 1851. This report was also published as *Report of General J. G. Totten, Chief Engineer, on The Subject of National Defences*. Washington: A. Boyd Hamilton, 1851.

_____ . *Merrimack River, Mass. and N. H*. H. Doc. 689, 75 Cong., 3 sess., 1938.

_____ . *Merrimack River, N. H. and Mass*. H. Doc. 649, 71 Cong., 3 sess., 1930.

_____ . *Military and Naval Defenses*. [Report of the Board of Engineers for Fortifications, April 18, 1836]. H. Doc. 243, 24 Cong., 1 sess., 1836.

_____ . *National Shoreline Study*. Vol. II, *Regional Inventory Report, North Atlantic Region*. H. Doc. 93-121, 93 Cong., 1 sess., 1973.

_____ . *Provincetown Harbor, Mass*. H. Doc. 600, 80 Cong., 2 sess., 1948.

_____ . *Public Works and Atomic Energy Commission Appropriation Bill, 1968*. H. Rpt. 505, 90 Cong., 1 sess., 1967.

_____ . *Public Works and Atomic Energy Commission Appropriation Bill, 1968, Conference Report*. H. Rpt. 820, 90 Cong., 1 sess., 1967.

_____ . *Public Works for Water and Power Development and Atomic Energy Commission Appropriation Bill, 1975*. H. Rpt. 93-1077, 93 Cong., 2 sess., 1974.

_____ . *Report of a Survey of the Connecticut River between Hartford and Holyoke*. H. Doc. 231, 58 Cong., 3 sess., 1904.

_____ . *Report of Proceedings to Date in Determining Value and Advisability of Purchase of the Cape Cod Canal Connecting Buzzards Bay and Cape Cod Bay, Mass*. H. Doc. 1768, 65 Cong., 3 sess., 1919.

_____ . *Report of the Board on Fortifications or Other Defenses*. H. Ex. Doc. 28, 49 Cong., 1 sess., 1886.

_____ . *Report of the examination which has been made by the Board of Engineers with a view to internal improvements, February 14, 1825*. H. Doc. 83, 18 Cong., 2 sess., 1825.

_____ . *Sea-Coast Defenses*. H. Ex. Doc. 271, 41 Cong., 2 sess., 1870.

_____ . *Survey–Connecticut River, &c*. H. Doc. 154, 19 Cong., 1 sess., 1826.

_____ . *Survey of Conn. River between Hartford, Conn., and Holyoke, Mass*. H. Doc. 136, 55 Cong., 2 sess., 1897.

_____ . *Surveys–Kennebec River, &c*. H. Doc. 173, 20 Cong., 1 sess., 1828.

_____ . *Surveys–Roads and Canals*. H. Doc. 83, 19 Cong., 2 sess., 1827.

_____ . *Surveys, with a View to Making Roads & Canals*. H. Rpt. 102, 19 Cong., 2 sess., 1827.

_____ . *Water Resources Planning Act*. H. Rpt. 169 To Accompany H. R. 1111, 89 Cong., 1 sess., 1965.

U. S. Congress. House. Committee on Rivers and Harbors. *Cape Cod Canal, Mass*. H. Com. on Rivers and Harbors Doc. 15, 74 Cong., 1 sess., 1934.

_____ . *Report of Colonel Edw. Burr upon the Cape Cod Canal: Its History, Operation, and Improvement*. H. Com. on Rivers and Harbors Doc. 3, 69 Cong., 1 sess., 1926.

302

U. S. Congress. Senate. *Coast Defenses of the United States and the Insular Possessions.* S. Doc. 248, 59 Cong., 2 sess., 1906.

———. *Land and Water Resources of the New England-New York Region.* S. Doc. 14, 85 Cong., 1 sess., 1957.

———. *Plymouth Harbor, Massachusetts.* S. Doc. 124, 87 Cong., 2 sess., 1962.

———. *Policies, Standards, and Procedures in the Formulation, Evaluation, and Review of Plans for Use and Development of Water and Related Land Resources.* S. Doc. 97, 87 Cong., 2 sess., 1962.

———. *Proposed Agreement with the Connecticut River Company.* S. Doc. 1067, 62 Cong., 2 sess., 1913.

———. *Public Works and Atomic Energy Commission Appropriation Bill, 1968.* S. Rpt. 574, 90 Cong., 1 sess., 1967.

———. *Public Works for Water and Power Development and Atomic Energy Commission Appropriation Bill, 1975.* S. Rpt. 93-1032, 93 Cong., 2 sess., 1974.

———. *Purchase of the Cape Cod Canal Property.* S. Rept. 924, 68 Cong., 2 sess., 1925.

———. *Report on the Means of National Defense.* S. Doc. 85, 28 Cong., 2 sess., 1845.

U. S. Congress. Senate. Public Works Committee. *Resolution for Passamaquoddy Tidal Power Study.* Adopted 21 March 1975.

U. S. Department of Defense. Corps of Engineers. Department of The Army. "Urban Studies Program. Proposed Policies and Procedures." *Federal Register* 39, No. 130, Pt.III, July 5, 1974.

U. S. *Statutes at Large.*

Publications of or in cooperation with Corps of Engineers districts and divisions

Boland, Edward P. " . . . both a blessing and a curse." *New England Leads the Way: The story of the world's largest flood control and hurricane protection system.* Department of the Army. New England Division, Corps of Engineers, and Motorola, Inc., [1970].

Buckelew, Timothy D. *Operation of LANDSAT Automatic Tracking System.* New England Division, U. S. Army Corps of Engineers, March 1976.

Charles River, Massachusetts, Main Report & Attachments. Department of the Army. New England Division, Corps of Engineers, Waltham, Mass., [1972].

The Chelsea, Mass. Urban Fire Debris Removal Operations, 14 October 1973 - 5 April 1974. Department of the Army. Corps of Engineers, New England Division, August 1974.

Comprehensive Water and Related Land Resources Investigation, Connecticut River Basin. Vol. I, *Main Report.* Connecticut River Basin Coordinating Committee, June 1970.

Connecticut River, Connecticut-Massachusetts, Navigation Study, Survey Report, Long Island Sound to Holyoke, Mass. Department of the Army. New England Division, Corps of Engineers, Boston, Mass., June 3, 1949.

Connecticut River, Hartford, Connecticut, to Holyoke, Massachusetts (Review of Reports). Department of the Army. New England Division, Corps of Engineers, Waltham, Mass., September 1973.

Draft, Feasibility Report on Alternative Regional Water Supply Plans for Southeastern New England. Department of the Army. North Atlantic Division, Corps of Engineers, November 1969. New England Division, Waltham, Mass.

The Earth Resources Technology Satellite Experiment and Flood Control in New

England. Department of the Army. New England Division, Corps of Engineers, Waltham, Mass., October 1974.

How to Guide Growth in Southeastern New England. Report of the Southeastern New England Water and Related Land Resources Study. New England River Basins Commission, Boston, May 1975. Review Draft/May 1975.

Interim Report on Charles River for Flood Control and Navigation, Lower Charles River, Massachusetts. Department of the Army. New England Division, Corps of Engineers, Waltham, Mass., May 1968.

Interim Report, Atlantic Coast Deep Water Port Facilities Study, Eastport, Maine, to Hampton Roads, Virginia. U. S. Army Corps of Engineers, Philadelphia District, North Atlantic Division, June 1973.

The LANDSAT Satellite and Flood Control in New England. Department of the Army. New England Division, Corps of Engineers, Waltham Mass., June 1976.

The Merrimack: Designs for a Clean River. A Feasibility Study prepared by North Atlantic Division, U. S. Army Corps of Engineers, in cooperation with New England Division, U. S. Army Corps of Engineers, Region I of the Environmental Protection Agency, State of New Hampshire, Commonwealth of Massachusetts, New England River Basins Commission, September 1971.

Merrimack Wastewater Management: Key to a Clean River. A Survey Study prepared by New England Division, U. S. Army Corps of Engineers, in cooperation with North Atlantic Division, U. S. Army Corps of Engineers, Region 1 of the Environmental Protection Agency, Commonwealth of Massachusetts, November 1974.

New England Division, Final Report, "Operation Noah," May 1958, U.S. Department of the Army, Corps of Engineers, New England Division.

New England Division, Preliminary Report, "Operation Noah." New England Division, Disaster Relief Office, Corps of Engineers, U. S. Army, Boston, Mass., November 1955.

New England Floods of 1955. 5 parts. Corps of Engineers. U. S. Army. Office of the Division Engineer, Boston, Mass., March-April 1956.

North Atlantic Regional Water Resources Study Report. Prepared by North Atlantic Regional Resources Study Group, North Atlantic Division, Corps of Engineers, U.S. Army, for the North Atlantic Regional Water Resources Study Coordinating Committee, June 1972.

Northeastern United States Water Supply Study, Millers River Basin Water Supply Project. Vol. I, *Main Report.* Department of the Army. New England Division, Corps of Engineers, Waltham, Mass., October 1974.

Northeastern United States Water Supply Study, Northfield Mountain Water Supply Project. Vol. I, *Main Report.* Department of the Army. New England Division, Corps of Engineers, Waltham, Mass., October 1974.

Northeastern United States Water Supply Study, Wastewater Management, Merrimack River Basin-Boston Metropolitan Area. [U. S. Army, Corps of Engineers, New England Division], December 1975.

Passamaquoddy Tidal Power Development, Final Report, and *Appendices to Final Report, October 23, 1936.* United States Engineer Office, Eastport, Maine.

A Plan for Long Island Sound. Vol. I, *Summary.* New England River Basins Commission, July 1975.

Principles and Facts Underlying Quoddy Tidal Power Project. Eastport District. U.S. Engineer Office, Eastport, Maine.

Report of the Southeastern New England Study, Summary. New England River Basins Commission, December 1975.

Reservoir Control Center, Annual Reports. Department of the Army. New England

304

Division, Corps of Engineers, Waltham, Massachusetts.

The Reservoir Control Center, Guidance Memorandum. Department of the Army. New England Division, Corps of Engineers, Waltham, Massachusetts, September 1971.

Wastewater Engineering and Management Plan for Boston Harbor-Eastern Massachusetts Metropolitan Area EMMA Study. Main Report. For the Metropolitan District Commission, Commonwealth of Massachusetts, by Metcalf & Eddy, Inc., March 1976.

A Water and Related Land Resources Study of the Pawcatuck River and Narragansett Bay Drainage Basins, Plan of Study. [U. S. Army Corps of Engineers, New England Division], May 1976.

Water Resources Development by the U. S. Army Corps of Engineers in Connecticut. Department of the Army. Corps of Engineers, New England Division, Waltham, Mass., 1975.

Water Resources Development by the U. S. Army Corps of Engineers in Maine. Department of the Army. Corps of Engineers, New England Division, Waltham, Mass., 1975.

Water Resources Development by the U. S. Army Corps of Engineers in Massachusetts. Department of the Army. Corps of Engineers, New England Division, Waltham, Mass., 1975.

Water Resources Development by the U. S. Army Corps of Engineers in New Hampshire. Department of the Army. Corps of Engineers, New England Division, Waltham, Mass. 1975.

Water Resources Development by the U. S. Army Corps of Engineers in Rhode Island. Department of the Army. Corps of Engineers, New England Division, Waltham, Mass., 1975.

Water Resources Development by the U. S. Army Corps of Engineers in Vermont. Department of the Army. Corps of Engineers, New England Division, Waltham, Mass., 1975.

Publications of State Agencies

The Journals of each Provincial Congress of Massachusetts in 1774 and 1775. William Lincoln, comp. Boston: Dutton and Wentworth, 1838.

Let's get All the facts about 'Quoddy. Maine Development Commission, Augusta, June 1950.

Massachusetts. Public Documents, 1860. No. 34, "Report of the Committee of Construction of Ship Canal between Buzzard's Bay and Barnstable Bay."

Massachusetts, Public Documents, 1863. No. 41, "Report of the Joint Committee of 1860 upon The Proposed Canal to Unite Barnstable and Buzzard's Bays."

Miscellaneous Documents

Connecticut Aircraft Nuclear Engine Laboratory, Current Facilities, Middletown, Connecticut, December 15, 1957. Pratt & Whitney Aircraft, Division of United Aircraft Corporation, CANEL, Middletown, Connecticut.

Information Sheet #2, May 1973, Natural Valley Storage. Charles River Watershed Association, Auburndale, Massachusetts.

Program, Ground Breaking Ceremonies, June 14, 1960, East Brimfield and Westville Dams and Reservoirs.

Newspapers

Boston Sunday Post, August 29, 1909.

Boston Sunday Post, December 25, 1955. "New England Salutes the Corps of Engineers."

Boston Traveler, August 23, 1955.

"Ecology 'spies' police the Charles," *Christian Science Monitor,* July 7, 1972.

Information Bulletin (New England Division, Corps of Engineers, Waltham, Mass.), November 1968, January 1969, February 1969, March 1970.

Washington Post, January 22, 1964.

Western Connecticut's Great Flood Disaster, August 19, 1955. Published by the Waterbury (Conn.) *Republican-American.*

Quoddy Courier, June 15, 1936.

Books and Articles

Abbot, Henry L. "The Corps of Engineers." *Journal of the Military Service Institution* 15 (1894): 413-27.

Alden, Carroll Storrs, and Wescott, Allan. *The United States Navy.* Chicago: J. B. Lippincott Company, 1943.

Alexander, Barton S. "Minot's Ledge Lighthouse." *Transactions of The American Society of Civil Engineers* 8 (1879): 83-94.

Allan, Carlisle. "George W. Whistler, Military Engineer." *Military Engineer* 29 (1937): 177-80.

Allen, John E. "Construction of Long-Span Concrete Arch Hangar at Limestone Air Force Base." *Journal of the American Concrete Institute* 21 (February 1950): 405-14.

Allen, John E.; Childs, Elliot F.; and Leslie, John Wm. "The Limestone Air Force Base." *Journal of the Boston Society of Engineers* 36 (October 1949): 458-81.

Barnard, J. G. "Biography of the late Bvt. Major General Joseph G. Totten, Chief Engineer, United States Army." *Historical Papers Relating to the Corps of Engineers and to Engineer Troops of the United States Army.* Occasional Paper, no. 16. U. S. Army Engineer School. Washington: Government Printing Office, 1904.

Barnard, J. G. "Lighthouse Engineering as Displayed at the Centennial Exhibition." *Transactions of the American Society of Civil Engineers* 8 (1879): 55-82.

Barnes, Lynn C. "Permafrost: A Challenge to Engineers." *Military Engineer* 38 (January 1946): 9-11.

Barron, Rita. "The Charles River: Engineering by Nature." *Appalachia* 40, no. 2 (December 15, 1974): 102-11.

Basso, Robert J.; Lincoln, F. L.; and Peraino, Joseph. "Rehabilitation of the Wharves and Piers, Army Base, South Boston, Mass." *Journal of the Boston Society of Engineers* 44 (January 1957): 70-97.

Beers, Henry P. "A History of the U. S. Topographical Engineers, 1813-1863." *Military Engineer* 34 (June 1942): 287-91, (July 1942): 348-52.

"Birth of a Base." *Life* 33 (September 22, 1952): 130-31.

Black, William M., director. *Pamphlet on the Evolution of the Art of Fortification.* Occasional Paper, no. 58. U. S. Army Engineer School. Washington: Government Printing Office, 1919.

Buzziard, Raleigh B. "Washington's Favorite Engineer." *Military Engineer* 40 (1948): 115-18.

Buzziard, Raleigh B. "Washington's Last Chief Engineer: Etienne Becket, Sieur de Rochefontaine." *Military Engineer* 45 (1953): 118-22.

Conn, Stetson; Engelman, Rose C.; and Fairchild, Byron. *Guarding the United States and Its Outposts.* Volume in United States Army in World War II: The Western Hemisphere. Washington: Department of the Army, 1964.

"Corps of Engineers, &c." *Niles Weekly Register* 29 (October 22, 1825): 121-22.

Cowdrey, Albert E. "Pioneering Environmental Law: The Army Corps of Engineers and the Refuse Act." *Pacific Historical Review* 44 (August 1975): 331-49.

Craighill, William E. "Breakwater at Sandy Bay, Cape Ann, Massachusetts." *Professional Memoirs* 8 (September-October 1916): 587-607.

Craven, Wesley Frank, and Cate, James Lea, eds. *The Army Air Forces In World War II.* Vol. 1: *Plans and Early Operations, January 1939 to August 1942.* Vol. 6: *Men and Planes.* Chicago: University of Chicago Press, 1948-55.

Cullum, George W. *Biographical Register of the Officers and Graduates of the U. S. Military Academy at West Point, N. Y.* 3d ed., rev. 8 vols. Boston: Houghton Mifflin, 1891-1955.

———. *Biographical Sketch of Brigadier-General Joseph G. Swift, Chief Engineer of the United States Army, July 31, 1812, to Nov. 12, 1818.* New York: Charles A. Coffin, 1877.

———. *Biographical Sketch of Brigadier-General Sylvanus Thayer, Superintendent of the U. S. Military Academy, July 28, 1817, to July 1, 1833.* New York: Sherwood & Co., Printers, 1883.

———. *Historical Sketch of the Fortification Defenses of Narragansett Bay since the founding, in 1638, of the Colony of Rhode Island.* Washington: 1884.

Dictionary of American Biography.

Dunnack, Henry E. *Maine Forts.* Augusta, Me.: Charles E. Nash & Son, 1924.

Fay, Frederick H., and Gow, Charles R. "The Boston Army Supply Base." *Journal of the Boston Society of Civil Engineers* 6 (March 1919): 67-113.

Fine, Lenore, and Remington, Jesse A. *The Corps of Engineers: Construction in the United States.* Volume in United States Army in World War II: The Technical Services. Washington: Department of the Army, 1972.

Forman, Sidney. "The First School of Engineering." *Military Engineer* 44 (1952): 109-12.

French, Allen. *The First Year of the American Revolution.* Boston: Houghton Mifflin Company, 1934.

Frothingham, Richard, Jr. *History of the Siege of Boston and of the Battles of Lexington, Concord, and Bunker Hill.* 2d ed. Boston: Charles C. Little and James Brown, 1851.

Geothals, George W. "Fortifications." *Transactions of the American Society of Civil Engineers* 14 (October 1904): 57-76.

Goodrich, Carter. "National Planning of Internal Improvements." *Political Science Quarterly* 63 (1948): 16-44.

Hall, William C. "Veterans Hospital Program." *Military Engineer* 39 (December 1947): 519-20.

Heavey, W. F. "The Corps in the Days of the Revolution." *Military Engineer* 31 (1939): 410-15.

Hill, Forest G. *Roads, Rails & Waterways: The Army Engineers and Early Transportation.* Norman: University of Oklahoma Press, 1957.

Holt, W. Stull. *The Office of the Chief of Engineers of the Army: Its Non-military History, Activities, and Organization.* Baltimore: The John Hopkins Press, 1923.

Huntoon, Daniel T. V. *History of the Town of Canton, Norfolk County, Massachusetts.* Cambridge, Mass.: Published by the Town, 1893.

Ickes, Harold L. *The Secret Diary of Harold L. Ickes: The First Thousand Days, 1933-1936.* New York: Simon and Schuster, 1953.

Ingersoll, L. D. *A History of the War Department of the United States.* Washington: Francis B. Mohun, 1879.

Itschner, Emerson C. "Missile Construction for Security." *Military Engineer* 51 (July-August 1959): 257-62.

Johnson, Emory. "Inland Waterways, Their Relation to Transportation." Supplement to *Annals of the American Academy of Political and Social Science,* September 1893, pp. 1-164.

_____ . "Rivers and Harbors Bills." *Annals of the American Academy of Political and Social Science* 2 (May 1892): 782-812.

Johnson, William. *The Papers of Sir William Johnson.* Edited by James Sullivan. 13 vols. Albany: The University of the State of New York, 1921.

Jones, Wilbur D. *The Confederate Rams at Birkenhead.* Tuscaloosa, Ala.: Confederate Publishing Company, 1961.

Kirchner, David P. "American Harbor Defense Forts." *United States Naval Institute Proceedings* 84, no. 8 (August 1958): 93-101.

Kirchner, D. P., and Lewis, E. R. "American Harbor Defenses: The Final Era." *United States Naval Institute Proceedings* 94, no. 1 (January 1968): 84-98.

Leslie, John William. "New Hampshire's Twin-Dam Reservoir." *Military Engineer* 56 (March-April 1964): 106-8.

Leslie, John W., and Minichiello, Anthony. "The Portsmouth Air Force Base." *Journal of the Boston Society of Civil Engineers* 43 (April 1956): 89-107.

Leuchtenburg, William Edward. *Flood Control Politics: The Connecticut River Valley Problem, 1927-1950.* Cambridge, Mass.: Harvard University Press, 1953.

Lewis, Emanuel Raymond. *Seacoast Fortifications of the United States: An Introductory History.* Washington: Smithsonian Institution Press, 1970.

Lippincott, Isaac. "A History of River Improvement." *Journal of Political Economy* 22 (1914): 630-60.

Lutz, M. K. "Military Missiles and Rockets." *Military Engineer* 51 (September-October 1959): 349-55.

Parkman, Francis. *A Half-Century of Conflict.* 2 vols. Boston: Little, Brown, and Company, 1892.

_____ , *Montcalm and Wolfe.* 2 vols. Boston: Little, Brown and Company, 1896.

Parsons, William Barclay. "Cape Cod Canal." *Annals of the American Academy of Political and Social Science* 31 (January 1908): 81-91.

Pitt, William. *Correspondence of William Pitt.* Edited by Gertrude Lelwyn Kimball. 2 vols. New York: Macmillan Company, 1906.

Porter, C. F. *A Brief History of Works Erected for the Defense of Portland Maine.* Occasional Paper, no. 18. U.S. Army Engineer School. Washington: Government Printing Office, 1905.

Putnam, Rufus. *The Memoirs of Rufus Putnam and Certain Official Papers and Correspondence.* Compiled and annotated by Rowena Buell. Boston and New York: Houghton Mifflin and Company, 1903.

Reid, William James. *The Building of The Cape Cod Canal, 1627-1914.* Privately printed, 1961.

Robins, Thomas M. "The River and Harbor Functions of the Corps of Engineers." *Military Engineer* 32 (September-October 1940): 325-31.

Scanlon, Jack. "Bangor's Big Stick." *New England Construction* 21 (January 21, 1957): 26-31, 78-79

Sibley, Alden K. "A Milestone in Flood Control." *The New Englander,* no. 427 (October 1959): 13, 30-31.

Smith, Clarence McKittrick. *The Medical Department: Hospitalization and Evacuation, Zone of Interior.* Volume in United States Army in World War II: The Technical Services. Washington: Department of the Army, 1956.

Sprout, Harold & Margaret. *The Rise of American Naval Power, 1776-1918.* Princeton: Princeton University Press, 1939.

Swift, Joseph Gardner. *The Memoirs of Gen. Joseph Gardner Swift, LL.D., U. S. A.* Privately printed, 1890.

Van Deurs, G. "And the Navy got its Wings." *American Heritage* 7 (October 1956): 78-79.

Winslow, E. E. *Lectures on Seacoast Defense.* Occasional Paper, no. 35. U. S. Army Engineer School. Washington: Government Printing Office, 1909.

Winsor, Justin, ed. *The Memorial History of Boston, 1630-1880.* 4 vols. Boston: James R. Osgood and Company, 1885.

Wood, Richard G. *Stephen Harriman Long, 1784-1864.* Glendale, Calif.: The Arthur H. Clark Company, 1966.

Miscellaneous Unpublished Materials

"After-Action Report for Operation Foresight, 1 March-16 May 1969." Duplicated. Department of the Army. New England Division, Corps of Engineers, May 1969.

"After-Action Report for Operation Foresight, February 1971-June 1971." Duplicated. Department of the Army. New England Division, Corps of Engineers, Waltham, Mass., June 1971.

Allen, J. E. "A Case History of the Cape Cod Canal." Paper presented at the Third Conference on Coastal Engineering at the Massachusetts Institute of Technology, October 22, 1952.

"Boston District Position Charts, 1 July 1946." U. S. Engineer Office, Boston, Mass.

Cowdrey, Albert E. "The Corps as Pioneer: The Case of the Refuse Act." Article accepted for publication by the *Pacific Historical Review.*

Fleming, Robert J. "Talk Before the Savings Bank Association of New Hampshire on 9 June 1956 by Brigadier General Robert J. Fleming, Jr."

"General Fact Sheet, U. S. Army Corps of Engineers," 1 January 1960. Mimeographed.

"History of the Boston District Engineer Office," 10 pp. typed. Prepared in the New England Division Office, January 1944. NED historical file.

"History of the Providence Engineer Office." 5 pp. typed. [December 31, 1943]. NED historical file.

Lafrenz, Rober F.; Taylor, Robert B.; and Davidson, Warren R. "History of the New England Division for Period June 25, 1950 through September 8, 1951." Mimeographed.

Leslie, John W., and Haines, Reuben M. "Design and Construction of Earth Dams in New England." Paper presented at the Milwaukee Water Resources Engineering Conference of the American Society of Civil Engineers, Milwaukee, Wisconsin, May 17, 1963.

Leslie, John Wm. "Water and Natural Resource Development in New England." Paper presented at the Regional Science Association Meeting, Boston, Massachusetts, October 24, 1964.

News Release. Department of the Army. New England Division, Corps of Engineers, 14 July 1971.

"Organization and Construction Projects." Typed. U. S. Army Engineer Division, New England, Corps of Engineers, Waltham, Mass., [1963].

"Organization Position Charts." New England Division, 1 February 1974.

Parks, Lillian D. "History of the U. S. Engineer Office, Boston, Mass." 6 pp. typed. May 22, 1943. NED historical files.

[Pearson, Richard W.] Address delivered at Norwich University Post, Society of American Military Engineers, December 2, 1954. NED historical file.

Personnel Directories of New England Division Office, 1 June 1945 and 16 December 1946, with Supplement, 22 January 1947.

"Program Review and Analysis," NEDOP 64. U. S. Army Engineer Division, New England.

"Program Review and Analysis." NEDOP 68. Department of the Army. New England Division, Corps of Engineers, Waltham, Mass.

"Program Review and Analysis." NEDOP 69. Department of the Army. New England Division, Corps of Engineers, Waltham, Mass.

"Program Review and Analysis." NEDOP 70. Department of the Army. New England Division, Corps of Engineers, Waltham, Mass.

Sibley, Alden K. "From Bunker Hill to the Bay of Fundy." Address delivered November 16, 1959. NED historical file.

_____ . " 'Passamaquoddy': A New Source of Energy." Address by Brigadier General Alden K. Sibley. U. S. Army Engineer Division, New England, Corps of Engineers, Boston, Mass. nd.

T. J. R. "Common Sense Flood Control in New England." 21 pp. mimeographed. New England Division, June 5, 1956.

INDEX

311

318